Making Sense of the Senseless:

Mild-Moderate Obsessive-Compulsive

Symptoms (OCS) Unveiled

Making Sense of the Senseless:

Mild-Moderate Obsessive-Compulsive Symptoms (OCS) Unveiled

Ron D. Kingsley MS, Ph.D., NCSP

The information contained in this book reflects the author's experience, research, and inferences, and as such is not for use as a replacement for competent medical, pharmaceutical, or other professional advice. Specific medical psychopharmacological and psychological opinions can be given only by qualified knowledgeable physicians, pharmacists, and psychologists who are competent and cognizant of each individual's particular developmental history and other relevant information. Always consult your doctor or the appropriate other professional for specific diagnoses and treatment.

This book was printed in the United States of America.

To order additional copies of this book, contact:
Xlibris Corporation
1-888-795-4274
www.Xlibris.com
Orders@Xlibris.com
15959-KING

CONTENTS

I dedicate this book to

All of us because
OCS is there in everyone and
knowing a bit more about it
can only enhance
each of our
lives.
It is my hope that all who read this
Will come away a little wiser
A little less judgmental
And perhaps just a little more compassionate.

I would especially like to thank the many OCS affected individuals who have come to me seeking assistance over the years and who ultimately have also helped me to better understand, recognize, make sense out of, and treat what I finally simply ended up calling OCS. This work would not exist without you.

Thanks.

Ron D. Kingsley

CHAPTER ONE

Lost in my own home . . . so alive . . . yet so alone
I should be loved . . . but feel I'm not
I wonder what went wrong
Inside I long to be . . . anyone else but me
Sometimes I'm afraid I'm living in a dream
Where no one else can see me . . . at all

It's true I have few friends
And most that say they are don't know who I am
Don't see the scars or pain
See the light . . . but not the rain
Don't know I sometimes wonder . . . if I'm sane
I'm told to wait . . . but I cannot
Though I try . . . somehow I'm caught
In this whirlwind that's my life
Where nothing that I do is right
And no one there to understand my plight

Hope's and empty dream . . . though I strive it seems
There's nothing I can do to change . . . my inconsistency
They tell me I'm to blame . . . I'm so lazy . . . what a shame
If I'd just try harder . . . I could learn to play their game
It's a shame

From the song "Lost" by Ron D. Kingsley

MAKING SENSE OF THE SENSELESS:

Obsessive Compulsive Symptoms Unveiled (Mild-Moderate Range)

Most professionals seem to agree that Obsessive Compulsive Symptoms (OCS) are expressed on a continuum that ranges from essentially no such symptoms to symptoms in the extreme. Those individuals with severe symptomotology are most often diagnosed as having a "disorder." Obsessive Compulsive Disorder (OCD), to be exact.

The individuals with mild to moderate OCS, however, do not fit the criteria for OCD and are, therefore, not considered to have a "disorder" (which, as it is now defined in DSM IV [Diagnostic and Statistical Manual of Mental Disorders: Fourth Edition], is correct). As a result, the needs of those with mild to moderate OCS have been, to a large extent, ignored. What are these needs? Do the symptoms really interfere to an extent that recognition, and sometimes, aggressive treatment, is truly warranted? How is it that this "problem" was not recognized and treated long ago? These are a few of the questions that efforts will be made to answer here in.

Research has demonstrated the effectiveness of the psychopharmacological agents known as the Specific Serotonin Reuptake Inhibitors (SSRI) in diminishing the symptoms of OCD. There is also compelling evidence that those individuals with mild to moderate OCS are also relieved of many, if not all, of their symptoms by the SSRI category of psychopharmacological agents as well. In fact, in my own clinical practice, I have seen and do see a significant number of individuals (both children and adults) that have been previously diagnosed as having such things as spoiled child syndrome, a hypochondriacal personality, Panic disorder, School phobia, separation anxiety, Major depression, Bipolar disorder, Cyclothymia, eating disorders, sexual deviancy, Generalized anxiety disorder, Oppositional defiant disorder, Conduct disorder, ADHD[Attention Deficit-Hyperactive Disorder], Intermittent explosive disorder, avoidant disorders, Agoraphobia, Social phobia, and so on. In the past 15 years I have discovered several individuals in every diagnostic and descriptive category listed above that were experiencing a variety of obsessive and compulsive symptoms. Once these were properly addressed and treated the result was a partial and often total remission of the previously diagnosed problems. This suggested to me that the obsessive and compulsive symptoms although not severe enough to warrant the diagnosis of OCD (via several DSM revisions) still seemed to be at the root of the individual's experienced difficulties.

In the beginning it was by chance that such a discovery was made. Then, as the pattern persisted, it began to gnaw on my awareness such that, in the last five years, or so, I have begun to fairly routinely use several questions in my preliminary clinical interviews to assess the possibility of OCS. This has become a standard practice whenever an individual has been previously diagnosed with ADHD, or Tourette's Syndrome. Also, this is done if the reason the individual was brought, or came, to see me was because of concerns that they might have ADHD or Tourette's. This is because there has been growing research evidence that ADHD, OCD, and Tourette's Syndrome are related (Rapoport 1992, Braun 1994). As pointed out by Braun (1994), "It is possible that the same general brain regions are involved in all three of these illnesses but that the functional interplay among them may differ, accounting for manifest difference in clinical symptoms." He further points out that "Evidence is mounting that the association between these disorders is genetic and they may represent different manifestations of the same gene."

In the last 10 years of my clinical practice when a child or adult has been referred to me for an already diagnosed ADHD that is not responding to traditional treatment with stimulants and yet is still causing significant problems even though stimulants have made an improvement, about 80 to 90% of the time there has been evidence of OCS at a mild to moderate level. Usually, with careful yet specific questioning, there is also a family history of OCS related behaviors and symptoms. Invariably these have never before been diagnosed (due to lack of clear symptomotology and severity), Grandma and Grandpa, aunts or uncles, and even parents, may be described as being, or having been, excessively rigid, demanding, "it had to be their way", strange, weird, eccentric, and sometimes downright "crazy."

In fact, in my experience, this idea of being "crazy," (i.e. the self sustained fear that "I" might be crazy), or at least that "something *must* be seriously wrong with me," appears to be one of the major factors relative to the difficulties practitioners have in making an accurate diagnosis. Other main factors involve practitioner's lack of experience and knowledge regarding specific mild to moderate symptoms, as well as the affected individual's confusion regarding symptoms, related dynamics, and how such symptoms can manifest themselves in day-to-day life.

The "confusion" referred to above typically results from a combination of things occurring over time. First, the symptoms are, research suggests, biochemically driven. Thus, it should come as no surprise that individuals often cannot come up with a reasonable explanation for their questionable actions, or thoughts. Second, the symptoms come and go and often change over time as well. Third, episodic stress, fatigue, and intense emotional experience all make symptoms worse. Fourth, individuals usually have at least partial voluntary control over symptoms which, as Rapoport (1992) indicates, "baffles and angers parents." It is also clear that these symptoms baffle, frustrate, frighten, and anger the affected individual as well. Fifth, individuals tend to adopt or rationalize almost any explanation that seems to "fit" their symptom picture. Sometimes the rationalization's source springs from the creative imagination of the individual, though, more often than not, the adopted cause is borrowed from the individual's specific societal belief system, that is to say, whatever is generally believed by the society in which the individual lives. Causation may also be borrowed from the media, or influenced by others' comments. Sixth, especially children, but many adults as well, will tend to explain specific symptoms by attempting to enter the belief system of the person demanding an explanation. In other words, since there is no recognized purpose for the symptom in question, the affected individual, often in desperation, tries to present an explanation that (even if not believed themselves) they think their interrogator *will* believe. Seventh, and perhaps finally, after a while (and sometimes immediately), the affected individual can come to believe with often an intense and frightening certainty whatever explanation seems to fit their particular symptom best. The more bizarre the symptom, the harder it is to create or find a reason that it's there, and the more likely it is that the individual will use a lot of time, energy, and effort trying to explain or hide it from other people. When thoughts are involved, they typically will not mention these to anyone. This alone can create major stress if the particular repetitive and reoccurring thoughts are considered blasphemous, "dirty", or wrong by personal or community standards. Thus, mental distress and confusion seem to be significant "side effects" commonly related to OCS.

When symptoms are severe, they are also much more likely to

be obvious. A person who experiences the need to wash his or her hands, dirty or not, 22 times exactly at varying intervals throughout the day whenever near a sink is going to be spotted relatively quickly. This same symptom, however, when in the mild to moderate range is very difficult, if not impossible, to spot by observation alone. This is because at a moderate level the "need" to wash may be only once or twice each time and only when real dirt is visible, and/or the individual has touched something believed to be "dirty" or something that others might consider likely to have germs. At a mild level the individual might be somewhat "fussy" about washing their hands. When dirt gets on the hands, they may start thinking about the need to wash them. This thought may then persist until the person is able to actually get them washed. Most often they will wash them only once, but the repetitive nature of the thought process causes a feeling of discomfort that simply won't go away until the hands are cleaned. Such individuals might avoid working on cars because of the tendency to get grease on their hands, which is hard to remove and can remain at least partially visible for days.

Should such a symptom at the mild to moderate level be aggressively treated? As a symptom in and of itself, the answer would typically be "no". When, however, one takes into consideration that such a symptom is rarely ever found in isolation, the treatment needs start to become clearer. Since many such symptoms may be active simultaneously, and each requires a bit of the individual's time (i.e., the time spent thinking about it, and/or spending energy performing compulsive actions), they take their toll. The tendency to be overwhelmed with even such mild to moderate symptoms as have been described is common. Observationally, the individual might be described by others as irritable, having a short fuse, angry, having a bad temper, worried, anxious, and so on. The longer such symptoms dominate in the mind, the more irritable an individual may become. Since no one else can perceive accurately what is going on within, and the individuals so affected commonly do not know what is happening either, misunderstandings abound, as might be expected.

As Rapoport (1992) has reported, research has documented

OCD in children as young as two years of age. Undoubtedly symptoms in such a young child would have had to be fairly severe, it seems, in order to make the diagnosis. Since so many individuals with OCS clearly make it all the way into adulthood without symptoms having ever been detected, one can openly wonder how the two-year-old with OCS in the mild to moderate range might present himself behaviorally. Clinical experience within the last ten years has presented me with the beginnings of what appears to be a consistent symptom picture for the young child with OCS. Research yet needs to be undertaken to either confirm or disconfirm these clinically derived hypotheses.

Some very young children have great difficulty sharing toys (especially their own), candy, other possessions, and even parental attention, or time with anyone. Of course there are many possible reasons for such behavior, all of which need to be explored, however, the potential explanation (that of biochemically driven OCS) in my experience is rarely even considered, if at all. The relative import of such a possibility, though, cannot be underscored enough. Such a diagnosis would have a profound effect, not only on the treatment plan, for the child, but also in helping the parents of such a child. An accurate diagnosis helps them to understand the nature of the problem, learn how to better manage its symptoms, and gain knowledge of what may yet be expected in the future. Accurate knowledge and awareness is one of the most powerful positive treatment factors in any form of treatment for any type of problem.

The very young child with OCS who is reluctant or simply refuses to share cannot adequately defend such behavior verbally, physically, or even intellectually due to obvious developmental limitations. As a result of this biochemical invasion of the will (for lack of more precise definition), it has appeared to me that these children lack awareness.

First of all they have no reference as to the reasons why they don't want to share, nor do their parents. The child is also commonly unaware of how extremely intense their resistance can become when attempts are made to force their compliance. Observers typically view such a response set as evidence that the child is selfish, spoiled, mean, a "bad seed," or the product of parental overindulgence, lack of discipline, or just plain poor parenting in general. It's no wonder many parents will not seek assistance for themselves or the child. Parents tend to be almost certain they are personally at fault for their child's behavior. When, however, OCS is a factor, this interpretation is simply not true. This is not to suggest parents have no impact on the behavior of their children, for indeed they do. Parents simply are not the primary cause for the biochemically driven obsessive and compulsive symptoms manifested by their offspring.

So, why do I believe it can be a symptom of OCS when very young children (and actually older individuals as well) are reluctant or unwilling to share? When OCS is involved, the behavior is persistent, as well as resistant, to most forms of discipline, punishment, and even rewards. When rewards do work, they are most often of an immediate well-liked consumable nature, or intensely desired already by the child. The idea of "intensity" will be discussed in more detail later on. Mostly, the efforts by parents to change OCS driven behaviors in their children meet with failure after failure. As a result, chronic frustration, anger, denial, and depression are common dynamics occurring in the parents of children with OCS.

An interesting sidelight to the idea that a child is unwilling to share is my own explanation for such OCS driven behavior. When OCS driven, the behavior seems to have nothing to do with a reluctance to "share" at all. My observations, along with clinical experience and interviews with older children and adults, suggest the symptom is related to an inability to let go of something that, for that instant, can be experienced as obsessively needed for no explainable reason. Sometimes it can result from an irrational fear the toy will be lost, or something awful will happen to it, like it might get broken.

Related to this tendency for OCS driven behaviors to persist in the face of all attempts to change them is another observed element in all significantly affected OCS individuals. In my experience, those with OCS will manifest many other symptoms in a broad range of environments and the initially identified Obsessive Compulsive symptom, almost universally, is only one of the many that will yet be identified.

Thus, when a symptom such as pervasive and consistent reluctance to share is identified, further exploration is not only warranted but also essential. Other symptoms that are observable by teachers, parents, and often in sessions with counselors/psychologists (especially during therapeutic play) include the following:

- *Tantrumming + Explosive Reactions* – These reactions tend to be frequent, although inconsistent, and often would be described as over reactive and/or extremely exaggerated. The reactions also tend to go on and on and on, long after reason dictates the person should be "over it". Parents of affected children are also confused, frustrated, and angry because the child is clearly over responding. Many times parents are not even aware of the triggering event and will indicate: "He tantrums over nothing." Or "over little things".

Note: The author realizes that all tantrumming is not related to OCS, and is not intending to suggest that it is. It is only that (given parameters suggested above) this is potentially important added information to consider such an underlying possibility.

When interfering OCS exists, the underlying cause of the tantrumming, explosive reactions, or the losing of control behaviorally and emotionally, appear to result from what I have called "the Cornered Rabbit Syndrome." These children are quite often believed to be (by teachers, peers, others, and sometimes even parents) overly aggressive, angry, unpredictable, mean, and to have conduct disorders. Generally speaking, most individuals with some knowledge of rabbits would not describe them as aggressive animals. If, however, as an experiment, we arranged for someone who had never seen a rabbit and knew nothing about them to observe a specific incident, it might be a different story. If through a two-way glass the observer watched as a man closed in on a rabbit that had already retreated to a corner of the room, a quite different interpretation is altogether possible. When a rabbit is cornered, it can lash out with teeth and claws in a way that is quite unusual for this typically timid animal. Under normal circumstances, rabbits universally choose flight over fight. Thus, the observer, seeing such a scenario, might easily determine that rabbits are indeed very aggressive and dangerous animals. The child with biochemically driven OCS is in a situation quite similar qualitatively to the one just described for the rabbit. The emotional response of the child with OCS experiencing an irresistible need for a toy that the parent is bent on forcing him to share is in a proverbial corner. The child does not understand this "need." However, the more cornered such a child feels, the more all-encompassing this "need" becomes. The child in this situation is likely is to suddenly lash out, behaviorally explode, or behave in some other, at the Moment, inappropriate manner. This holds true for adults as well. Often within a period of 15 to 45 minutes, the child is acting as if nothing ever happened and, when questioned about the incident, may not remember it at all. Much of the time he may also have a quite distorted memory when compared to that of the others who may have been present. I have come to believe this is not a conscious distortion but, rather, seems to result from the bioneurochemical interference relating to the emotional intensity of the Moment.

Tantrumming for the very young child is nearly the only means with which to express intense feelings of displeasure over what is going on. Interestingly, even older OCS affected children and adults will tantrum, although it is a bit more sophisticated than that of a child. Children have neither the words nor the capacity to put them together for meaningful communication as do older children and adults. So, when parents are going out for the evening and the child is experiencing an excessive need for them to stay yet they leave anyway, tantrumming occurs, usually for quite a while depending on how intense the need or fear may be. Frequently the fear is that something horrible or awful may happen and they won't come back. Typically, such behavior will also happen again and again and again because it is driven biochemically. This is not to suggest parents should stay home. When parents go ahead and leave in spite of the screaming, crying, and extreme reactions, they are in one of the best treatments, outside of medication, that research has documented can have a positive outcome for Obsessive Compulsive symptoms. It is a behavior modification technique known as Exposure and Response Prevention. This technique is explained quite well and described in great detail in the book *Getting Control* by Lee Baer.

Since OCS responses such as those being discussed are not simply "learned responses," but also have that biochemical component, the resulting behavior is typically quite difficult to extinguish or diminish the response to acceptable levels that can be tolerated. Often (and perhaps most of the time) exposure and response prevention, when applied correctly over time, can reduce compulsive urges and even diminish the frequency and, thereby, power of obsessive thoughts. The ability to better manage stress and life can then be enhanced.

However, in my opinion behavior modification does not "cure" OCS/OCD. It can be a useful tool, often in conjunction with medication, in the management of the problem even though the "trigger" is biochemical. Over time parents of OCS affected children may have to engage several (and sometimes many) different babysitters as they too become severely frustrated and overwhelmed. If parents can help the baby-sitter to better understand the reasons behind the child's behavior and offer a few suggestions in how best to handle specific difficult and abrasively persistent behaviors (and perhaps pay a little more as compensation), chances are they may find babysitters who last.

What about bedtime? It is not uncommon for children as well as adults with OCS to have difficulties initially getting to sleep. It is not yet clear if the problem with falling asleep is the reason very young (and older too) children will often actively resist going to bed. They may be obsessively insecure at night when out of sight of parents and/or older siblings. They may experience irrational fearful thoughts or strong generalized emotions of fear. With older children and adults, initial insomnia appears to result from an inability to shut down trains of thought and/or urges and compulsions to get up and "do" something.

Bedtime Routines

Interestingly, in my clinical experience, I have found that many individuals with OCS can get to sleep quite a bit sooner when listening to some kinds of music. Generally, if the music is too slow or too fast it will not help. There is a range, however, around the tempo of the human heartbeat that most often seems to best enable getting to sleep. This appears to be especially effective when a group of favorite or often-heard songs at that particular beat can be put on a cassette and played nightly at bedtime. Unfortunately there are also some for which this does not work.

It should be pointed out that trying to reason with an OCS affected child, adolescent, or adult, or attempting to talk her into bed or talk her out of a particular OCS driven behavior is not a good idea. Doing so usually results in a frustrating sense of failure on the part of the one attempting to do the reasoning. Establishing a consistent "bedtime," along with a nightly routine immediately before this scheduled time for going to bed, can make it much easier for a child to "settle down" and actually "get there."

One family began a nightly ritual, which began approximately thirty minutes prior to the specified time for the children to go to bed. Parents would announce, "All right, kids. It's time to get ready for bed." First, the children would go to the bathroom where they would brush their teeth and then be directed to get their pajamas on and "Get your books." Each child would choose two picture books from the family's small library. The Father and/or Mother when he was not there (he worked two nights a week) would then read each of the children's books to everyone. Instructions when the reading was completed were, "Okay, put your books away and kiss Mom and Dad good night." After this was done they would be instructed to "go potty" and hop in bed, at which time the Father (who played guitar and sang a little) would get his guitar and sing a few songs to them as they lay in bed. When this routine was followed without deviation, their OCS affected children would respond like at no other time before this routine was set up. Bedtime went from a nightly battlefield to a smooth, easy-to-handle (although somewhat time-consuming) transition.

There are other groups of individuals that have similar needs for consistent daily routines. The most notable of these and perhaps the most severely affected (generally speaking) are those diagnosed with Autism. The similarities between some autistic behaviors and OCS behavioral responses to sudden and unexpected changes in the environment and/or the child's daily routines are striking. Perhaps the same biochemical component driving the loss of behavioral control and tantrumming of the autistic child when introduced to especially abrupt changes in routine is the same mechanism as in the child with OCS. The most obvious difference between the populations is the severe communication difficulties of those diagnosed with autism. For the specific issue in question relating to the changes in expected routines, though, both may be manifesting OCS driven behavior.

The OCS child can be said, at times, to badger parents unmercifully. Once a desire to do and/or get something is experienced and expressed, there is often a period of time in which the child cannot "let go of" or get the thought or idea out of the mind. Interestingly, the idea of "badgering" hinted at above seems to occur whether the parental response is positive or negative. Similar "badgering" also occurs with adolescents and adults, although it is manifested somewhat differently. Irritation seems to be the most common by-product of the child's badgering. Let's say, for the sake of understanding, that you have a child with OCS and that child has decided she needs new crayons. The intensity of the child's focus on a single idea and the way in which this is displayed can be almost frightening. When parents are made aware of these symptoms and begin to understand, this intensity often becomes a tip-off that the child is exhibiting an OCS driven need. Knowing this ahead of time can significantly lessen the frustration and anger typically felt by parents as the scene progresses. When the parental response is positive, the child will often respond with varying degrees of excitement usually exaggerated quite a bit more than what might be considered a "normal" response. The next thing that commonly occurs because the idea of getting the "crayons" is still persistently pressing at the forefront of her mind is a tendency to begin asking things such as "When can we go and get them?" "Can we go now?" If the parent is not specific and says something like "later" or "in a little while" the parent is setting him self up for additional badgering. Even though the parent has agreed with the child's request, the biochemically influenced need persists, driving the child towards obtainment which would then satisfy the urge, obsession, and/or compulsion. Thus, when a parent is non-specific, the child will typically start in with, "How much later?" "When will it be a little while?" "Is it later, yet?" "Why can't we go, now?" And so on. I know of many such situations in which the parent barraged by the child's nonstop harassment has eventually become so irritated, frustrated, and angry that their ensuing reaction was along the lines of, "If you don't *shut up* and leave me alone . . . we're *not* going to go at all." This, of course, can reopen to debate the child's initial request. She may begin to wonder if she will ever get the crayons. She also may fear that she won't get them, which may then trigger the need for reaffirmation of the original parental agreement. Thus, the child queries, "Can I get them? Can I get the crayons?" or "So, are we going to go get them now, Dad? Are we?" This is why parents, teachers, babysitters, and others need to understand this and be made aware of OCS and its associated dynamics. The ability to manage the child's symptoms, redirect blame, and depersonalize the child's behavior is greatly enhanced and allows for possible development of better and more fulfilling relationships. When parents understand the biochemical nature of the problem and are able to thereby internalize it, they, as well as teachers and others, become capable of controlling their own reactions and significantly reduce the otherwise typically experienced frustration and anger.

The response of the OCS affected child to a parental rejection, or negative reaction, to his stated desire (going back to the crayon example), is similar to that which occurs with a positive parental response in that the child cannot "let go" of the thought or idea and experienced need. There is, however, one typical immediate difference. When the-asked-for-thing is an OCS manifestation and the parent's first response is a flat-out "no" the child will often react in an over-exaggerated manner. Immediate tantrumming is not uncommon, nor is over reacting by crying, whining, and intense sulking behavior. Because the obsessive or compulsive urge is underscored biochemically, when the desire is thwarted, the child's emotional experience is incredibly multiplied. As a result the reaction tends to be catastrophic. Children and adults in clinical interviews describe feeling, at these times, that if they do not get what they need, think they need, or don't get to do what they feel compelled to do, it's as if the "whole world is going to end". Although such a statement seems a little crazy, and in a calmer Moment even the OCS affected will often agree that it is, in reality, an extreme exaggeration, at the Moment this need is thwarted or interfered with, these individuals often dramatically lose emotional control. Later on, when calm and in control once again, they will often spontaneously and sincerely apologize for their inappropriate behaviors and/or the comments made during that period of time in which they were out of control. The parent or teacher hearing such an apology again and again and again may have difficulty accepting it and also may have trouble believing it is truly sincere. They may think, and sometimes say, "If you were really sorry you wouldn't act that way anymore" and the like.

Other situations likely to bring on periods of emotional loss of control in both children and adults include the following:

A.) **Interference with obsessive needs:** When an OCS affected individual is already engaged in an activity (especially if it's one they greatly enjoy), it can become intensely obsessive and/or compulsive in nature (although not always). At those times when it does, if anyone or anything interferes with the activity before its completion, several reactions may occur as follows:

1.) An emotional explosion.
2.) A flat refusal and/or inability to acknowledge the interruption (no response).
3.) A verbal acknowledgement such as "Okay, Mom," or "Be right there, Mom," without having processed a thing that was said and the activity is continued as the child remains unaware interference of any kind had actually occurred.
4.) Tantrumming.

possible responses

Once an activity becomes OCS driven, the child commonly experiences a "need" to continue to be engaged to the activity's conclusion and/or at least until the biochemical intensity diminishes. When forcefully interrupted, the child's reaction is usually quite intense but often dissipates quickly and many times within 10 to 45 minutes, appears to be totally forgotten. It's as if whatever caused the distress had never really happened.

B.) **Unexpected changes in plans and/or routines:** When the individual with OCS is expecting to go and/or do something that has been planned ahead of time and there has been a sudden change of plans, they usually do not handle it well. There may be significant anger, explosive episodes, and a refusal to become involved in the unplanned event. Tantrumming, crying, pouting, and the like, are also all too common responses.

C.) Criticism and/or discipline: Rebelliousness, anger, and amplified emotional reactions in response to discipline or criticism appear to be rooted in the person's biochemically driven irrational need to make no mistakes. This "need" leads to what looks like an intense resistance to being disciplined. Clinical experience has suggested to me that the discipline itself is not the thing that's being resisted. The often-obscured underlying issue of resistance is really the ever-present need to "make no mistakes". Other expressions of this same need include the inability to admit to any wrongdoing; the need to be right all of the time; the need to be the best and win in all contests, and the inability to admit a mistake was made. To have made a mistake is like wearing a badge that all can see, showing the absolute worthlessness of this to be despised, horrid, person who has been caught making a mistake.

The emotional connections with obsessive and compulsive symptoms seem to become somehow "supercharged" to the point that cognitive distortions (mental misunderstandings) also often occur. The brevity of these emotional reactions seems to be dependent upon how long a particular obsessive thought or compulsion has been present as an active symptom. The longer a symptom has gone round and round in the mind, the stronger the expression of the emotional reaction as well as the length of time that the reaction seems to last.

As a result of these super-charged feelings triggered by the underlying biochemical/bioneurological imbalance, the reaction that occurs appears similar to the heightened energy-state experienced during the well known "fight or flight" adrenaline response. This also tends to be of brief duration. During such a reaction individuals experience exaggerated strength, endurance, and resolve. This quickly dissipates after the danger is gone. One cannot help but wonder what might occur if this same exaggerated experience happened after most of the events and actions that are experienced every day of our lives. In my mind I can easily see this wretched and beleaguered little man tiptoeing down the hall (so as not to trigger a reaction). His beady eyes shift nervously from place to place with each new sight or sound, whether imagined or not. He is weary. At any Moment he knows he is likely to lash out emotionally. He's never sure exactly what it will be that triggers the reaction. He has no idea why this keeps happening to him. Over the years he has heard many possible explanations and has believed in a score of them from time to time. His current favorite is that he must have spent his early childhood years in a war zone, which traumatized him to the point that he can't remember. He was, after all, adopted and never knew who his real parents were. He still doesn't know. So . . . maybe, he was the illegitimate child of an American doctor and an American nurse who were stationed together in Vietnam in about 1969. That would be about right for his age. Both the doctor and the nurse had spouses back home. He'd wanted her to consent to an abortion. She adamantly refused. A bitter struggle ensued. The mash unit's very isolation was her saving grace. The doctor did not want that baby born. It would be a constant reminder of his infidelity. The nurse, even though she promised that she wouldn't, probably would look him up after the war someday. By then he would be a successful "rich" doctor, and she would demand back payments on child support.

When working in the same tent together he avoided looking at her; and when he did look, well, if looks could kill the growing baby within her wouldn't need to be aborted. She knew of his feelings and was terrified he might slip her something when she wasn't looking. Put something in her milk. Maybe he might even "accidentally" trip her. She had to do something, and soon.

The story the little man believed was that the nurse ran away, had the baby, and then spent the next three to four years running in Vietnam. She was branded a traitor and had to keep running in order to stay out of jail as well as to stay alive. The little man imagines him self as an infant, then as a toddler with bombs going off left and right amid the constant crack of sniper fire. He sees him self running from place to place with his harried Mother until finally a sniper's bullet kills her. Eventually he's adopted and sent to America. Buried in his subconscious though, are these memories that would surely make anyone jumpy, or likely to over react to even small or seemingly insignificant events. Though he can't remember if this "really" happened, he clings to the possibility because it is believable and makes a strange and surreal kind of sense. Such a belief can eventually become so strongly held in the consciousness of an individual that, for them, it becomes "truth." A truth that will not be easily changed or let go of.

<u>Negativity</u> Many times, though certainly not "always", the person with significant OCS will seem seriously over focused on the negative side of things. This tendency may actually be the result of the over focused, or obsessive, need to do things a certain way or redo them until it seems or "feels right." When such a dynamic is occurring, anything but that "right" feeling is stridently rejected as inadequate. Since it is often very difficult to get everything one does "just right," the individual may give the impression that, for them, nothing is going the way it should, and probably never will. Also, because the OCS affected's emotional experience and expression both tend to be extremely intense, their reactions to things not going like they should can be so consistently negative that no one wants to be around and/or interact with them. This negativity is commonly not something these individuals can readily accept or even see. Their lack of awareness in regard to their own negativity is understandable since it is biochemically driven. They don't see themselves or their behavior as "being" negative. The things that have happened and keep happening to them are what's negative. These people appear aggressive, angry, never satisfied, and even downright mean. They expect to do things right the "first" time and when they don't, the failure to do so seems to need to be rationalized or be justified via an emotionally expressed negative reaction that will then allow them to continue on. A typical alternative reaction is to simply give up, or refuse to try. Giving up, or refusing to try, is tantamount to depression. Anger and depression appear to be among the common secondary reactions to mild-moderate OCS.

<u>Selfishness, Egotism and Egocentrism</u> So many ideas, thoughts, and needs invade the mind and consciousness of individuals with significant OCS that they appear to be extremely self-focused. Others describe this as the tendency (or need) to always do what

they want to do with a disregard for anyone else's input. There can be no argument with this observational interpretation, as this is exactly how it would appear to another. The individuals themselves are almost always unable to even consider the idea that they are, or might be, self-centered. This is because they often do not experience the things they do as being self-absorbed. To them their actions seem almost never focused on themselves. Thus, how can anyone possibly view them as self-centered? In fact, many affected individuals will openly argue that they are "far from" being self-centered, and for someone to even suggest that such might be the case is a grave insult. There may be an eruption of anger, along with a tirade of examples loudly shouted as absolute evidence of their truly altruistic behaviors. One of the problems can be that although the action undertaken is meant to be for another, or to help another in some way, that other may not want the thing that's offered. Similarly they may not desire to be helped, or may not want the help in the specific fashion that it has been given. The individual with OCS is viewed as someone who wants to be helpful for the benefit of only him self or herself rather than for the person helped. The affected individual, however, does not see it that way at all. To them they were offering help from the viewpoint that makes the most sense. If not done exactly in the way proposed, they believe it should not be done at all. This appears to most observers to be quite self-centered, or self-focused.

Cause-Effect Learning Problems OCS appears to inhibit the learning in cause-effect situations. Actually, as is true of so many other situations, cause-effect learning only seems to be inhibited. Because the behavior, actions, and/or thoughts are triggered by an underlying biochemical insufficiency, whenever this "trigger" is in effect the individual may be incapable of accessing previously learned material. Thus, inappropriate behaviors tend to reoccur again, and again, and again no matter what the immediate consequences (reward or punishment) may be. After the fact, affected individuals almost always either become aware themselves or, when confronted by another, are able to verbalize that "Yes, they've done it again". Sometimes, though, this awareness can be delayed for a long time. To others this tendency to repeatedly act inappropriately even though aware they shouldn't is a truly puzzling behavior, to say the least. Others typically want to know "why". "Why do you do this time and time again?" "You *know* better than that!" and so on. This is perhaps the most aggravating situation for an individual with OCS to find themselves in because invariably the honest answer to the question "why" is genuinely "I don't know." As children, however, affected individuals learn quite thoroughly that the response "I don't know" is usually unacceptable to others, and is almost always believed to be an excuse or even a lie. This is commonly the underlying dynamic that can lead to the acceptance of false causation and the sometimes creative manufacturing of believable expressions of causation, as discussed already. Why do these children and adults engage in the telling of so many falsehoods and slightly "bent" stories? I believe it is because the literal truth is so often considered by others to be completely unbelievable. How is it possible to not know why you did something? How can a person forget that they know a certain behavior is wrong and not to be engaged in, and if they haven't forgotten, how could they deliberately engage in such an activity again? The common conclusion being, "She must be behaving that way on purpose, just to get me." The key word in the above example is "deliberate". This is a pejorative interpretation and, as such, is an emotional distortion of the common community or socially held belief that "all behavior occurs for a reason." Since those so affected vow that they had no reason, it must mean that it was purposeful and done "just to irritate me." This distorted belief can then lead to yet other distortions, which may then also be similarly misconstrued. It is no wonder that significant OCS is so difficult to diagnose and trace back to an underlying biochemical insufficiency.

The ADHD-OCS-Tourette's Connection These are important relationships for professionals working with any one of these disorders to be aware of (Please see Neurobiological relationship of Tourette Syndrome, Obsessive Compulsive Disorder, and Attention Deficit Hyperactivity Disorder . . . article). Some motor tic and vocal tic symptoms are so intertwined with compulsions as to be virtually indistinguishable (this appears to be especially true for complex tics). Unless quite severe, motor and vocal tics prob-

[handwritten margin note: They don't know why they behave the way they do, so they make up / answers / stories.]

ably should not be actively treated, at least, pharmacologically. Most of the time, side effects, or potential side effects, in my experience, seem to outweigh the benefits of such treatments. The medications most often used to inhibit such tics have been documented through research (Rapoport) to sometimes worsen OCS in susceptible individuals. This appears to be due to the action of the drugs. The medications used in the treatment of Tourette's tend to be Serotonin blockers while those most often used in the treatment of OCS are Serotonin Reuptake inhibitors (which, essentially, allow for more Serotonin availability between the affected synapses instead of less). In my experience the most successful treatment of Chronic Tic Disorders and Tourette's Syndrome from mild-moderate, and even severe, has been accurate knowledge. Also important is the sharing of this knowledge with all those likely to be regularly working with or likely to have significant contact with the affected individual (i.e.,workplace, social gatherings, church officials, school personnel from teachers to principals, psychologists, and playground aides, as well as classroom peers). Someone who understands the condition and also knows the affected individual should share this information. Tourette's Syndrome, when demystified in this manner, is more easily accepted and, if not accepted, tends certainly to be viewed with more compassion and significantly less fear.

It seems plausible to me that the 30% or so of the individuals identified by Barkley (1995) as having ADHD, whose symptoms don't seem to respond to the established traditional psychopharmacological treatments for ADHD, may be in a large part those individuals whose attention difficulties are primarily OCS related. It has also occurred to me that the "Antidepressants" that research has consistently demonstrated as "effective" for many individuals diagnosed with "ADHD" may, in reality, be treating the unidentified mild-moderate Obsessive Compulsive symptoms.

Stress tends to exacerbate all symptoms of ADHD, OCS, and Tourette's. Thus when an individual, for example, with both OCS and ADHD, who has been diagnosed with ADHD only (the OCS yet to be recognized), is treated with a stimulant, and ADHD symptoms are significantly lessened, as is also a significant amount of stress, both at home and at school. This, then, often will also reduce the obsessive and compulsive symptoms indirectly. Depending on the strength of the OCS, or severity of the underlying biochemical problem, OCS may no longer interfere with day to day functioning at all. Sometimes, however, symptoms that are significantly diminished by lowered stress levels from the effective psychopharmacological treatment of ADHD will, in time, return. This results in the acting out of behaviors thought to signify a return of ADHD because many of the observable symptoms of OCS are practically indistinguishable from ADHD at times.

Some of the most common symptoms that can result from either ADHD or OCS include the following:

-Short attention span
-Attention span not increased by punishment or reward
-Erratic, flighty, or scattered behavior
-Easily distracted
-Seems to show little respect for authority
-Does not finish things he/she is doing; jumps to something else
-Does not seem to show common sense
-Becomes over-excited easily
-Seems to be over-active and restless
-Follows academic directions poorly
-Seems to lack impulse control
-Is unaware of what is going on around him/her
-School work and homework often not done or incomplete
-Seems to lack control of self; will speak out or leave seat indiscriminately
-Can seem stubborn and uncooperative
-Denies responsibility for his/her own actions
-Quickly frustrated and often loses emotional control
-Seems to almost welcome punishment
-Acts silly
-Plays the clown of the class
-Significant problems with transitions

The above-related behaviors are not "always" present in ADHD and OCS. The last 15 years of clinical practice have suggested to me, however, that often variations of these seem to be the common denominators when OCS is misdiagnosed as ADHD. This seems also true when both disorders are present with significant interfering symptoms.

Some of the more commonly seen symptoms and associated symptoms seemingly more specific to mainly OCS are as follows:

-Questions indicate a worry about the future
-Does not ask questions
-Upset if makes a mistake
-Perseverates, significant trouble shifting responses or tasks
-Overly concerned about fairness and all things being equal
-Shows over-remorse for wrongdoing
-Cannot seem to forgive others
-Is upset if things don't turn out perfect, or "just right"
-Blames self if things go wrong
-Shows many unusual fears
-Seems to display a don't care attitude; does what he/she
    wants
-Appears tense
-Worries too much
-Appears nervous
-May avoid physical contact in play
-Becomes angry quickly
-Acts as a non-conformist
-Becomes angry if asked to do something
-Is rebellious if disciplined
-Wears unusual clothing styles
-Associated with loners
-Does things his/her own way
-May not engage in rough and tumble with others
-Explodes under stress
-Many tend to reject classmates in a hostile manner
-Will not take suggestions from others
-Flares up at classmates, siblings, or parents if teased or

pushed
-Style of behaving seems deliberately different from most
-Sulks
-Is difficult to get to know
-May seem dependent on others to lead him/her around
-Appears unhappy
-May show little feeling when others are upset
-May seem over-obedient
-Withdraws quickly from group activities; seems to prefer to
   work by self
-Avoids competition
-Seems to want to boss others
-Seems shy
-Seems to deliberately put self in a position of being criti-
   cized
-Is easily frustrated and gives up passively
-Tends not to show feelings
-Wants others to do things for him/her
-Feelings easily hurt
-Often seems to cling to adults
-Appears disinterested in class or in work of others
-May appear to be depressed
-Seeks constant praise

The above-related descriptions are not necessarily symptoms, in and of themselves; rather, they represent common behavior observable to others that often occur as a result of OCS. Thus, trying to eliminate (or treat) these specific behaviors without taking into consideration the underlying cause (when OCS related) often leads to partial or complete treatment failure which can then bring on despair, anxiety, anger, and/or depression.

Obsessions are defined as persistent ideas, thoughts, impulses, or images that are experienced as intrusive and that cause marked anxiety or distress (DSM IV). Compulsions are repetitive behaviors the goal of which is to prevent or reduce anxiety or distress (DSM IV).

Trapped . . . but only I can see the walls around me
They say relax . . . it's something I can't do until I know the truth
But what is truth

Is it what we think or believe . . . or could it be everything we feel?
It always seems so real
Sometimes I think I know the answer . . . and then I don't
As it slips away . . . into another day
In the story of my life . . . I can't remember . . . I can't remember

I just want to live my life and not be misunderstood
I want to discover all the truth
I want somehow to find myself . . . anyway I know I should
But sometimes . . . I just don't know what to do
(There are times when I just don't know what to do)

Stripped . . . of everything I need to be sure of who I am
They slip . . . into my mind these lies and I don't understand
Perhaps in time I can
In this world of make believe the masks are up . . . everywhere we go
Didn't you know?
I'm not sure what you may think . . . but in the mirror . . . I don't want to see
A different me . . . in the story of my life
I can't remember . . . I don't remember
Trapped . . . but only I can see the walls around me

From the song "Trapped" by Ron D. Kingsley

THE OCS/OCD CONTINUUM:

THE CRAZINESS IN US ALL

Have you ever wondered if you might be *crazy?* At one time or another we have all probably considered this possibility, however briefly. The very fact that you are able to actively wonder about this is a very important and powerful argument for your sanity. True *crazy* people tend to be unaware that they've lost touch with reality. They typically don't wonder if they're crazy because they are absolutely certain that they are sane. The strange things they may think, do, or say do not seem strange to them. It's this lack of awareness that makes *craziness* such a monumental problem. Thinking strange thoughts and sometimes doing strange things is not crazy. It's when the individual believes that the thoughts and actions that they engage in are not strange when everyone else would agree that indeed they are, that the loss of touch with reality truly occurs and *craziness* or insanity may be present.

As I explain the mild-moderate OCS condition to clients for the first time, they will often ask a question something along the lines of, "Well . . . Yeah, but doesn't everybody do that?" My reply tends to be pretty much the same. I tell them that many people, if not all of us, undoubtedly do and that the key to determining if it is a true problem or not is to try and figure out if the identified symptoms are interfering in one's day-to-day functioning. If so it is worth treating and even if not thought to be of significant inter- ference, it is still valuable and healthy for individuals to under- stand such symptoms when present and how they can affect their decisions and ultimately their life.

Clinical experience has suggested to me that a continuum of obsessive and compulsive behavior, characteristics, or symptoms exist that seems to be related to the Serotonin levels in the brain. There are undoubtedly other factors at work that influence and affect these behaviors, but the Serotonin levels appear to be at the heart of the matter, at least from my experience. Since every hu- man has Serotonin and it does the same things for every one of us, it makes perfectly good sense that most of us are going to have characteristics of obsessiveness and compulsiveness at some level or the other. The trick is recognizing it for what it is and in not allowing it to interfere with and/or run our lives. Easier said than done, I know.

The continuum theory would explain why some individuals need higher doses of medication for relief. Mild-moderate OCS adults tend to respond to Prozac, for example, at 20–60mg per day in my experience while the literature reports OCD (the severe form, remember) responds at 40–80mg per day. This is similarly true for the other SSRI as well. It has been my contention for some time now that the depressions responding positively to the SSRI medications are so responding due to the amelioration of underly- ing OCS that was never recognized or diagnosed. This, in my opin- ion, is why the literature reports that depression may take 3 to 6 weeks to begin responding to these medications. First, the under- lying obsessive and compulsive symptoms must improve signifi- cantly because together, they are what has caused the depression. In the mild-moderate range, improvement of these symptoms be- gin within days of starting an appropriately dosed SSRI, providing there are no interfering side effects. When an individual is plagued with 30 or 40 such symptoms (even though in only the mild-moderate range) that are manifested throughout the course of a day, it can be frustrating and ultimately quite depressing. Over time as this continues, other dynamics become involved that are not directly connected to the Serotonin levels and depression sets in. Thus, when enough OCS symptoms get better, it follows that the related depression would also thereafter begin to get better as well. Hence the three to six week time period before depression starts to lift. If, however, you are tracking specific symptoms of OCS, a change in the positive direction is quite often experienced almost immediately.

Given that I am suggesting these *symptoms* as I've called them are present in everyone, it is reasonable to suggest that we don't necessarily want to rid people completely of all obsessive and compulsive like behaviors. The goal is to relieve those symptoms that are clearly excessive in nature, temper others, and be made aware of them as many as possible. Education is still the best and most important treatment factor for just about anything. When you know what you are dealing with and begin to understand its implications, dynamics, and related features, you are in a position to make changes that will be more likely to last. This may be why depressed people who have been successfully treated with an SSRI tend to, when the medication is discontinued, become depressed again. The underlying OCS, having never been identified or discussed, returns when the medication is stopped and recreates the very same conditions that initially caused the depression that was being treated. Since no knowledge of this underlying cause was made available, the person could not anticipate nor work to block the reemergence of the depression by circumventing and/or changing their responses to these returning underlying symptoms.

When people are educated regarding the OCS prior to the start of a medication, they can see which specific symptoms are getting better and why ultimately the depression lifts. This allows them the time needed to develop new skills and new ways of being in the world without the interference of their symptoms. Then, when the medication is reduced or stopped and the symptoms start creeping back in, they can better see them for what they are and respond accordingly. Sometimes this happens in the head. You recognize a symptom as it's trying to occur and sort of say to yourself something like: "oh no, I'm not doing that one anymore" and you don't. You are able to do this because while on the medication, those new skills you developed along with the relief you experienced really do enable you to respond in a different way than you once had. Sometimes, because you no longer feel so overwhelmed all the time, your response to a given symptom's attempts to reenter your life can now be one of simple and successful flat-out resistance.

The tendency for symptoms to persist over time and grow in either number or strength is why those who are significantly OCS affected often feel so incredibly overwhelmed. After being treated for a time with appropriate medication, this symptom accumulation effect no longer has the power to overwhelm. As each symptom comes round again and is dealt with in a different and a more effective manner than before, the build up of emotional distress that used to occur no longer becomes so big and heavy. No longer does it simply overwhelm the individual and the resulting frustration, anger, and eventual depression can be averted.

You may be asking yourself the question, "so, if everyone of us has this OCS thing, doesn't that mean I'm . . . like . . . normal?" Yes it does. That's exactly what it means.

Recent research has reported teenagers who seem to have developed a type of lethargy (apathy or indifference) towards everything as a result of long term use of the SSRI group of medications and/or too high a dose. This group of medications consists of Prozac (Fluoxetine), Zoloft (Sertraline), Paxil (Paroxetine), Luvox (Fluvoxamine), and Celexa (Citalopram). This reported lethargy actually makes sense and fits in rather nicely with the hypothesis of a continuum. If very-very low Serotonin levels result in OCD (Obsessive Compulsive Disorder), and levels a bit higher but still lower than the norm result in OCS (Obsessive Compulsive Symptoms in the Mild-Moderate range), then it stands to reason that if the Serotonin levels were actually too high the resulting behavior might just be the opposite. On one end of the continuum you have individuals who care enormously about what is going on and are constantly *driven* in their responses to themselves and the environment. On the other end you should have people who aren't driven to do much of anything and don't care. This may be exactly what is going on.

Do we want to actually treat and eliminate all obsessive and compulsive types of behavior? I think not! This appears to be what gives us the desire or motivation to go beyond ourselves, to invent, to become really great in art, music, or sports. We don't want to lose these capacities; we want to enhance them. The goal, therefore, in the treatment of significant OCS is not to completely abolish the symptomotology, but to temper it just enough so that the affected individual can become aware and reactive to more than just the drives within him or herself. This dynamic is what makes the OCS affected look so selfish and self centered all the time. We also want the affected ones to become more conscious of their actions and responses and more sensitive to the impact that their own behavior has on others and on the environment.

CHAPTER TWO

WHAT WILL BE GIVEN ME TO OVER COME IN THIS LIFE
WHAT WILL I NEED IN ORDER TO SURVIVE
IF WE COULD JUST KNOW AHEAD OF TIME PERHAPS WE COULD PREPARE
FOR THE TRIALS IN LIFE . . . WE ALL HAVE TO BEAR

YOU KNOW, THE THINGS I'VE SEEN MAKE IT EASIER
EASIER TO UNDERSTAND
HOW SOME COULD CHOOSE . . . COULD CHOOSE . . .
YES COULD CHOOSE ANOTHER PLAN
WE ALL WANT SO MUCH TO KEEP OURSELVES
FROM HAVING TO FACE THE TRUTH
WE REALLY ONLY GROW FROM THE STRUGGLES IN LIFE
WE GET THROUGH

SOME HAVE NO LEGS . . . SOME FEEL THE NEED TO RUN AWAY AND HIDE
OTHERS CANNOT HEAR . . . SOME HAVE NO SIGHT
AND THERE ARE THOSE WHO CAN'T CONTROL THE WAY THEY MOVE . . .
SOME . . . THEY LIVE ALONE
OTHERS HAVE TWO HOUSES . . . AND SOME NO HOME

WHATEVER MAY OCCUR I WILL STRIVE TO LET IT BE
THE KIND OF THING FROM WHICH I LEARN I WHAT IT'S TEACHING ME
I'VE GOT TO TRY AND REMEMBER IT'S NOT . . . NO . . . NEVER JUST WASTED TIME
I'VE GOT TO SOMEHOW . . . SOMEHOW . . . HOLD THE LINE

From the song "The Struggles in This Life" by

Ron D. Kingsley

The Near Sighted Archer

"I don't want a pill controlling my life."

So said a young lady to me as I attempted to explain the potential benefits and positive reasons for considering a psychopharmacological treatment for her mild-moderate Obsessive Compulsive (OCS) and attention deficit hyperactivity disorder (ADHD) symptoms.

"If God had wanted me to be different . . . "she started to add in that old pat and well-worn argument that never really explains anything.

It occurred to me, however, that, although that argument

doesn't explain away anything, it certainly does demonstrate the depth of this young lady's convictions, or fear.

This got me to thinking. Just what does it mean in the life of a given individual, or to us, to be on, or in need of, what are known as psychoactive medications? The term psychoactive is defined as "mind altering", "mood altering", "affecting the mind or behavior", and/or "having an effect on the mental state of the user." Various synonyms are also widely in use but have essentially the same definition. These include the psychotropic, psychopharmacological, psychopharmaceutical, psychopharmacological, psychoactive, and, rarely, psychochemical.

Webster defines the term psycho itself as: *A victim of severe mental or emotional disorder.* Is it any wonder that when medications carry the prefix "psycho," the average individual is none too thrilled in the taking of it? These medications are already perceived in a negative light. The general public tends to shy away from medicines that primarily affect the mind and/or behavior. It seems obvious that the media has played a large role in the general public's perceptions of various specific psychotropic agents as well as these pharmaceutical agents in general. Another seemingly very important factor relating to the ways in which the general public perceives these medications must be of a spiritual, religious, and/or community awareness direction.

It has been suggested that individuals can generally be defined by the communities to which they belong. To a certain extent I believe this is true. A given individual may belong to several communities, each of which would have a general set of rules, guidelines, and beliefs to which they (more or less) ascribe. Because some differences must exist in the definition of a community (for it to exist as a separate community) an individual may be more strongly involved in one, or a few, and less so in others, and it stands to reason that one cannot belong (truly) to communities that are strongly disparate in their views. The entire world is, perhaps, our largest whole community as people. It may also be the one in which most people are the least actively involved simply because of its size alone. The United States of America is a community, as is England, Brazil, and Japan. The countries of the world form large communities followed by states, cities, towns, and neighborhoods. The family itself is perhaps the smallest community. Other communities include the schools we attend (from grade school to college), parent/teacher associations, the place at which you work, others who share in your profession, various religious communities, and so on.

At the heart of most (if not all) true communities is the belief that each individual has within themselves the capacity to grow and become whatsoever he and/or she may wish. This capacity, however, depends upon the wholeness of the individual. Expectations for those perceived as "less whole" are not equal to those thought to be "whole" because of a strong naturally occurring bias that the less whole are obviously also less capable. Thus, the one legged man is expected to lose the race against the man who has both legs. He is also often perceived as less than, or not as good as, the man with both legs intact is. The boxer with only one arm cannot be considered a serious contender against he who has both. Practically the only time such expectations are not held against the "less whole" is when their wholeness is not obviously in question. When others cannot easily see whatever it is the person may lack. That, or when in some ingenious fashion the less whole are made whole once again.

A near sighted archer, provided with corrective lenses, effectively erases the problems generated by her aspect of being less than whole. She can now compete on equal grounds with those individuals who retain their sighted wholeness.

If we, however, follow the logic of the deep seated community-laden belief system like the young lady at the beginning of this article, one might easily arrive at the conclusion that providing corrective lenses for this near sighted archer is the same as "cheating."

I can hear the argument even now.

"If God had wanted that archer to see clearly . . . he would have . . ."

It sounds quite silly right now, does it not? And yet the use of such lenses to correct a flaw in sight is theoretically no different than the taking of a medication for something such as ADHD or

OCS. The "pill" in this case represents the corrective lens, and the biochemical insufficiency represents the flaw in eyesight.

"Wait a minute!" I can imagine this hypothetical young lady's next argument. "Glasses don't change the person. They don't make her into somebody she's not. They don't make her into somebody different!"

"Ah, but they do indeed," would be my follow up response. Of course, just how much of a change occurs depends on how severe the flaw, or aspect of being less whole, actually is.

The near sighted archer, with corrective lenses, can once again win the archery tournament, or, all other things being equal, now achieve a much higher score for her efforts. She will also be able to read signs earlier and more easily, as well as recognize with greater ease and assurance friends and acquaintances from a distance. She may begin to smile more often and more readily. A spring may return to her step, or, in the case of never having seen too well, the spring may arise for perhaps the first time. Such movement is a common reflection of a strong inner confidence. It says, "I can see clearly now . . . the pain is gone." She becomes surer of herself, of her actions, and also her reactions.

Other's perceptions of this near sighted archer will similarly change. From an incompetent bumbling fool of an archer to a competent, prize-winning, expert in the field who is now admired rather than condemned. From a perceived stuck-up and aloof self-focused loser (or brat) who ignores friends and acquaintances on the street or across a crowded room; to the warm, observant, and conscientious friend who always notices and acknowledges the presence of friends and neighbors, associates and acquaintances in every possible situation.

Does getting glasses change one's behavior? Of course it does. Do glasses also affect the mood? Yes they do. Can it be that these foreign instruments of intervention (glasses) actually alter one's mind? Oh, yes they can! Can others perceive these changes and respond accordingly by altering their previously biased viewpoints? You bet!

Can the self and/or others develop new prejudices and negative perceptions resulting from the corrective lens intervention?

Sure they can. After all, life is no bed of roses. The thorns come with it as well.

"Four-eyes! Four-eyes!" Children are often cruel without the full realization of what it is they are doing. In fact, this has to be the primary reason for the creation and popularity of contact lenses.

And, what-do-you-know? Isn't this a similar situation to that of the pill? Well, yes and no. There is many a child, though, who upon receiving prescription glasses will for a time refuse to wear them. Some, too young to actually refuse, will lose them, forget them, break them, and wear them only until they get on the bus or are dropped off at school. Once out of parental eyesight, the glasses are quickly shoved to the bottom of their backpack and left there until the return trip home.

Not all of this reluctance related to wearing glasses can be blamed on the reactions of others, though. There is also the very real discomfort initially experienced in the actual wearing of the glasses, even given today's super-light lenses and frames. The weight alone irritates and puts pressure on the sides of the nose in spite of advances made in the construction softness and comfort of the supporting nose pieces. The weight similarly rubs and pulls at the ears which, however downplayed by others, can be quite painful for the first few weeks to a month. It takes a persistent and dedicated effort to get used to wearing them. When taken all together, these factors created a place for the invention of contacts. Contacts allowed teenagers and adults to escape the fairly frequent appellations of "bookworm," "brainer," and perhaps the most dreaded label of them all, "nerd." Contacts also enable these "less than whole" individuals, for all intents and purposes, to look as if they are "whole." One should never underestimate the psychological power that this "illusion of wholeness" holds for those who perceive themselves as "less than whole."

The child finding herself in this situation denies the need for corrective lenses.

"I can see just fine!" She proclaims loudly to any inclined to listen. "I don't need glasses," the child shouts out her wholeness. If it's said enough times, at just the right decibels, and with enough conviction, perhaps it will come true, or so they may pray in their hearts.

The teenager and adult say, "Gimmee contacts." These individuals are no longer able to effectively deny that a problem exists. The effects are openly obvious and the problem, at this time of life, is typically too severe to be ignored, so, they opt to hide it or make sure the physical evidence and effects are the least obvious as is currently possible.

Thus, the illusion of wholeness comes into play and enacts its subtle and insidious masquerade of wholeness on us all.

This is but one lone example of the myriad's of such masquerades of wholeness perpetuated on a daily basis by most, if not all, individuals and communities of the world. These charades eventually begin to fool even the individuals engaged in their use into believing in their own complete wholeness which serves to further enhance the unspoken community held notion that unless one is completely whole they are somehow inferior.

B.F. Skinner discovered, along with others, the very real behavioral principles that rocked the world community and became instruments of liberation for many. His work is at the heart, either directly or indirectly, of nearly every behavioral modification technique in use today and his insights regarding the whys and wherefores of behavior significantly enhanced the world's understanding of disordered behavior at all levels. Skinner seemed; however, to be suggesting that human free will does not exist. He appeared to feel that all actions and behavior labeled as, or thought to be, the result of free will, or individual choice, were in fact examples of operant conditioning. The idea that all behavior can be shaped or controlled if one had absolute control of the environment, in the opinions of many, is an extremist position. Skinner's work seemed to lead him down this road.

The human community, though, needs to believe in individual choice and ultimate free will. How else can punishment, or consequences, be justifiable in relation to an individual's unacceptable, asocial, and/or deviant behavior? If all behavior is learned and is the result of operant conditioning principles, then, personal responsibility is little more than a figment of the imagination. How then can communities hold individuals responsible for their inappropriate actions or, for that matter, applaud and reward others for those behaviors considered appropriate and/or outstanding in some way? This slight diversion of thought from the main point, or purpose, of this article seemed necessary to add depth to the contention that some beliefs and ways of thinking seem capable of being traced through physical boundaries and even those of time and show up in all parts of the world throughout recorded history. Free will is one such "world community" ideal.

"I don't want a pill to control my life!" she (and a true host of others) have said.

"So," I respond to this statement. "You would rather be controlled by a biophysical chemical deficiency (insufficiency) which you barely understand and don't yet have a clue how extensively has influenced (and still does influence) your life's choices, insidiously dictating much of what you do?"

"Yes," many have, and do respond to such a question. They mostly don't come right out and say "yes" but their actions (active denial) or lack of action (inactive denial) is essentially saying the same thing. They tend to not want their behavior influenced or changed by a pill. They simply do not realize that the deficient brain chemical is already influencing (often for some time) and changing behaviors that, without those brain chemical deviations, would have been significantly different and probably within the typical expected ranges of most others. Thus, just as weak or damaged eyes may require corrective lenses to correct the deficiency in eyesight (or, if you will, to change visual behavior). Insufficient brain chemicals that relate to other behaviors may require the intervention of a pill (a chemical booster) to correct the chemical levels which then will have an effect on behaviors dependent on these adequate chemical levels. Corrective lenses do not "control" the individual engaged in their use nor even the eyes, themselves. The correction simply clears up the vision so that the individual can experience the same or similar clarity that is common to most human beings. This clarity then allows the treated individual to behave differently than they had prior to the intervention. The lenses free the individual from being forced to respond to their environment inadequately, or in deviant ways, due to their faulty vision. Individual responsiveness is not forcibly changed. Behavioral options are broadened and the corrected eyesight enables the individual to now choose new behaviors that were not available to them prior to the intervention. Actions previously limited and controlled by poor eyesight are controlled and limited no more. The individual is now freer than ever before in all her response/ behaviors related to, or dependent upon, good eyesight. The intervention itself is not a chain lock tying the individual down for life; rather it is a liberator. Without the intervention the individual is already chained and restricted. Corrective lenses are a management tool helping the poor-sighted individual compensate for this weakness which simply does not respond to a strong will and/or a desperate desire to see more clearly. The individual is not to blame for poor eyesight. It is typically a genetic weakness completely out of their control. It is true that corrective lenses will probably have to be used throughout life, if the individual desires to have clear sight. So what? Lens prescriptions typically will need to be recalibrated or changed as time goes on (usually made stronger) as the visual deficiencies worsen due to damage, age, progressive disease and so on. This is consistent with the common course of events in all biophysical functions. These functions all weaken, some more than others, with age and eventually many individuals who never had to before will require aides (or interventions) if sensorial and bodily functions are to be kept at previous (and/or) adequate levels. Otherwise, significant behavioral changes will follow these functional deteriorations. Eventually, no intervention in the world can correct and/or prevent the functional deterioration brought on by age. Some nevertheless try to lessen this deterioration anyway, but it is always a losing battle.

Now, let's go back to biochemical intervention once again. Interventions within this realm of functioning are yet in their infancy. Corrective lenses have been in use and constantly refined for over seven hundred years. This is not true for the biochemical. There are far too many people who not only remain unaware and therefore have trouble believing when told. Some either refuse to believe or, for a variety of reasons, are incapable of believing that brain chemicals affect behavior in some of the ways that they do. Community beliefs and mores have a lot to do with this. So, also, does the media.

The discovery that chemicals of the brain have powerful influences on human behavior is much like the discovery that behavior is learned through operant conditioning. Many, when presented with such an idea have fears that, once again, scientists have come up with a theory that takes away human free will. Those in the know, however, realize that biochemical causation, or influence, is only a partial causal factor resulting in only some of the overall behaviors engaged in by those so affected. Like learned behavior, it accounts for only a percentage of behavioral responses and even these often remain under the partial control of affected individuals or can vary within certain specific parameters, making it appear as if complete control is actually available.

This on going discovery of biochemical causation doesn't exclude free choice or free will. It enhances our understanding there of. Most behaviors relative to OCS have elements of learned behavior too, and behavior modification may be the most effective, and therefore best, intervention or treatment when evaluation determines this is the primary, or most likely, underlying causative factor. Some behaviors are biochemically induced and psychopharmacological intervention may prove most effective when evaluation indicates this probability. Interestingly, there is a wealth of research demonstrating that many of the identified (so-called) behaviors making up the behavioral disorders with known or suspected biochemical origins are most effectively treated when both behavior modification and psychotropic agents are used as intervention strategies together. When behavior is primarily related to a physical deficiency (other than brain chemicals) and the treatment corrects, or compensates, for the deficiency (as in the case of the near sighted archer), the behavior, of course, dramatically improves as well. Up until the true root of the behavior is identified and corrected, or compensated for, interventions aimed at the behavior itself will be less than adequate. The intervention may be somewhat effective because behavioral causation is rarely, if ever, completely the result of only one component. Factors are combined, often with one or two as main contributors. Thus, treatment specific to one causative factor will usually have a positive effect on the related behaviors, yet not much of an effect (if any) on behaviors relative to other causative factors, although often indirect positive effects do also occur.

The ability to choose, or free will, is (in my opinion) yet another element responsible for some behaviors. Those behaviors relating to this factor may be most effectively treated by knowledge gained through education and such educational strategies are myriad in number. Knowledge alone, however, as everyone knows, is frequently not enough. The reason for this, it seems to me, is that the behavior in question is the result of one or more determinants beyond that of free choice not yet identified or compensated for. Thus, a combination of intervention strategies, it makes sense, are more-than-likely going to be necessary when intervening behaviorally for most problems in order to achieve the most effective outcome.

To the common parental cry of, "I've told you a thousand times!" I suggest the appropriate answer to a parent with this complaint might be, "So, out of that thousand times, how often did you actually strive to insure your child was completely capable of performing the expected task adequately? Did you assist and support him until there was strong evidence indicating he was entirely capable of satisfactory independent performance? Or, did you simply provide information and verbalize what you wanted the child to do, assuming that because of age, or anticipated maturity level, his capacity to perform the task adequately must be present?"

A parent doing the above is assuming that free will, or choice, is the only element involved in the behavioral repertoire necessary to perform the requested action. This, however, may or may not be the case. If it is, then there may be some justification for the parental anger that so commonly accompanies that frustrated cry of a thousand times.

The parent usually believes that the child chose purposefully not to follow their instructions, directions, demands or rules. This can have a devastating affect on the parent child relationship. As a result of this "partial control" that exists, the parent (teacher, or adult) feels justified in their belief that the child is actually in complete control and deserves every bit of consequence that strict adherence to rules demands. Parents are also frequently so "fed-up" and/or frustrated by such behavior that no compassion is available to soothe the distraught child. The general experienced feeling is one along the lines of: "She made her bed . . . now let her sleep in it!"

The insidious intertwining of behavioral causation is often so difficult to disentangle that they become mistaken one-for-another. When this happens interventions may miss the mark and/or only prove partially effective. This is true of dual or more than one, biochemical causation as well.

A good example of such a biochemical situation exists in the common (genetically connected) co-morbid disorders of OCS, ADHD, and Tourette's. It is not unusual to see ADHD and effects early in life and also to confuse the two because symptoms result in so many similar observed behavioral responses. Both problems are exacerbated (made worse) by anger, fatigue, emotional excitement, and/or stress. Both are also primarily due to related yet different biochemical deficiencies and, as such, respond to pharmacological interventions of dissimilar origin and/or activation.

Thus, not only can behavior result from different components but it can also arise from subsets within an identified main component. Differing physical problems (i.e., eyesight, hearing, etc.) can bring about behavior that is atypical and/or problematic that needs quite different intervention strategies (i.e., corrective lenses vs. hearing aids). So, also, can there be learned behaviors that require different kinds of intervention as in specific learned phobias, which respond to desensitization. Furthermore, the behavior of learned tantrumming (although not all tantrumming is learned) may respond to several behavior modification techniques, as well as the biochemical interventions (i.e., OCS and the SSRI and ADHD) such as various medications. Interestingly enough, it is my contention that similar problems arise within the realm of free will. In other words, there are different ways of communicating knowledge that may or may not inspire one's free will to kick in and take over (The humorous approach, factual approach, lecture, insight oriented and so on).

The important thing to remember is that "no behavior is an island." There is almost certainly a combination of causal factors coming together to create all behavioral dysfunction. This is why it is particularly important when psychologically or psycho-educationally evaluating individuals (especially children) to rule out vision and hearing problems and possibly some others as primary factors relative to their behavior and/or day-to-day functioning. Unfortunately, we are not yet at a level wherein biochemical influences, learned behavioral interference, and free will can be readily determined. Nor can we separate them into neat little percentages that might tell us how much influence each may be generating on a specific given problem or group of inappropriate behaviors. However, in order to intervene with the greatest chance of success, efforts should be made to discover, in-as-much-as-possible, all potential influences before deciding on the initial direction that intervention's should take.

For example, if a large portion of problem behaviors are similar to behaviors exhibited by a group that is known to have a strong biochemical root, such as OCD and/or OCS, the most appropriate initial treatment option may very well be medication. With medication for these particular problems (especially in the mild to moderate ranges) as much as 50 to 90 percent of the problematic behaviors and responses may improve dramatically. Thus, the remaining behaviors would fall into the other three categories and, hopefully, physical has already been ruled in or out, leaving mainly learned behavior and free will. These two typically respond both to awareness or education and behavior modification. In cases where biochemical influences are involved, the initial treatment therein can drastically reduce many of the problem or target behaviors needing intervention. In the OCS/OCD case, this initial psychotropic intervention typically can change the entire focus of a therapeutic/counseling plan of action. Issues of previous therapeutic import and clinical focus often simply melt away and/or may need to be significantly reframed in light of the frequent, fairly dramatic changes in the psyche as well as the behavior. Prior diagnoses may need to be reconsidered or at least broadened just a bit. Now, behavior modification techniques for any problematic behaviors that remain, as well as awareness and education, will be at their most effective because the biochemical influence is no longer a primary interfering factor.

Appropriate interventions enable both clinician and client to begin the process of disentangling the contributing causal factors and determining, in-as-much-as-is-possible, how much of an influence each has been exerting on the referral problem, or problems.

This also gives the treating clinician and professionals the opportunity to consider common co-morbid and related disorders that may need additional psychopharmacological interventions, as in the case of the genetically related ADHD, OCS/OCD, and Tourette's syndrome. Since ADHD and OCS (not the full-fledged diagnosable disorder, but the symptoms that vacillate within the mild to moderate ranges) are in many ways very similar (especially to the untrained observer), it is helpful when the clinician, aware of this, is prepared to consider this dual diagnosis. When the ADHD and OCS related biochemical deficiencies are both found to be significantly interfering or influencing the behavior, then both may require psychopharmacological interventions of a different (yet related) genre in order to maximize treatment effectiveness. When either ADHD or OCS is misdiagnosed, one-for-the-other, the knowledgeable clinician will suspect this is the case quickly, as typically the ineffectiveness of the prescribed medication is often quite obvious, and suggest that an alternative related diagnosis might be the actual primary contributing factor. When this is the case, a recommendation to change to an appropriate medication can be made early on.

Thus, the task of the clinician, counselor, psychologist, and/or therapist is to, as-thoroughly-as—possible, investigate all prospects relating to an individual's reasons for the troubles/problems initiating the referral. As has been suggested, these tend to fall into several clusters as follows:

    Learned Behavior: stemming from environment, experiences, punishments, rewards and etc.

    Physical Causation: manifested by weak eyesight, poor hearing, organ failure, deformities, and loss of limb and so on.

    Biochemical Causation: manifested by brain chemical deficiencies and inconsistencies such as Serotonin levels relating to OCS/OCD and Dopamine/Norepinepherine in relation to ADHD and etc.

    Self-directed behaviors/Free will/and/or choice: manifested by an individual's capacity to control and dictate, or govern, actions and behaviors as they so choose.

As indicated previously, there are causal subsets within each of the above-related main precipitating components. Any and all such components of their subdivisions can influence or interfere with typical behaviors directed or caused by other components or factors. Thus, although a contention of this expose is that free will does indeed exist as a foundational agent in the formation of many behaviors, this does not automatically mean that free will is completely and totally free. An example may help to get this concept across.

Let's go back to the near sighted archer briefly. Although this archer has the ability to choose to study and work at the sport of archery she is not free to perform at her highest potential no matter how much she practices and no matter how persistently she demonstrates the will to do so. Her free will may want to choose to work hard to become a master archer. Her weak vision, however, is taking away a portion of that free will and therefore her free will alone is ineffective in changing or making a difference in this chosen avocation no matter how strong her will may be.

Free will, however, was surely a major factor that enabled us to recover the partial loss of behavioral selection due to poor eyesight. The invention of the corrective lens was the result of an individual who was bound and determined to regain the ground and freedom lost to this weakness in visual perception. Thus, the visually weak, or impaired, rather than being chained by, limited to, or restricted by the use of corrective lenses, are in reality liberated in the reclaiming of a variety of behavioral options that were indeed lost as a result of this weakness in vision. The same, I believe, is true in relation to the biochemical realm.

As in the example above, behavioral options belonging to the free will are lost, significantly influenced, and/or interfered with when the foundational biochemical system within each individual is compromised in some way. Brain chemicals in excess, deficit, inconsistent availability, and/or absence will have their effects and jeopardize once again the consistency and ready availability of a host of typical behaviors. We are free, and yet depending upon the forces in play, we are also not free, in a very real way.

The freedom to choose has always been recognized as a human characteristic dependent on other factors within the specific environment and circumstances wherein one exists. The free will, or choice to take a walk whenever one has the desire, can be severely modified and even completely taken away for periods of time, spanning the briefest of Moments up to an entire life time. Prisoners, or inmates, experience a loss of free will in their ability to take a walk that is proportional to the seriousness of the crime they committed. Serious crimes usually result in a greater loss of personal freedom and, hence, a loss of free will.

Sometimes I find myself wondering why it seems so easy for most people to accept that a compromise in the environment can seriously impact our free will, and yet many of these same individuals can't accept, or even acknowledge, that free will can be similarly affected by learned behaviors and biochemical elements. I also think, or am presumptuous enough to believe, that I know why the above may be true. This, in turn, causes me to wonder why I even wonder? Enough of that, though.

The reason biochemical and learned behavioral causation are conceptually difficult it seems to me, has a lot of do with how visible or obvious actual interfering environmental factors are viewed by practically everyone. There can be no real argument that an inmate locked in a cell has had his or her free will to take a walk seriously compromised. We can visualize the cell. We can easily imagine how such a factor as being locked up would interfere with our own free will. It is as obvious as discerning the night from the day.

Let's imagine that a particular inmate has been locked up in his tiny cell for the first five years of his ten-year sentence. The warden of this imaginary prison is not especially prone to treating the inmates in a humane and reasonable manner. He has left this inmate in his cell, and only his cell, for the entire five years. Food has been brought to the cell when made available at all. There is a toilet in the cell that sometimes doesn't flush. Thus, there has been no need to open our inmate's cell door. It has never been unlocked in five years. The inmate is now severely depressed. Therefore, given the described situation, most of us should easily be able to visualize this and feel as if we understand. We can sense that anyone treated in such a manner would probably be very depressed; heck after five years, you might even wonder about our inmate's sanity and seriously doubt your own ability to withstand such apparently abusive conditions.

Now, let's assume that at the five-year mark the prison's warden had a sudden change of heart. No, let's not go in that direction. That's too unbelievable. Let's just say he left the prison for undisclosed reasons. A new warden is hired from out of state. This warden is humane and she believes in certain inalienable rights of all inmates. One such belief is an inmate's right (free will) to take a walk, in-as-much-as-is-possible, pretty much whenever they so desire (of course, within the confines of the prison facility).

Suddenly our inmate finds a large portion of his free will to walk miraculously (or so it must seem) returned. Although he remains incarcerated in the very same cell that he has occupied the last five years, the door is now left unlocked from eight a.m. to eight p.m. daily so that he can take advantage of his newly recovered freedom. This procedure is much more humane than before. The hapless inmate's free will in this area yet remains not entirely his own, but under the new management he is much more free than he had been under the old warden's now historic five-year-plan.

After a week with this new policy in place, the new warden pays a visit to the inmate. She's very concerned. In the seven-day period since the inmate was given back a portion of his free will, not once has he chosen to exercise even a single freedom relative to those that were returned? He has not ventured forth at all from his tiny cell. He has not so much as even touched or approached the unlocked door of his cell, let alone opened it. He might just as well have still been on the old five-year plan with his cell door irrevocably locked.

This is where it begins, conceptually, to get a little harder to follow, understand, and eventually to even consider as possible. Of course, in a real life situation it is never as simple as suggested in the example being created herein which is being purposefully oversimplified, for the sake of explanation and hopefully better, or more comprehensive understanding of human behavioral causation.

The identified inmate's cell door remains unlocked during the specified times on a daily basis. The warden has visited him several times. So has the prison's psychologist. The psychologist has diagnosed the inmate as experiencing a Major Depressive Disorder. He doesn't even care that his door is unlocked. He's too depressed to go anywhere or do anything. The psychologist doesn't even try to conceal her amazement that the inmate is still eating.

Although the inmate is clearly in control of a significant number of new behavioral options, he steadfastly refuses to act on them. It's as if he believes these options don't exist. This particular example, in its simplified one-dimensional form, is primarily the result of the "learned behavioral causation" category and can be conceptualized as a product of what has become known as "learned helplessness." This factor is now interfering with this inmate's free will and seriously limiting him. These limits are in exactly the same dimensions as were originally established by the environment of his imprisonment. Why?

Rather than attempt a detailed explanation as to how it can be possible that our inmate's free will remains restricted in spite of his obvious freedom, I hope that you might be able to accept even just the possibility that such a story as that of the inmate is entirely plausible. This is one of the first steps to ultimate understanding. The belief that something *is* possible.

Physical causation, like many of the learned behavioral origins, is easier to conceptualize and accept, again I believe, because of its widespread visibility along with the long held world community experience and belief systems. Corrective lenses, hearing aids, wheel chairs and etc., are not perceived as having the potential to actually change the who-we-are. Such things are generally not believed to act as potentially personality altering interventions even though they absolutely can be, and almost always are, exactly that.

Free will itself is difficult to conceptualize and accept as a definitive reality (in spite of its having a strong, worldwide, community held and long standing acceptance as real). This, I believe, is essentially because of its invisibility. Furthermore, free will cannot be touched, measured, heard, smelled, tasted, or depended upon (in many instances). Biochemical factors are similarly invisible. When brain chemical fluctuations are actively influencing behavior and thereby considered primarily causal elements interfering with an individual's free will, these chemical fluctuations cannot be seen, felt, heard, smelled, or even tasted. The interference is invisible. Since the biochemical influence has usually been life long, whatever influence and/or interference is already occurring in relation to an individual's free will: it is nearly a universal perception by those affected individuals that their free will is entirely intact. When such a belief is in place, it is quite understandable that the treated individual fear that the behavioral changes associated with the psychopharmacological intervention are affecting and changing their basic personality structure. The individual often feels terrified at the prospect of having to redefine the very person whom they have long believed themselves to be. As described herein, though, the individual becomes caught in the illusionary trap of experience. They only know themselves as who they currently are and always have been. The chronic lifelong nature of underlying biochemical causes makes it nearly impossible for them to consider the "who-they-might-be" without having had the constant biochemical interference and influence. Their perception of the self has often been insidiously distorted. This distortion has been on going for such a long period of time that they simply cannot conceive of themselves as changing or becoming different from how they are now, unless (and herein lies the kicker) the intervention used *is* actually somehow altering their basic personality structure. Much of the reason such a belief persists seems related to how very quickly significant behavioral changes can occur, take a pill and, voila, within an hour, specific behavioral patterns can become altered. For some disorders, change occurs in days, and for some in weeks. Often no discernable effort to alter behaviors other than the act of ingesting the pill at the appropriately prescribed time intervals has been made by the individual being treated. This, many see, as the most powerful available evidence demonstrating there is indeed a change in personality occurring. The people who react in this way, I believe, out of no real fault of their own are perceiving the situation in reverse, and since most have been given no reason to consider or believe otherwise, this inaccurate perception remains steadfast in their minds. Such a perception may hover around the fringes of their thoughts, making it a struggle, at times, to continue with prescribed psychotropic interventions.

As briefly touched upon previously, I believe those encountering biochemical behavioral interference almost always have an incredibly difficult time accepting the idea that their belief in who they really are could be a false or mistaken perception. The chemical intrusion has always been there. Thus, when this interference is suddenly eradicated, either completely or partially, how can they be expected to see such often dramatic change as anything but an actual loss of who they are, rather than a successful intervention or attack on the actual problem? Such a loss can be extremely disconcerting to the treated individual for all of the reasons already explored herein, and undoubtedly others as well. The uncertainty this situation engendered within treatment responders' places them extremely high up on the personal vulnerability scale. This vulnerability can fairly easily be translated into the role of victim. The victimizers may be the media, well meaning (and I suppose some not so well meaning) friends, acquaintances, perceived authority figures, distant relatives, and even immediate family members. Individuals in vulnerable states are frequently more easily influenced than when not experiencing such emotionally fragile frames of mind. Emotions and perceptions can sometimes be tipped from one side to the other almost as quickly as a ping pong ball gets batted back and forth over a net. This is a tenuous period.

Fortunately in my experience, a good percentage of those initially diagnosed with OCS and ADHD (and their immediate family members) do see the psychopharmacological influenced behavioral alterations as a positive transformation. Distraught parents sometimes view children's responses as a much sought after return to previous higher levels of functioning. Over the last fifteen years as I have worked extensively with children and adults in the initial diagnosis and treatment of OCS/OCD, ADHD, and Tourette's Syndrome there have been several occasions in which Mothers of treated children have thanked me. This has been done either via phone, in a written letter, or personally during a session, for "returning their child" to them.

So many times in early sessions, parents attempting to explain their child's problematic behaviors that caused them to be brought in to see a clinical psychologist are "caught between a rock and a hard place." Usually by the time events bring their child in for treatment, their child's actions and behaviors have typically reached a point of constant intolerability. Almost without exception, as parents unfold the story (as they perceive it) about their child, they, at some point, are struck by the discrepancy between the description that they are painting and how, in the depths of their souls, they really care about and feel for their child. Often they exclaim in anguish, " . . . but she really is a wonderful person . . ."

" . . . He truly is good in his heart, you know . . ." and so on.

Frequently such admonishments are repeated many times throughout the course of initial sessions. I often get the impression that many of these parents are hanging on by a thread of belief and hope that their declarations of goodness really are true. Many seem to be searching for reassurance that what they believe about their child is the truth. They want, sometimes desperately, to hear the psychologist, counselor, therapist, or whomever tell them,

"Yes! You're absolutely correct. He does have a good heart."

"Yes! She is wonderful." in spite of the observable behavioral evidence suggesting the opposite.

The parent hopes for this reaffirmation and at the same time also fears (often at an unconscious level) the "professional" will proclaim the child to be the vile, loathsome, evil creature their behavior seems to be shouting to the world that they are. The biochemically driven individual can appear to others (and even to themselves) to be all of the above and more. Fortunately, I can honestly report that in all my years of private practice and extensive work in the public school setting, the parent has, every time in the case of their declaration of goodness, been absolutely correct. The child is good. The real problem is that something else is interfering with the child's ability to demonstrate their true inner goodness in a consistent enough way that others are able to see it and respond to this goodness, rather than to the interference. I do not believe I have ever worked with an "evil" child, although I readily admit to having worked with many who, for all intents and purposes, certainly appeared to be that way, at least initially. Invariably, children who seem malevolent are those who truly have biochemical dysfunction as a primary underlying cause for the observable behavior. Usually there are learned behaviors stemming from the influence of the biochemically driven behaviors that may be a lesser, though sometimes equally important, contributing or supporting factor as well.

Interestingly, in the cases I have come across wherein the initial treating professional has told the parents, was seen as telling them, that the future prognosis is poor because there is something a bit nefarious about this particular child, the seeds of mistrust and doubt have been invariably sewn. Parents reject such a pronouncement in their hearts even while often attempting to follow the recommendations of this "expert" who must know at least more than they do regarding what is going on. Sometimes parents have seen numerous "professionals" and are understandably discouraged and weary. The biochemical causative factor is still in its infancy, although I believe it is even now merging into childhood. There is much that remains unknown. Professionals quite often have simply not had enough experience or training in the recognition and/or treatment of behaviors caused or significantly influenced in this way.

As this is written, cases flood my mind relating to the three inter-related, inherited, and bioneurochemically driven disorders of which I am most familiar with and for which I have worked hard to become an "expert" (in continuous training, I would add). These are the aforementioned disorders of ADHD, OCS/OCD, and Tourette's Syndrome. Many of my clients seen in private practice (with these particular disorders) have been to several (and some quite a few) previous counselors, therapists, physicians, and/or psychologists. There they have received incomplete and/or improper diagnoses which have frequently led to interventions being applied that may have resulted in some improvement which, either doesn't last, or simply isn't helping enough for continued treatment to be pursued. This can result in the parents doubting their inner feelings and "gut instincts" relating to the commonly held belief in their own child's goodness.

Once previously undiagnosed ADHD, OCS, and/or Tourette's is finally recognized and treated appropriately (usually with a combination of education and insight, psychopharmacological interventions, behavior mod techniques, and a therapeutic disentangling of personal, social, and family dynamics related to the problem) the light goes on in the parents' eyes as well as in their hearts. "Yes!" they say. "This feels right." It also explains how the affected individual can seem so wicked and vile and yet, in reality, be so very good.

Adults recognized as having one or more of these three disorders, when treated appropriately, are often relieved of long-carried and accumulative burdens of guilt, frustration, and irrepressible anger directed at themselves in relation to how badly they feel about their own misbehaviors. Anger is very often aimed at parents and significant others as well for a lack of understanding and the resultant responses that occurred. Awareness and appropriate treatment provides the affected adult an opportunity to reframe their recollections of the past in a new light of recognition and understanding of the true underlying problem(s). Reframing historical recollections can (and usually does) free the individual from immediate as well as what can be enormous emotional stockpiles collected over the course of a life time of guilt, self-hate, and self-directed fury, as well as misappropriated anger leveled at parents and others. This experience alone can significantly boost the individual's energy levels, enable important old emotional wounds to finally heal, and provide the desire and motivation to persist in this difficult journey of discovery, liberation, and healing. The treatment process is on going and includes continuing education, appropriate interventions, and an acceptance that these particular bioneurochemical disorders are managed more or less successfully over time and not cured.

As I ponder what I've written herein thus far, I can't help but think treatment for the biochemically driven problematic behaviors would be so much easier if, like learned behavioral and physical causation, we could see, touch, hear, smell, or taste the elements involved. We can't though, anymore than we can do the same in relation to free will (which, by the way, is why some may reject its presence as a causative factor and/or its existence altogether).

There is however, it seems to me, at least one other (as yet undisclosed) way in which the recognition and treatment of specific biochemically driven behaviors and disorders can yet be perhaps made easier. Since the five senses, as indicated, are at an incredible disadvantage relative to biochemical recognition, an alternative pattern of recognition is needed. This pattern, in my opinion, can be seen vicariously as the affected individual connects with similar behaviors and actions that are described in the stories and descriptions offered by another. The discovery of the self in the anecdotes of another can be a powerful confirmation of previously misunderstood and hidden truths. The connection created by such recognized truths can be sufficient to motivate the affected individual, or parent/guardian of an affected minor, to actively seek out appropriate professional assistance.

One of the biggest problems relating to the recognition and

treatment of most of the biochemically influenced problems and disorders is that left untreated, the affected individual is not likely to die anytime soon as a direct result of the disorder. Although occasionally the behaviors can lead to possible serious injury, and even death, theses dreaded consequences are not directly related to the biochemical problem. Individuals don't die from a lack of impulse control. The moving car their impulsive behavior influenced them to run out in front of can, however, injure and/or be the instrument of their early demise.

Individuals in the helping professions are constantly searching for examples, or real life experiences, that can be compared to the psychoactive biochemically originating behaviors. This is done in an attempt to create vicarious experiences and connect with these affected individuals or significant others in order to facilitate understanding, and ultimately, treatment.

Several years ago in a casual conversation with one of my trusted friends and long time colleagues he shared an example that he would normally use. This physician indicated that when trying to enable parents and/or affected individuals to understand and accept the need for psychopharmacological intervention in cases of ADHD and OCS/OCD or depression, he would compare it to insulin dependent diabetes. This analogy, however, somehow did not ring true in my heart. As we talked I felt his explanation darting through my conscious (and perhaps unconscious) mind, searching for that all-important connection. It did not happen. I spoke up and indicated to him that, for some reason, this comparison (at least for me) was weaker than logic dictated it ought to have been. As I gave voice to these thoughts, it occurred to me that this lack of recognition and lack of a truly powerful connection was due to one major difference in the treatment of these disorders versus diabetes. All are primarily treated via a medication. All, when untreated, significantly influence behavioral responsiveness. The insulin dependent individual, however, if left untreated is very quickly in danger of death and will soon die as a direct result of his biochemical insulin-related problem. This direct relationship to physical expiration is the reason my gut told me this factor belongs in the physical causation group; nevertheless, it is a biophysical chemical disorder. My colleague's use of this inexact analogy, even though similar in some important ways, to the OCS/ADHD/depression experience, created enough dissonance in my mind and heart that I felt compelled to share the eye-glass comparison that I had developed for similar situations.

Thus, we have gone full circle and returned to, (you have probably easily surmised), that's right, the now hopefully infamous Near Sighted Archer. The comparison of the interventions involving corrective lenses and psychotropic agents for OCS/ADHD/depression connects with me, as I hope it does for you. If an individual with mild-moderate visual problems who needs glasses does not get them, she will absolutely not seriously injure herself or lose her life as a direct result. She may, however, be injured and even experience death from the speeding car that her poor vision just might interfere with enough to influence her to step out in front of.

Out of her misery. The only way out. Depressed individuals frequently do not think clearly. This is widely known. People who aren't thinking clearly sometimes do things they otherwise would not do.

I hear her callin' . . . callin' out to me
And I can't help thinkin' . . . it's time to let it be
This world keeps turnin' . . . days go swiftly by
And my heart keeps yearnin' . . . way down deep inside
And I know she knows . . . who I am and I'll yet be depends on just . . .
What I want and where I go and what I need and so . . .
She goes right on believin' that there's no way out
In the struggle for ascension there can be no doubts
Yet she doubts
I see her runnin' . . . runnin' in my dreams
And she's also dancin' . . . dancin' wild and free
And she knows I know . . . who she is and she'll yet be depends on just . . .
What she wants and where she goes and what she needs and so . . .
I go right on believin' that there's no way out
In the struggle for ascension there's no room for doubt
But I have doubts
And this world keeps turnin' . . . years move swiftly by
And we go right on learnin' . . . it's what keeps us alive
And I know you know . . . who you are and you'll yet be depends on just . . .
What you want and where you go and what you need and though . . .
You no longer feel that there is no way out
In the struggle for ascension there is always doubt
We all have doubts
Everybody doubts
There's always doubt

From the song "Doubts" by Ron D. Kingsley

CAMOUFLAGE: OCS OVER TIME

The absolute most common reason given by the OCS affected
for their frequently irritating and sometimes inappropriate behaviors is; "I don't know." At least this is the most common response
initially. That is to say that early on in life this tends to be the
response. It doesn't take long, though, for the affected individual
to learn that others do not like or appreciate such an answer even if
it is true. People tend to believe in the power of reasons. It is fairly
often believed that unless the reason for a behavior, or action, can
be determined, it will be difficult, and/or impossible to change it
or stop. Also, once a person makes sense of, or understands why a
thing happens, the world (environment) becomes a less frightening place in which to live. When the cause for a behavior is known,
a person may feel comfort as well from the newly obtained ability
this provides to predict their own or another's actions.

Since many obsessive and compulsively driven behaviors in
the mild-moderate range closely resemble other behaviors in the
general population for which the accepted cause is from a different

source and well known the truly biochemically caused OCS related actions tend to be erroneously considered the same. In other words, the generally believed reasons for the "popular" behaviors become the believed reasons for the OCS driven behaviors as well. Individuals with OCS will commonly begin to accept that the popularly held reasons for certain behaviors must be the very same reasons at the heart of their own unacceptable behaviors, as they typically have a hard time coming up with acceptable explanations themselves. Although such mistaken beliefs may be tentative at first, eventually (with no better explanations forthcoming) this faulty thinking can become so strongly embedded into the affected's belief system that they become incapable of even considering the possibility that an alternative cause actually might exist. This, experience suggests, is one of the main reasons why mild-moderate OCS is so frequently misdiagnosed.

Another important element that tends to interfere with the OCS affected's ability to accept the idea of an alternative cause is *fear*. These persons often strongly feel that they *must* have a reason for *everything*. Thus, when they finally accept whatever they believe the cause is for a behavior, this acceptance can become *locked* in and absolute. Knowing the source of things reduces anxiety and fear. To let go of a well established believable reason is to invite fear and anxiety back into the picture. It tends to be much easier to instantly dismiss all other possibilities in order to avoid the misery such uncertainty usually brings. Frequently there is a need to not only have had an explanation for all things available; but these explanations also had better be believable too. Some of the OCS affected may fear that if their interpretations for their behavior are not believable, that others will surely conclude they are crazy, weird, or insane. Sometimes the explanations provided are exactly what the OCS affected truly believes and sometimes these accounts are cover ups, or flat-out lies. Quite often such false explanations are developed because the affected one simply has no other explanation for their behavior or actions. They don't know why. They are often afraid that others simply would not believe them if they told the truth. It is incredibly difficult for people to believe and accept that there are actions and behaviors that some of us engage in without having an understandable reason at all. So, those who are OCS affected often can become very good actors. Another way that could be used to describe this is that they become very good liars. This represents a fairly common part of the reason why so many of the affected have serious social problems. A believable explanation, even if the individual isn't sure it's true, can eventually serve to convince the affected one that there really is nothing wrong with them which further helps them to keep anxieties and fears in check. Thus, there is often a strong internally experienced need to believe in and subsequently refrain from questioning, doubting, or changing already held beliefs. This can be true even when the accepted reason or explanation doesn't quite fit the OCS behavior it is supposed to explain. Active confrontations early on or challenges made by a therapist/counselor or psychologist to the OCS affected's belief system may result in massive and extreme denial, which can result in premature therapeutic termination.

Children with OCS soon learn that parents and teachers don't really want them to be honest. Although these adults may tend to emphatically declare and even insist that they only want the child to tell the truth, the OCS child's experience in attempting to do so eventually teach them that this statement is false. When first asked to explain why a given (OCS driven) behavior has occurred, or continues to occur, the child will tend to respond openly and honestly with something like, "I don't know". Typically the adult authority figures hearing this will become upset and believe that the child actually does know the reasons for their behavior and is simply refusing to tell. In time adults involved with such a child can begin to feel or believe that he is a liar. They may even begin to confront and call him a liar right to his face. This places him in a double bind or no-win situation. The fairly common OCS tendency for extreme self-doubt may even get its start from experiences like these.

Another, more specific example of this same dynamic is demonstrated in an actual case that I was involved with years ago. A 10-year-old boy's parents wanted me to work with their son whom they indicated had been long before diagnosed with ADHD, and more recently with school phobia. This diagnosis was by a counselor in conjunction with a psychiatrist who they initially began to see because these professionals were covered by their insurance plan. This boy, however, (let's call him Billy) continued, in spite of being actively treated, to demonstrate extreme resistance in relation to going to school, such that his Mother was only able to get him there two or three days out of the week. The morning fight prior to school was exhausting her and sometimes she just did not have the physical energy or the emotional strength needed to win the daily battle it took to get him there.

In checking with Billy's teachers, something the psychiatrist/counselor team had somehow neglected to do, several important and interesting facts were discovered. Once Billy's Mother was able to get him successfully to his classroom, there would be no further observable evidence whatsoever that he had a problem with being in school. Furthermore, Billy had apparently been quite successful in convincing his Mother (as well as his treatment team members) that the reasons he didn't want to go to school were many and very *real*. These included the following: other students didn't like him, teased him, and even got physical (pushing and hitting him). The teachers were mean, did not like him, and treated him unfairly. Finally, he complained (quite believably) that the school work was not only too difficult for him, but that the teachers also refused to provide him with help when he needed it. Teachers, when interviewed personally by me, refuted and were surprised in regard to each and every allegation Billy had gotten his Mother and these others to believe.

Prior to his arrival at the school wherein this was happening, the teachers to be involved in his education had been informed prior to his arrival at the school regarding Billy's status as a diagnosed student with ADHD and modifications and accommodations had already been set in place. Billy was also an identified student with specific learning disabilities and received special education resource services of which all teachers had also been made aware. No teachers, lunch aides, or recess aide had ever seen another student push, hit, tease, or be unkind to Billy, and his teachers generally felt that he was well liked by his peers. As a result of the accommodation plan, homework was only being sent home with

Billy if teachers were absolutely certain he would be able do the work on his own. Furthermore, teachers indicated that he would hardly ever ask for help, nor would he indicate that he needed any. He similarly did not demonstrate a willingness to accept one-to-one teacher assistance even when a given teacher thought he might be struggling and made an offer to assist him. At such times he would inform these teachers who'd offered that he was not in need of assistance.

All of the above-related information was obtained prior to my first visit with Billy. I found him to be very well defended against any and all types of intrusive questioning. Shutting down and completely refusing to respond, however, was his most common response the Moment a personal question was asked. He seemed unwilling to disclose any information whatsoever that might be of interpretive value relating to him self or his family. After developing a relationship over a long period of time, however, this changed and Billy shared more information.

Billy, it turned out, had three older brothers who had been diagnosed with ADHD as well as co-morbid depression and had a Mother similarly diagnosed. According to available information, his Father was in denial and probably could have been diagnosed as well. Furthermore, even with the somewhat limited information I had obtained in the beginning, there was evidence of obsessive and compulsive symptoms throughout Billy's own as well as extended families. The possibility of significant obsessive and compulsive symptom interference had never before been evaluated or even considered.

During the approximate nine-month period that I was involved in working with Billy and his family, the following dynamic picture was eventually pieced together. The underlying factor for Billy's school refusal, which had been on going for several years and returned at the start of each new school year, was that Billy experienced intensely felt thoughts that something awful or horrible would happen to his Mother while he was away at school. The related compulsive part of this was that if he stayed at home nothing would happen, or if it did, he would be there to help her.

He had no rational reason for such thoughts, nor was he able to come up with any. With time in counseling, he remembered trying to tell his Mother about these fears long ago when the situation had first occurred. He was also able to remember (rather intensely), the emotional distress he experienced resulting from this confession. At the beginning his family members tried to reassure him with words that there was nothing for him to worry about and otherwise simply ignored this, to them, irrational idea. Eventually they began to ridicule and poke fun at him, stating their disbelief that such a silly fear could even remotely be the real reason that he didn't want to go to school. Finally, his parents began to demand sternly and even yell at him that they wanted him to confess the true reason for his not wanting to go to school. This is why he eventually came up with the reasons stated earlier in this article (i.e., kids teasing, work too hard, teachers unwilling to help and etc.).

Billy's early part of the school year avoidance had been on going for about four years prior to the time I became involved. During this period he had been taught inadvertently that the truth, as he saw it, simply would not be accepted as true. The fear and intensity related to the actual reason for his school avoidance had been steadily growing each year. By the time I came in contact with him, his fear had become so powerful that, irrational or not, Billy simply felt that he *must* stay home at all costs. Thus, he began to come up with excuses that his Mother and others might more readily believe. He *had* to be there with his Mom in case something awful happened to her because he couldn't shake the thought that if he wasn't there it just might.

The deep internal awareness of his own deceptiveness stemming from his earlier attempts to tell the truth appeared to be at the heart of his tendency to shut down and become totally non-responsive whenever threatened by questions. Prior to coming to see me, no one had really believed that he could actually have a fear such as he'd described that could result in such literal and extreme school refusal. It made no sense! Neither had anyone provided him with even a glimmer of hope of ever understanding how such a thought could exist and persist for so long and so strongly unless of course, he was crazy. He had secretly been afraid for a very long time that he might just be out of his mind.

There were, it is essential to note, many other indicators of possible OCS in regard to Billy's behavior in evidence all along. Had this not been the case, a different diagnosis would have been sought out and found that would have been considered as more appropriate.

Many individuals with OCS are chronic self-doubters. This leaves them open to the influence of anyone who adamantly insists that they may have the answer or that they *know* the truth. The symptom of excessive self-doubt often creates a gullibility problem which is, essentially, the tendency to believe in, at times, even the wildest sounding stories that may be told. A child with OCS can become an easy mark for those children who seek to feel powerful by teasing and putting others down. When it occurs, this problem only heightens the feelings of inadequacy already created by the presence of the mild-moderate obsessive and compulsive symptoms (OCS). When other children call an OCS child "stupid," the affected child often secretly wonders if he just might be stupid. He may also harbor a growing fear that he is indeed stupid and this only makes sense as his peers see it too.

The confusion regarding the whys and wherefores of OCS symptoms creates a sort of impenetrable cloud around these individuals from which understanding and light are seen inconsistently and in only an intermittent fashion. In other words, the real reason for OCS related behavior tends to be well hidden or camouflaged. Without consideration of the whole picture well meaning individuals in the helping professions can unintentionally add to the confusion by suggesting possible causation related to specific pieces of the overall picture that they may briefly see clear evidence for. Many OCS driven behaviors mimic behaviors that do result from alternative causation. The OCS affected may even celebrate this explanation offered by the unwitting professional as "the answer they have for so long been waiting for." After all, reason suggests this *is* a professional who is making the diagnosis, and those with OCS have frequently been searching for such a long time for the answer that they quickly jump at the chance of finding one. Since the professional explanation may appear accurate, work on the area may take the forefront in therapy for some time. Techniques, however, that are typically and generally effective for those who really do suffer from the assumed specific cause, tend to fail when applied to the OCS affected, as well they might be expected to. There are also times when a specific treatment technique can be effective as in the use of Exposure and Response Prevention, which should when practiced correctly, reduce the strength of specific OCS behaviors.

By the time the OCS affected individual reaches adulthood, a clear direct connection to a given symptom may be hidden by years of misperception and faulty reasoning regarding its origin. As a result, it may seem nearly impossible to trace back to underlying mild-moderate Obsessive Compulsive (OCS) causation. When a given symptom *is* detected, defense mechanisms may set in and cover it up so quickly that awareness has no chance to set in. In other words, the possibility that a specified behavior might be a single symptom of a much broader biochemical/neurological condition is beyond the individual's capacity to believe at that particular Moment in time. Thus, the symptom is denied, rationalized away, or used against the therapist/counselor to demonstrate his obvious incompetence and sessions may be justifiably terminated. As in the earlier example of the "school phobic" boy, it was much easier to believe in school phobia than it was to believe he could actually be afraid something might happen to his Mother to the extent that it would serve to motivate him to avoid school.

Over the past decade or so, it has become very clear to me that OCS is a viable diagnosis and that it is on a continuum for us all. All human beings have Serotonin in their brain that does the same thing for them. If Serotonin availability is extremely low, Obsessive Compulsive Disorder (OCD) as defined in DSM IV may be present. This is the severe form of the problem discussed herein and when OCD is present, in this day and age of mass information accessibility, most people would recognize it, although they may not truly understand or believe that it is *real*. If Serotonin levels are insufficient yet higher than those levels that bring on OCD, then mild-moderate Obsessive Compulsive symptoms (OCS) may be present. These I tend to categorize into high-moderate, moderate, low-moderate, and mild levels. Symptoms at these levels tend to be very difficult to identify as resulting from OCS because they so often mimic other conditions and problems that have very different roots. Most people have some of these "symptoms", if you will, and this may be a necessary component to human motivation. Whether or not treatment is actively begun should depend on recognition of the symptoms and a determination whether or not these tendencies are interfering with an affected individual's day to day functioning. The camouflage, however, tends to be extremely good.

CHAPTER THREE

INSIGHTS INTO OCS

Where do I go from here . . . nowhere I fear
Sometimes I want to find a way to disappear
I used to be able to see . . . oh . . . and take care of my needs
And now I can't seem to remember what I believe

It's been dark so long I can hardly imagine the light
'Til the pain is gone I'll pray for the night . . . yeah the night
It's so cool and dark there . . . I can safely hide
In the night . . . oh . . . the night . . . yeah the night
Even though I'm afraid . . . I know I'll survive

In some things I've found release . . . ahh . . . but no lasting peace
As the chains of habit grow tighter each day I am less free
I know what you want me to say . . . but I've got to find my own way
If I'm ever really going to make it . . . I've got to strive for my own light each day
I'm not made of steel . . . . . . I think and feel
I want to learn to run from the fake and go for what's real
And if I believe I can be whatever I want to be
Then I'll begin to do all the things that I need to get free

From the song "The Night" by Ron D. Kingsley

DISSATISFACTION . . . GUARANTEED

Most of those affected with OCS (Obsessive Compulsive symptoms and characteristics in the mild-moderate range) will experience bouts of negativity off-and-on throughout the course of their lives. This is one of the most commonly occurring and pervasive of the dynamics associated with the condition. It makes nearly perfect sense.

Although there may be Moments and even somewhat extended periods of apparent "happiness," this is not the norm for the typical OCS affected individual. These individuals could better be described as "chronically unhappy." Think about it. Since, for these individuals, nothing is ever perceived as good enough, right enough, or exactly what they wanted. It makes sense that, overall, true happiness would be like the elusive butterfly, often just within reach, but terribly difficult to catch and hang onto.

The tendency to obsess over every tiny perceived personal lack that is experienced during the course of a day at school and/or work leads to dour and irritable moods that frequently unfold, or unravel, upon arriving home for the day. Even success itself is too often perceived by the OCS affected as, in reality, failure nonetheless because it wasn't the "right kind" of success and/or it wasn't successful at the level desired, and/or expected. This, I believe, is frequently the hidden dynamic that drives the workaholic, never-say-die, OCS affected businessmen to continue reaching for more, far beyond the levels of success already achieved. To them they are not really successful. No matter how much wealth or societal acclaim they receive in their deepest thoughts, they have not yet arrived at the zenith of true "success." The OCS affected never do and so are driven on and on and on. A group of them are anyway.

There is yet another group within the OCS affected population that are similarly driven, but do not have the talent, the genius, the luck, the favorable environment, or perhaps are symptomatically just a bit worse off (more severe) than the "successfully unsuccessful" described above. For this group the personal responses and emotional reactions to perceived failures are stronger, linger longer, and are significantly more painful. Instead of jumping on the treadmill of continually striving to reach the unreachable true satisfaction and success that they desire, individuals in this group tend to start giving up. "Why even try" when you are already sure that failure awaits you at the end? These individuals begin to wallow in negativity, self-defeating thoughts, and heavy-duty depressive episodes. The old adage, "You can lead a horse to water, but you can't make him drink," comes to mind. You can point out to an individual in this group her successes and accomplishments, but you can't make them think (or believe) that this means she is successful, or that these things are even really successes at all. The OCS affected can always find something wrong, or some reason why a given accomplishment or degree of expertise is really not what it appears to others to be.

A high school diploma means nothing to a young man who will tell you, if you ask, that the only reason he got the diploma in the first place was that his counselors felt sorry for him. As a result the counselor somehow arranged for him to graduate even though he didn't deserve it. HEY, isn't that what all high school counselors do? Similarly, it means very little to the young woman who will quickly inform you, if you ask, that she wouldn't have graduated if her parents hadn't been continually pushing, nagging, and in other ways influencing (forcing) her to do her homework. She'll tell you flat-out, "It's their diploma, not mine!" Thus, a highly respected and valued accomplishment (obtaining a high school diploma) can be perceived with such negativity that it's achievement can actually work against, rather than for, the recipient. There is a man (and I expect there are many more, both male and female) who, upon receiving his fourth college degree, experienced fearful and anxiety provoking thoughts such as, "What if they find out?" (I don't really deserve this), and "So, *big deal*, you've got a Ph.D. Now what?" Truly it's not hard to imagine that it was one of the OCS affected who came up with the tart and sassy definition for the oft heard acronym relative to the degree of Ph.D., "Piled higher and deeper."

Exactly what is it that leads some of the OCS affected to become the driven "successfully unsuccessful" wherein they are deemed clearly successful in society's eyes and yet not in their own? What is it that influences others to become chronically depressed and worthless underachievers (often solely in their own eyes, at least initially)? Some possibilities have been alluded to already in this treatise. Others surely exist. Much investigation and research needs to be done in this area, nevertheless, an attempt will be made herein to explore some of the OCS related possibilities.

First, and perhaps foremost, when the OCS symptom picture is evident and significantly pervasive, it is a good bet that the brain chemical Serotonin levels are insufficient. Serotonin deficiencies are frequently associated with varying levels and degrees of obsessive and compulsive symptomotology and/or characteristics. Treatment in the form of medication that is either a Specific Serotonin Reuptake Inhibitor (SSRI) or has a strong Serotonin reuptake inhibiting component as a part of its active ingredients frequently diminishes the OCS affected's negativity and perceptions of chronic failure quickly and obviously. In fact the individual's response, or change, is often so dramatic that parents, siblings, and significant others not uncommonly refer to it as "Amazing". Initially the affected (and treated) individual often does not fully appreciate this "change" because, being biochemically driven, their previous actions were not self-perceived as "negative" and/or unreasonable. Frequently they do seem to sense that others are reacting to them and treating them a little differently but they truly may not understand why. To them they are still the same old "Joe" or "Jill" that they always were. Since the initial change is internal, biochemical, and has nothing to do with thoughtfully planned actions with the express purpose of achieving behavioral change, the initial responsiveness simply may not be viewed personally as a "change". It is simply the way it is. This would explain why, when treatment is of short duration, the one being treated quite often reports the belief that the medication trial has not been effective. Unless treatment continues for a sufficient length of time and the individual begins to discover for themselves more dramatic changes in the disposition and behavior of others in relation to themselves, it is difficult (although not impossible) to see and believe in their own personal behavioral transformation. You cannot see or feel the healing occurring internally after suffering a severely broken leg. You can only trust in the actions of physicians and thereafter follow the instructions given so that these will result in the leg's healing. You cannot know it is truly healed until, when running and jumping, you no longer experience weakness and pain. The OCS affected often begin to truly experience an awareness of their own healing (symptom relief) as it is reflected in the actions and reactions of others towards them.

Another factor that would seem to be involved is the OCS affected's intense drive to either continue chronically to succeed or to finally give in to defeat. This is the frequently simultaneously occurring (thought to be genetically connected) condition known today as ADHD (Attention-Deficit-Hyperactive Disorder). For this particular discussion relative to the intense energy often behind the chronically driven OCS behaviors, the consideration is for the ADHD-primarily hyperactive type. It makes sense that, perhaps, the underlying force (drive) behind the never-say-die "successfully unsuccessful" might just be the biochemically driven hyperactivity component of ADHD. The always on the go, never needing much-sleep, always needing to be doing something restlessness of ADHD. This, in combination with OCS, may be the more part of the explanation relating to the driven (societal perceived successful) individuals who are never satisfied, that nevertheless won't often give up or lapse into depression, but usually will go on-and-on-and on, in spite of the current levels of "other perceived" success. At least in part it may explain the group that seems unable to go on and simply quit trying. Perhaps, these individuals simply don't have the needed energy to continue on in the face of all odds.

Then there is, of course, the levels or strength of the symptomotology. This may correlate with the degree of the Serotonin deficiency. It would appear to make sense that this is so. When treating diagnosed OCD (severe Obsessive Compulsive symptoms) with, for example, Prozac, the typical dose range needed for successful treatment is quite high (40–80mg daily). However, when treating mild to moderate OCS, the typical effective dose ranges from 10–40mg daily.

Next there are conditioned or learned behaviors that commonly develop relative to and result from the OCS symptom's becoming secondarily and tertiarily related to the primary biochemically driven thoughts and behaviors. These are those behaviors that might also be related to the environment, modeling from parents and/or others and may also be the ones that tend to persist and hold maladaptive patterns together, even though biochemical conditions may have improved. This also makes sense. An example of such a case might be as follows:

Let's say the biochemical, as it often does, triggers an emotionally laden hypersensitivity which becomes expressed each time a mistake is made, or something doesn't go right as perceived by the individual. The individual's subsequent reaction each time this occurs is to become significantly emotionally distraught so much so that others begin to take notice and react. Some of them become irritated or angry and advise the individual to "Shut up!" and/or "Quit whining!" Some resort to name calling, "Oh . . . you big baby!" and "What a weenie!" Still others may attempt to console the affected one by reassuring him, saying, "Don't feel bad, everybody makes mistakes," or, "Just try to shake it off, it's no big deal," and so on. These reactions of others generate secondary reactions from the individual. The individual may begin to feel picked on or singled out unnecessarily and start to verbalize this idea angrily in return. This may then lead to the individual's appellation as a troublemaker and/or essentially as a "bad seed." Eventually he may come to see himself as "Bad." This perceived "badness" could begin to permeate everything he may do and say. The attitude that is fostered and begins to be expressed, as well as the perception of being bad, can further set the stage for the entrance of a group of behaviors. These behaviors, although not directly caused by the biochemical element, probably would never have occurred at all were it not for the reactions that did occur and *were* directly chemically related. Yet, because these behaviors evolved out of the reactions of others, misdirected and/or misinterpreted as they may have been, they tend to remain in place for some time even though the underlying related biochemical deficiency is being treated effectively.

Thus, in spite of the directly biochemically driven hyper-emotional response becoming significantly ameliorated, diminished in intensity, or no longer present, the complex intertwined behaviors connected to this symptom should not be expected to dramatically be affected or changed immediately. This is because, over time, these inter-related responses have been born of other factors having no direct ties to the biochemically caused emotional hyper-responsivity. Thus, appropriate medical treatment may take weeks, months, and perhaps even years to demonstrate the full positive effects that are potentially possible. As the underlying biochemically driven foundation gives way, eventually the entire structure will fall. The key word herein is "eventually." Many of the behavioral inter-related responses and behaviors associated with OCS can be so complex that it is im-

handwritten margin note: This is Cooper—and he tends to gravitate toward the "bad" or rebellious things & act like he loves them & are cool—I feel like it's an act, & it was probably a result of our reactions to his reactions. Can this be counteracted

possible to quickly and clearly see the connections leading back to their biochemically driven origins whether considered by the professional or the affected individual. In such cases these connections only become clear with extended medical and therapeutic treatment and analysis, after the fact. When the walls tumble, the previously unobserved decaying foundation can be easily connected to the fall. Fortunately, the very complex behavioral structures originating from the biochemical foundation that was built years in the past are usually surrounded by sufficient symptomatic behaviors more closely and obviously connected so that the diagnosis of OCS can still be made. It is not, however, unusual for the strong-willed to find alternate, equally believable (and sometimes more so), causative factors and explanations for the existence of these very same behaviors. Historically this type of response has been typically considered to be a form of "denial," that could be conscious or unconscious, that is meant to protect the individual from finding out about or having to deal with bad news. With the OCS population, it appears that such a psychodynamic interpretation is often inaccurate and therefore counterproductive.

The OCS affected individual frequently comes to believe, having no better explanation, in a host of reasons or possible causes for their otherwise unexplainable behaviors. These reasons typically center on the commonly believed behavioral interpretations to which they have been exposed. Thus, "I just have a bad temper like my Dad" becomes the accepted reason for seemingly inconsistent angry outbursts related to the biochemically driven hyper-responsivity and so on. This is not to suggest that all angry outbursts are biochemically driven. They are not, of course, and herein lies the problem. Many individuals, especially in the lay population, have never even heard of, let alone been taught that sometimes, angry outbursts can be due to a biochemical insufficiency of the brain. These same individuals, however, have witnessed such outbursts in family members and been told stories of such outbursts in extended family members for all of their lives. They have also heard such explanations as: "You've got a bad temper, child. You must've learned it from me and I learned it from my Dad, I'm sure." Such a belief system, when present, often makes it very difficult for them to even be able to consider possible alternative explanations for their behaviors. When this occurs it is not denial (although it can and may develop into such), it is simply ignorance.

As mentioned earlier, the OCS affected "successfully unsuccessful" individuals (forever dissatisfied in all aspects of life) usually do not perceive themselves as chronically negatively focused individuals, although most others who know them would. Rather, they tend to see themselves as "realistic," "genuine," "sincere," and "authentic" in relation to life's experiences. They are reality based and prefer not to feign success and/or positive outcomes where none exist. They are serious and sober observers. They don't want, or need, to exaggerate the positives in order to feel a measure of success. Success, to them, is a "never ending story," and so on. The underlying dissatisfaction and thereby negative viewpoint has become so insidiously entrenched into their belief system through extremely complex intertwining that the affected adult very rarely is able to disentangle themselves from the intricate and long standing webs of deceit. The threads have been there for too long and are much too powerful to recognize and overcome alone. If caught in time, though, the youthful versions encapsulated by this insidious symptom can be successfully treated. Early treatment may enable such individuals to prevent the accompanying negativity related to the chronic personal dissatisfaction with the world that so irritates, consumes, and chafes the OCS affected who are older and untreated.

As with other specific symptoms, the chronically dissatisfied also have a polar opposite. Individuals in this group hardly ever seem to show up for treatment. This may be due to the fact that relatively few of the OCS affected end up at this symptom pole. It is more likely, though, a direct result of the symptom's effects on others in the world and these other's ultimate perception of the behavior as not a symptom at all, let alone something for which one might seek out or need treatment. If not already guessed this is the ultimate Pollyanna, optimist, continually elated, chronically happy, self satisfied, always triumphant positive thinker. These individuals gloss over and often will not or simply cannot accept or acknowledge the negative side of things at all. They cannot allow themselves even the smallest resentments, laments, disappointments, negative attitudes, or to be dissatisfied with anyone or anything. Of course, such an extreme case as related above, if any, is the one most likely to end up in a treatment situation. Most, however, are on a continuum and not nearly so extreme. Since, a positive attitude and optimistic outlook tend (in most cases) to be highly valued behaviors, or attributes, these individuals are rarely, if ever, identified as possibly symptomatic. Those who are truly symptomatic, though, can irritate and grind on the nerves of others that must deal with them on a daily basis (similar to their polar opposite, negative cousins). The reason for this is because of their persistent and irrefutable positive outlook, no matter the situation. Such optimism can appear far-fetched, tenuous, and even fraudulent when present.

As with other symptoms that are demonstrated in a bipolar pattern, the OCS affected individuals may cycle from leaning more towards one of the poles and then suddenly shift to the other. Further research is needed to try and determine why some affected individuals go back and forth from positive to negative poles, while most seem to lean towards, or only take a hold of, just the positive or just the negative side. Thus, the unyieldingly positive and/or negatively focused individual may be displaying evidence of underlying OCS causation. As with other symptoms, though, if this is so there will be a myriad of other elements suggestive of the same diagnosis. When supporting symptomatic components are not found to be present after thorough assessment, an OCS diagnosis should not be made and other possibilities should be sought out instead.

"There's nothing wrong with my heart . . . there's nothing wrong with my eyes
My life is not falling apart . . . and I am not losing my mind
But with you I can never be sure . . . exactly where it is I stand
Should I be running away from you . . . or holding tighter your hand

And the tears that you see running down the length of my face
Are not in any way meant for you . . . they're just out of place
And yours too . . . I'll bet . . . must be about the same
Ain't it funny how we can both shed tears and yet still pass on the blame . . ."

Excerpt from the song "There's nothing wrong with my Heart" by Ron D. Kingsley

HEY! DON'T LOOK AT ME . . .

IT'S NOT MY FAULT

The exact title for this particular paper in my ongoing discussions of behaviors, the emotional experience, and dynamics related to Obsessive Compulsive Symptoms (OCS), which I have repeatedly defined elsewhere as *NOT!!! OCD* was difficult to choose. Remember, OCS as I have defined it, is the mild-moderate version of OCD. The underlying cause remains the same (biochemical): related to Serotonin levels in the brain. The differences between a diagnosis of true OCD (as defined in the DSM IV) and OCS lies in the severity and/or intensity of its observable and experienced symptoms or characteristics.

As pointed out and explained in earlier writings the OCS affected typically cannot see, or even conceive of, their problems, symptoms, and experiences as relating to those that are characteristic of a true OCD diagnosis. When professionals unfamiliar with OCS suspect obsessions and compulsions and confront the mild-moderate OCS affected with the DSM IV diagnostic criteria (symptom questions) relative to OCD, the OCS affected tend to be quite puzzled. The OCS group simply do not see a connection between the suggested OCD characteristics and their own symptoms and rightly so. There is a connection but, for a host of valid reasons, these connections are well camouflaged and the relationship to OCD quite difficult to follow. Suffice it to say that clinical experience and research in OCD has led me to the conclusion that obsessive and compulsive symptoms are on a continuum. This continuum ranges from relatively few, if any symptoms, all the way up to those that, when defined, make up the diagnosis known today as OCD (severe and extremely persistent symptoms).

The context of this particular discussion is centered on a very common set of OCS symptoms and related dynamics that tend to be especially troublesome both for those who are OCS affected as well as those others who must live, deal with, and in any way consistently relate to them. Thus, the title of this paper could have just as easily been one of the following: "**Lies, Lies, Lies . . . and More Lies;**" or "**Don't Blame Me . . . I Didn't Do It;**" or "**A Million and One Excuses . . . For Everything;**" or "**Storytellers Anonymous;**" or "**The Rationalization and Justification of a Life;**" or "**The Irresponsibility Syndrome.**" Perhaps these titles provide a sufficient image to get the point across, though I believe I could have easily gone on. The bottom line is the common tendency and need for the OCS affected to actively avoid blame and often redirect it towards anyone nearby or any set of circumstances that, virtually, could be conceived of as possibly related at the Moment. The emotional intensity the OCS affected display during these Moments make them extremely convincing and their explanations and stories tend to be very difficult for others to resist, even when involving highly unusual and/or unlikely circumstances.

An OCS affected teenager recalls a time when a family moved into her neighborhood not long after their rather large house had been completed. The teenager had been about 10 years old at the time and there had been a girl in the family that was close to her same age.

On the occasion of the new girl's first visit to (let's call the affected party Jill) Jill's house, a story emerged. Jill remembers feeling belittled and great shame (keep in mind that the OCS affected tend to be hypersensitive and experience events and emotions at significantly heightened levels when compared to the non–OCS affected).

Apparently after the new girl had been given a tour of the house and its surroundings, she made comments relating to the "small size" of the house, Jill's room, the swimming pool, and etc.,

Jill began to experience an undeniable *need* to somehow justify and explain her home under this perceived attack.

She suddenly found herself telling the new girl all about how the previous owners that had actually had the house built were a family of midgets. As implausible and silly as this may sound, Jill with her details and emotional investment in the telling of the tale, made a believer out of this new girl. This brought Jill immediate relief from her inner experienced intense shame for living in what the new girl had badmouthed and implied was such a "small" house and one that somehow didn't "measure up".

The other girl's focus had been shifted from apparent depreciation (perhaps out of a need to feel "special" or superior herself) to one of awe and admiration. Jill now became the "special" one. The need to deflect and/or defend against perceived personal attacks (or judgements of others) is often unrelenting and very powerful. Defenses are instantly constructed with no thought of the potential consequences. The inner experienced "need" becomes the momentary sole focus of attention. Thus, the irrational and illogical can and sometimes do occur.

Jill described this memorable and important incident as one of the never-forgotten examples often shared with others by her parents of their early twinges of concern and fear that their daughter was becoming a liar. The new girl had been so taken in by Jill's sincerity in the telling of the tale that she had gone home directly and shared the story of the midget house with her own Mother. Jill might never have been found out had the new girl's Mother sometime later not made the off-hand comment at a social event she'd attended with Jill's Mother, "So, your house was built by midgets, huh?"

The defense of self is frequently an all-important event not unlike a gunshot. When the trigger of a gun is released and it strikes the bullet, this projectile is immediately driven out of the barrel in an undeviating course until friction and gravity overcome it's initial empowering thrust and gradually pull it to the earth. Once struck, a bullet cannot be called back, "Hey, wait a minute. I don't want you going in that direction. In fact, why don't you come on back and we'll just forget that I ever fired you at all." This, however, isn't going to happen. Bullets can't be talked into coming back or into changing the direction of initial flight. They can't. The OCS affected's reaction to a perceived attack on the self (the trigger) is much like that bullet, once triggered; the path of defense becomes immediately all consuming and the direction undeviating.

The inflexible nature of the reaction, as well as the immediacy of the response, drives the symptom picture. Numerous other variables can also be components that disturb and influence the triggered response; much like a bullet is affected by gravity, friction, and anything else that may be in its path. Thus, the reactions, embellishments, stories, and lies are typically quite diverse and variable. The reaction depends on the specific environment, previous experience and learned behaviors, as well as the OCS affected's capacities, creativity, and overall strength of the underlying biochemical drive or perceived needs.

Another example may help clarify even more the insidious nature of this problem. In the previous example a child was the center of focus. In this one let's look at an adult's response to the need to resolve one's self of blame.

> Sherry related the incident of having just come into the family living room with a glass of water in hand to work on the computer. Upon entering, she found the furniture rearranged somewhat by her husband who had temporarily moved things around so that additional space would be available. He'd made the space for a structure that would not be there for very long. On the coffee table was their 15 year-old son's newest 1000 piece puzzle that was about 90% completed. The table had been shoved up next to the stool where Sherry had seated herself at the computer. She set her full water glass down on the edge of the coffee table closest to where she was sitting. As she reached back towards the rear of the computer for the switch to turn it on, she was dismayed that she seemed unable to reach it. She kept stretching her arm out to the side of the computer and

the cabinet wall wherein it sat. Finally, she could just feel the switch panel. It was at her fingertips.

She had to lean in a very awkward position and stretch. Suddenly she hit the water glass which then spilled all over the nearly completed puzzle. She knew it had been ruined. She mopped up the water as best she could anyway, hoping that it just might dry out and be okay. Later that day she confronted her husband with a degree of subdued anger regarding what had happened. She informed him it was his fault. It never would have happened if he hadn't rear-ranged things and in doing so, placed a side table behind the computer cabinet which was on top of the cords. The positioning of the table had pulled the switch box to the very back of the cabinet and made it impossible for her to reach it and turn on the computer. If he hadn't done that then she wouldn't have knocked over that water glass by trying so hard to reach it and their son's puzzle would not have been ruined.

The logic of this woman's argument almost seems sound but there are a few holes in it. If she wasn't symptomatic for OCS, she might have been better able to accept the responsibility and real-ize that she had set the water down too close and on the same table as the puzzle. Then she had knocked it over herself. Had she slowed down long enough to assess the situation, she might have realized the danger and removed the glass to another position to avoid knocking it over.

The OCS individual, when facing blame, sometimes cannot bear the thought that something might be their fault. Sometimes it's because to accept the blame would mean accepting that they make mistakes that they feel no one should ever make. This, of course, would mean that they are flawed in some way and that is what they cannot bear the thought of. It may also mean that oth-ers will see that they are flawed and then think things about them and so on.

The OCS affected often appear to be unable to handle failure of any kind, whether perceived or real. Typically the implications of failure, usually in thoughts or words, swirl within the minds and hearts of these people. To simply shrug it off and continue on, and/or keep trying in the face of failure is not something they can easily do. The irrational belief, or feeling, that "all is lost", or in their own "worthlessness" and sometimes the perceived impression or need that they deserve to be punished for being "so stupid" is very real to them. Like the bullet, once fired, they cannot be talked out of the direction, or pathway they may suddenly find themselves on. They must go on until released from the path as the drive weakens over time and/or something else interferes with its course.

A reported incident in the life of Thomas Edison (whom I believe clearly had ADHD as well as OCS) seems to be a good example of what is being discussed herein. It is said that a reporter once asked Mr. Edison in relation to the experience of inventing the electrical light bulb, how it felt to fail 2,000 times (the reported number of experiments that occurred before achieving a workable bulb). Mr. Edison's quick reply seems, in my opinion, to demonstrate the common OCS inability to accept, admit to, or even conceive of personal failure. History records his response.

"Fail?" he said. "Fail? I never failed. It was a 2000 step process!"

The making of mistakes, not doing something right, not understanding a taught concept, and so on, in the mind of the OCS affected, is so intensely experienced as "a bad thing" that, it too, must be defended against. Thus, if such cannot be out-rightly denied, the next best thing that can still protect the extremely sensitive and fragile OCS self is having a viable "reason" or cause. Another common description of this very same thing is known as "the excuse." The OCS affected tend to be the grand masters of the excuse. Yet another definition that, it could be strongly argued, is also a synonym of "the reason" or "excuse" is quite frankly "the lie" or untruth.

This fact, that others can interpret a given OCS response as "a lie," creates a fascinating anomaly for the OCS affected individual. The telling of a lie is wrong and as such the OCS driven individual often cannot openly allow one to be told. Thus, because it does occur, when confronted he must defend his own defense. In other words, he must be able to convince him self that such a response, in some way, is ultimately the truth. If unable to do so the excuse is often used, once again, to explain, rationalize, and/or justify the (I'm sorry you say it that way) lie.

At this point one can begin to sense how incredibly complicated the OCS affected's life can become. It is often, though not necessarily consistently, overwhelming. Most of the time, after the fact (being caught in the lie or mistake or whatever), the OCS affected is as frustrated and disheartened as everyone else is about her behavior and reactions. Some of the reasons and lies are over such inconsequential and trivial things that even she has no clue why she or anyone else would even consider, or feel such a need to cover up for, defend, and/or lie about it. It literally makes no sense. This very fact, however, is actually one of the important indicators that can help us to make sense out of and actually begin to understand these behaviors and reactions.

Behaviorists long ago successfully mapped out learned reactions and pathways to behavior that, when certain specific principles are consistently applied, change undesirable and maladaptive patterns. These principles are powerful change agents, unless the behavior is not learned or reinforced positively or negatively, but rather, is due to something else. The tremendous positive impact of behavioral methods brought psychology out of the dark ages and into a new era and cannot be ignored. These very methods and ways of presenting the underlying causes of learned maladaptive behavior, though, can (and often do) interfere with the diagnosis and treatment of OCS.

Biochemically driven behaviors typically do not stand-alone. There are learned behaviors as well that develop around, support, and/or are connected to those behaviors that are directly attributable to the biochemical. Thus, the professional promoting and utilizing behavioral methods and principles of understanding behavioral causation will have some success working from this behavioral perspective with the OCS affected because many of the secondarily and tertiarily related responses are in fact learned.

When working purely from this perspective with the OCS

driven population, however, experience suggests that overall successful behavioral change may be somewhat limited. This is because responses and behaviors directly, (or primarily), connected to the biochemical are not maintained by reinforcement schedules whether positive and/or negative. This may very well be the real reason for those long documented reports of times when behaviorists apply their methods to a specific troubling behavior and diminish its effects or extinguish it entirely, only to have another different, though similarly maladaptive behavior start up in its place. It's not, in my opinion, due to some unconscious need or repressed incidents of the past. Rather, it is the untreated biochemical incongruency, which continues to drive, or create, tendencies, and reactions that are then expressed behaviorally. So, extinguish that behavioral response and do nothing to affect the underlying biochemical problem and it becomes understandable how another behavior might replace one that was treated behaviorally with success. It makes sense because the specific treated behavior, in such a case, was the observable expression of an underlying chemical problem that would continue to push for expression unless the chemical problem itself is treated successfully via the behavior modification techniques. Success may be inconsistent and/or fleeting. In such cases, blame for the failure of these behavioral techniques is often thought to result from misapplication of the techniques on the part of those responsible for implementing the strategies. Therefore, quite often, parents and/or teachers (who else?) get the blame once again.

Diagnosis and treatment of OCS can also be delayed because parents, teachers, and the affected individuals come to believe that their symptoms and maladaptive behaviors result primarily from learned patterns, experiences, poor parenting, and the like when they actually do not. A great many of OCS driven symptoms and related behaviors look so similar to well known, well researched, and well accepted, learned patterns, experiences, trauma, and so on. As a result, no one can truly fault the parents, teachers, and in some cases, the professional, for treating symptoms behaviorally and for having such strong and unrelenting preconceived notions.

In the paper (OCS: Camouflage Over Time), I discuss how, over time, the OCS affected's symptoms become hidden in layers of inaccurate beliefs and reasons for specific responses and behaviors. This, then, serves to make it all the harder to detect the underlying OCS mechanism and ultimately the biochemical instigator at the bottom of the pile. It is easier to believe in behavioristic principles (learned behavior) because historical research has demonstrated its effectiveness in a great many cases as both an explanation of cause (the reason for the behavior's presence) and as an effective treatment strategy. Thus, when the biochemically driven responses and behaviors resemble well known and well documented behavioral patterns and principles it often results in a behavioristic point of view and explanation by lay persons as well as professionals. It is the easiest explanation to believe because we know the specific behavior in question truly could have been learned. We have all that research behind us. This enables us to make sense out of the behavior. "Oh yeah," we say, "that's got to be it."

It is much, much more difficult for us to accept that the behaviors we are seeing are ultimately the product of a brain biochemical imbalance. This becomes particularly hard when there are so many other causative possibilities that seem to have stronger connections with the reasons in which we already believe. However, in the beginning, the general public, as well as professionals, had a similar extremely difficult time accepting most of what the behaviorists were saying too.

As I have discussed in previous writings, the early life of the OCS affected individual is typically plagued with doubts, misunderstanding, frustration, fear, and frequently anger. When old enough to be questioned by adults about their behavior, the most common response relating to the purpose and/or the reason for a given action or behavior is: "I don't know." This is because, when biochemically driven, the OCS affected do not know why they behave in the ways that they do. They are responding to an inner mechanism over which they have no, or little, conscious control. Hence, they do not know why they think the way they do, nor why they do what they do when symptomatically driven. Often their behavioral responses make no sense either to them or to anyone else. Thus, the search for motive, reasons, and/or causation begins.

This common human need to find meaning and to understand behavior and figure out why it occurs often actually hinders the OCS diagnosis. Self-recognition and awareness of the symptoms often works as an active influence to keep these individuals from actively seeking out treatment. Let's go back to the title of this paper.

Frequently the OCS affected end up accepting the apparent obvious explanations for their chemically driven (otherwise unexplainable) behaviors. Since this may satisfy their typical human need to know why they do what they do, they can then get back to the business of living their life secure with the knowledge that they understand themselves and the reasons for their behaviors. If the chemical imbalance is not too severe and stress remains at a constant range within their capabilities to handle it, such an individual will not become actively engaged in seeking out help, and/or treatment.

"Treatment? Help? For What?" they might ask. They already have an explanation for their behaviors. There is no need for another. Thus, early intervention and treatment can be delayed, or may not occur at all. Many who do seek out professional help become very frustrated by a lack of long term, and/or consistent progress. They may give up and seek no further assistance. They may become embittered because the so-called "professionals" have not been very helpful, and sometimes, because some professionals may imply, or actually state outright, that the causes for their lack of success lie with the parents or with the individual themselves.

The search for behavioral meaning, or for the reasons why behaviors occur, also frequently becomes an unconscious tool used in response to a very common symptom's need. The OCS affected typically have a need to be free from blame and also to not make mistakes, or to be considered by others or even themselves to be at fault for anything. They cannot bear it emotionally.

This, of course, makes no sense because making mistakes is a human certainty. By recognizing our mistakes and working hard to minimize them until fewer and fewer are made, we progress or become more proficient in all things. The OCS affected, however, often cannot stand even the thought of their own personal culpability, blame, and/or fault. At least not initially or immediately.

Perhaps the OCS affected's dilemma is already tugging at your own conscious mind as this is being read. If the OCS affected can't handle being wrong or deal with it when they make a mistake, "how do they ever make it through life?" This is a very good question.

Usually, these people learn, and become very good at, justifying and rationalizing their actions and behaviors. Since they can barely, if ever, admit to wrongdoings and mistakes that they make, they instead place the blame, fault, or reason for their actions on something or someone else. They cannot be held responsible or be considered at fault when the reason for their actions or response lies outside of themselves and is not under their immediate control.

This is the dynamic that I believe is at the heart of the common OCS inability to accept responsibility for their own behaviors and actions. When they can conceive of a reason for their actions that is beyond themselves, they are able to admit a mistake was made, but since it was not their fault, the mistake they made was not truly their own. This then protects them from the intensely multiplied inner turmoil and emotional distress the OCS affected experience when forced to confront the human reality that they do, as do all of us, make mistakes.

The obsessive thought process experienced by these individuals when something doesn't go right and they are unable to shift the blame can be incredibly self-deprecating and trigger long lasting hyper-emotional responses such as anger, explosiveness, and depression. As a result, they may behaviorally or verbally act out or shut down completely. The emotional pain accompanying the response each time it occurs can be such a devastating and intensely experienced event that it becomes traumatic and something to be avoided at all costs. In situations like this, a lie becomes the lesser of the two evils. So powerful are these internal needs, however, that even the lesser evil of the lie usually must be put in such a way that the individual can somehow conceive of it as being the truth.

One of the major problems related to this dynamic is that frequently, individuals who are unable to admit personal errors and mistakes and accept responsibility for their actions are also unable, unwilling, and/or unmotivated to see a need for/or have a desire for personal change. After all, if it's not my fault, why should I be the one to change? This may be stated openly but its presence is usually observed rather than shared. Over time this pattern quite often becomes so ingrained and automatic that to think of it as resulting from a combination of underlying biochemical causes and a subtle inter-twining of learned behavior seems ludicrous. Pointing a finger at this person would only result in an immediate turn of the head to see who was at fault behind them. To attempt and pin the blame on this individual is to risk immediate retaliation, often in the form of an explosive and vehement denial.

The OCS affected do not see themselves, however, as making excuses for their actions. To them it is not an excuse, but the very reason that explains what happened. To think differently is to invite the intense and unrelenting flagellation from their own unforgiving mind. The OCS affected, however, are typically unaware of this relationship.

One of the most revealing aspects of this pattern diagnostically (suggesting possible OCS presence) is the fact that the response pattern tends to be the same no matter how inconsequential or insignificant a particular incident or situation may actually be. Thus, the misspelled word to this individual may be perceived internally as a mistake or error of equal severity to actions such as breaking the law. The error may not affect the individual noticeably until pointed out as such by someone else. This is a common trigger associated with the OCS defensive mode.

Significant others, parents, spouses, teachers, and friends simply cannot understand why anyone would make excuses for and/or deny having played a part in some of the silly and incredibly trivial mistakes that occur. It often seems so ludicrous to think that any one could possibly become so defensive that it even becomes very difficult to believe. Thus, when an individual consistently excuses their inappropriate actions and behavior no matter how comparatively insignificant the actions seem to be, it should be considered a strong indicator for possible OCS and an underlying biochemical causation.

At the Moment of confrontation regarding maladaptive behavioral responses, and/or the pointing out of an error, the defense mechanism erupts without so much as a second thought about the matter. The harder others push for the OCS affected to recognize and accept responsibility, the harder those affected may deny their part and/or stand by their initially proposed explanation relating to the event in question. Ever on the defense, they frustrate and tire to the point of exhaustion nearly all those who must deal with them on a consistent long term basis. They literally wear down their opponents.

Of course, it is important not to forget that this behavioral response to the biochemical can be as black-and-white, and all or nothing, as most other OCS behaviors, and thus it is also sometimes manifested in the form of its polar opposite. That is to say there are some OCS affected individuals who not only will accept responsibility, blame, or fault for the things that they've done, but they also accept it for things they haven't done as well. Such an individual cannot let go of the idea, or thought, that something they might have said or done may have somehow tipped the scales or caused the problem. They may come to believe that they are at fault for every mishap, mistake, misunderstanding, and misperception that might occur, no matter how remotely involved their participation, or influence might have been. It makes sense that this OCS dynamic is not nearly as common as it's opposite. Taking the blame for everything is quite depressing and tends to lead to more serious and frequent bouts of depression, hopelessness, and suicidal ideation in general.

Thus, when individuals demonstrate a seeming inability to accept blame, fault, and/or responsibility, or seem to blame themselves first in all things. When they act as if they are responsible for the woes of the world and everything in it, or seem to vacillate between these two extremes blaming the self at times and then everyone else at other times, OCS may (it's a good bet) be present.

Recognition and awareness is a big part of the successful treatment battle. Without awareness, no war can be mounted against the symptoms. Change is not sought after, nor does it occur where it is not recognized as being needed.

I used to think . . . if they could just see
The one I know that's really me
Then they . . . would surely understand
Somehow I knew . . . something was wrong
Though I didn't know what . . . it was so strong
I was like an ostrich . . . with its head in the sand
But all they believed of me . . . just wasn't true
They couldn't see into the heart
So many things I'd do . . . were so often misunderstood
And then they'd turn away . . . whispering . . . that boy's no good
But I believe we can be what we want to be
If we put in the kind of time and effort it takes
All we have to do is try . . . and never give up . . . though we may ache
To stop . . . to quit . . . to run . . . in fear our dreams will break

Somehow I sensed . . . that I could stand
All by myself . . . as we all can
When we believe . . . it's something we can do
And though I may fall . . . a thousand more times
I'll get back up . . . 'cause that's a part of life
I know I'll make it . . . if I just keep on . . . I've learned this is true

'Cause all they believed of me was from their own point of view
They couldn't see into my heart
So many things I'd do . . . were so often misunderstood
And then they'd turn away . . . whispering . . . that boy's no good

From the song "They couldn't see into the Heart" by Ron D. Kingsley

LITERAL THINKING

(I'm Not Blind, Stupid, or Deaf . . . Just Extremely Literal)

"DON'T YOU *LIE* TO ME, *BOY!*"

His mind whirled. A gesture of confusion surfaced immediately . . . "But . . . I'm not . . . ."

"A lie on top of a *lie!*" his Father shrieked.

"No!" the boy stammered, "I'm not . . . You don't understand."

The older man crossed his arms and stood up straighter, just a bit. "Oh, I don't, huh?"

The boy barely allowed his head to nod.

"Let's just look at the facts," his Father took a notepad and pen from the stained left breast pocket of his faded blue workshirt, "shall we?"

The boy said nothing.

"Were you at the scene of the crime on the night in question?" his Father began.

"No," Ryan replied without hesitation.

"NO!" Mr. Coye shouted. His pen ripped right through the top sheet of the tiny spiral pad. He quickly tore the rest of the sheet from the pad, crumpled it in one hand, and threw it towards the blue-gray carpet. "No?" he repeated. "Now you're trying to tell me you weren't even at the party?"

Ryan's brow began to furrow ever so slightly. "I didn't say that."

"Yes! You *did!*"

"No, *Dad*, I did not."

"You did! You lying little . . . I just asked you if you were at the party on the night of . . ."

Ryan cut him off. "No you didn't," he stated with drop-dead intensity. "You asked me if I had been at the 'scene' of the crime."

"Same thing," his Dad shrugged.

Ryan crossed his arms. "There was no crime!"

"Guess that depends . . ."

"Depends!" Ryan's teeth chattered mid clenches. "Depends on what?"

"On whether or not you were the victim, of course," Mr. Coye smirked.

"Dad, there was no victim . . ." Ryan scurried to his left and bent his knees just enough to retrieve a battered old dictionary from the bookshelf. He madly flipped through the pages until he reached the V's. When he finally got to the page with a "Vic," he was all over the page scanning with his eyes several times before being able to mentally remind him self the words were in alphabetical order. He silently cursed him self for this lifelong slow, slow process he faced whenever searching for information. It was always the same. The Moment his eyes took in the morass of information crammed into the one little page, it seemed as if they would rebel. It was like they were immediately overwhelmed and saying "Whoa . . . look at all that stuff we've got to look through!" Then apparently in a sort of "shock," his eyes would begin to scan through the myriad of words and phrases with no rhyme-nor-reason whatsoever. He always found what he was looking for. That wasn't the problem. It just took him a lot longer than everyone else (or so it seemed to him) to finally get there. It made tasks tedious. It was a pain in the butt!

His eyes settled in on the page "Vic." As he commenced moving from word to word down the page, he sang in his head, "A,B,C,D, . . . E,F,G . . ." This was another annoying routine he'd catch him self in, again and again. If he didn't sing the alphabet song as he compared each letter on his way to "Victim," he'd invariably get lost and have to retrace his initial steps and start all over again. At least he didn't have to sing the ABC song clear to the end for each letter he found.

Sure enough, he had to turn the page. Fortunately at this point in the process his letter by letter focus would keep him from being overwhelmed by the amount of information on the next page. Ryan continued considering word after word until he arrived at "Victim."

"And for the fourth time! Ryan!" his Father's arms were bent with hands clenched into fists that were poised on his hips. Never a good sign. "What *are* you doing?"

"What am I doing?" was his Dad joking? Ryan looked up from the dictionary. "I'm showing you," he answered with conviction before returning his gaze to the book.

Mr. Coye threw up his hands. "You haven't heard a word I've said."

"Dad," Ryan insisted. "Listen . . ." he began to read from the dictionary. "Victim, a person or animal killed as a sacrifice to a god in a religious rite," he skipped over the number two definition and continued with the third. "A person who suffers some loss, especially by being swindled." Ryan kept reading and included some of what was under the word "Victimize" for good measure. He read, "to kill, destroy, and to dupe or cheat . . ."

"Ryan . . . ," Mr. Coye breathed. He was clenching and unclenching each fist at his sides. Again, not a good sign.

"There was *no victim*, Dad," Ryan reiterated. "Do you want me to look up the word *crime* for you too?"

"No!" the man screamed. He could contain himself no longer. "I don't want you looking up *CRIME*. I don't care about *VICTIMS* either! We're discussing the party and what you did, son. I don't care if it's a little white lie or a felony."

Ryan dropped the dictionary. The big toe of his right foot broke the book's fall. He bit his bottom lip and held his breath. Ryan dared not respond to the pain. Beads of sweat formed on his forehead and at his temples.

"Now!" his Father continued.

Ryan, head bent just a bit, stared at the tiny circular stain on the carpet.

"Did you, or did you not, purposefully set out to embarrass and humiliate a classmate of yours by the name of Jill last Friday night at the school's eighth-grade Halloween-slash Festival-slash Party?"

"No," Ryan half whispered.

"WHAT DO YOU MEAN . . . NO!"

Ryan squeaked, "No . . . sir?"

His Dad was clenching his teeth now too. He began sucking in great gulps of air. It reminded Ryan of a snorting bull getting ready to charge. He'd seen one do that on a Spanish channel he'd flipped to not long ago. Just before heading full-tilt towards the cape swirling Matador, the bull snorted and sniffed and blew gusts of air into the dirt with sufficient force to cause a miniature dust storm around its front legs and bobbing and darting head. The strong behavioral resemblance between that animal and Ryan's huffing and puffing Father caused the beginnings of a smile.

"You think this is funny?" Ryan's Dad remained livid. His cheeks and the tip of his nose were fiery crimson and well on the way to mottled purple.

Ryan took a step back.

"I don't know about you, son. You deliberately hurt someone, lie about your part in it, and then have the nerve to laugh about it?"

"I wasn't laughing about *that*!" Ryan tried to explain. " I . . . . I . . ." he stammered.

His Dad's red-hot-face hovered only inches from his own. One or two degrees more and his Father's heated breath would surely burst into flames. Ryan thought better of what he'd been about to say. He tried to move back but an unyielding catamaran halted his retreat. His knees were shaking badly. Interestingly enough so, also, were his Father's.

"There . . . were . . ." his Father stated evenly, taking a new breath after each word, "witnesses."

Ryan stood his ground. He knew he had not intended to hurt Jill or even embarrass her, not really. It was just a joke, a harmless prank. He would never be able to admit to what his Father had accused him of having done. It would be a lie.

"Son," the man seemed to be trying so hard, "the psychologist said your behavior can't be changed unless you first admit to it."

"But I didn't do what you said."

"You did," his Father's voice had become suddenly flat and

void of emotion. "Maybe we ought to quit that psychologist. Six months we've been seeing him and nothin's changed."

That was okay with Ryan. He didn't like the guy anyway. His Dad was talking softly to him self.

"Why would the teacher call me and tell me that he did it if he didn't do it?" He glanced at Ryan. That boy can be so convincing. He wanted to believe him. Heck, he used to believe everything the boy said. That was up until the principal got involved a while back. Mr. Johnson had forced Ryan's Father to rethink his position. If Ryan had lied *that* time, maybe, just maybe, he'd lied to him before as well. It unnerved him a bit. All those times he'd come to his son's defense, telling and even yelling at other adults and parents that "my boy wouldn't lie!" That's what he had once thought. Reality can bring you to your knees in an instant.

Ryan watched his Father walk away still mumbling. As the man shuffled into the kitchen, though, Ryan heard the words his Father obviously had meant for him to hear quite clearly.

"I wouldn't plan anything for awhile," he said. "I don't think you'll be going anywhere soon. I won't tolerate lying, son, not from you. Not from anyone."

But, he hadn't lied. Why wouldn't his Dad believe him?

And, in fact, Ryan truly had not lied. This scene is not a demonstration of a lying child, even though it may initially seem to be just that. Rather, it demonstrates an insidious and very common dynamic relating to those with OCS that often wreaks havoc within the family constellation and in most other relationships as well. This can be better reflected, perhaps, by the use of several good descriptive words and phrases. These might be as follows: **Rigid Thinking; One Track Mind; Tunnel Vision;** *All* or *Nothing* **Responses; Exactitis;** and there are undoubtedly many more.

We already know most of the OCS affected typically have an obsessive need to be right or, more specifically, not to be wrong. To be wrong is frequently an emotionally devastating experience, particularly when it is pointed out publicly. Making a mistake is another form of being wrong. It could be literally any kind of a mistake, no matter how tiny or insignificant it may seem to others. This need can be so relentlessly held to that, the affected person can become immobilized should a mistake actually be made. They may need to start a task over no matter how close to completion it may have been before the mistake was made. It's not as if they walk around thinking constantly, "I can't make a mistake." It's not conscious. When they make one, they simply over react in varying degrees and intensities depending on their personal symptom levels (mild-moderate, etc.).

These individuals similarly tend to hold others unconsciously to their personal standard. This may be the single most significant factor in relation to the continuous intra-individual communication breakdowns, misunderstandings, distortions, and misperceptions common to the OCS affected. The scene between Ryan and his hapless, frustrated Father is a classic example of this miscommunication problem. Let me share another example that is not quite so complicated as was Ryan's scene before attempting to make better sense out of his situation.

In this scene the OCS affected family has just finished dinner. One child starts to leave the table without clearing his personal implements used during the meal.

"Wait a minute, Joey," the Father's voice booms out.

Joey stops and turns.

"Don't forget to take your dishes to the sink," his Father reminds him. "You know the rule."

"Yeah, okay, Dad." Joey's reluctance seeps into his vocal tones but he moves to comply.

Seeing this, his Father leaves the table him self.

As Joey moves away from the kitchen towards the hall, his Father raises up a bit from his position on the couch and takes a quick glance back at the table, just to be sure.

"Joey," Mr. Greene shouts, "*You get back in here*, NOW!"

"What?" Joey returns from the hall looking frustrated. He pokes his head back into the living room.

"What is it, Dad?"

"I thought I told you to take your dishes to the sink?"

"Yeah, well . . . I did."

Immediately Mr. Greene rises to his full 6'5" height, towering over the mere 10-year old Joey. He points towards his son's place at the table, "Then what do you call that?" he demands in accusing tones.

Joey glances back at the table, "Call what?" he asks genuinely surprised.

"You can't see the fork, spoon, and knife you left that I specifically told you to take to the sink?" His Father's vocal tones were rising as he spoke.

Joey, exasperated him self, shot back at his Father, "You told me to take my dishes to the sink. You didn't say anything about the fork and stuff. I thought someone else was going to pick 'em up."

"Why, you little impertinent . . ." Mr. Greene returns, "You get your smart little . . ."

"NO!" Mrs. Greene interrupts. "George, don't you dare say what I think you're about to say."

The authority in her voice stops him cold.

Looking at his Father, Joey was sure, "If it were at all possible, steam would have been shooting out of the man's ears just like it does from the spout of a teapot on the stove."

"Get your Butt . . . your behind," his Father stammered with a quick roll of his eyes towards his wife, "over there and finish picking up your place." Then with exaggerated emphasis and a very slow tempo, he added, "Take your fork . . . your spoon . . . Oh, do I need to spell them out too?" he added sarcastically.

Joey shook his head.

"And don't forget the knife!" With that he plopped his two hundred and sixty pound frame back onto the couch. Dust mites got an unexpected free ride to anywhere in the room. Some might have even made it all the way out to the hall.

Joey quietly removed the offending pieces of silverware and carried them to the sink. He could hear his Father muttering to his Mother, or to him self.

"I can't believe that little . . ." He was saying. "What is he, stupid? Does he think we're stupid? Of course not! He's just trying to get my goat. He doesn't want to do a damn thing. That lazy little . . ."

Joey was almost to the hall.

"He knows he's supposed to take his dishes to the sink. We only do it every meal! He thinks he's funny, I suppose. Oh yeah, he's hilarious." His Father quickly glanced back towards the table once again. He became suddenly silent.

There, left at Joey's place, was his milk glass.

It's not hard to imagine the kind of response Joey's Father probably had the Moment he discovered that glass. There's no need to add it to what's already been written. This situation may sound ludicrous. It is not. Part of the difficulty in accepting and comprehending such a scene as possible is the fact that this scenario literally mimics, at least observably, the long theorized and well known behavior and response patterns that can result from an individual's passive-aggressive attempts to get even with, and irritate others. Thus, doing literally only what parents, teachers, and other authority figures of any kind require of them, and nothing else, can actually be a predetermined response relating to one's otherwise inexpressible anger meant to irritate and get back at, in return, an offending other. This particular passive-aggressive response pattern has been so thoroughly entrenched into the belief-system of most of the world's societies that, when such actions are present, it is frequently the foremost and often the only consideration thought to be possible.

Another theory put forth as an explanation (although in my mind a weak one) is that Joey, in the scene presented, might just have had a desire or need to be in complete CONTROL. This viewpoint would suggest that Joey's efforts relate to the emotional satisfaction experienced when his actions, or lack thereof as the case may be, cause his Father to become

Under the CONTROL hypothesis, as well as that of the potentially passive-aggressive hypothesis, the child, weaker individual, or the one in an employee/boss relationship is unable to confront the more powerful "Authority Figure." As a result, the only way to express internally experienced anger relative to the figure of authority, is to do it clandestinely. In other words, this means to demonstrate this control, and in the other case demonstrate anger and revenge. Actions are either in secret so that nobody knows who did it, or in such a way that the behaviors, it can be argued, were done in such a way that it looks innocent although it was not. These behavioral patterns have been described by experts for generations, written into the World community's books and literature, and performed in theater as well as displayed in the movies. Thus it is not surprising that when such patterns do exist, they are generally thought to result from dynamics such as those just described.

In my experience over the years working with OCS I have become convinced that an equally viable alternative explanation for behavioral responses such as those discussed is primarily biochemical in nature. When mistakenly diagnosed for either the passive-aggressive or control versions, behavior problems are unavoidable. Treatment strategies designed for the first two tend to be ineffective when the biochemically driven OCS is the actual underlying reason for the manifest behavior.

The primary OCS driven explanation for Joey's situation can be difficult for most people to believe due to the previously suggested biases that frequently exist. If OCS is present, however, the many prior failed interventions and chronic misdirected attempts to understand can suddenly (or eventually) begin to make sense.

The OCS driven tend to be just that, driven. Frequently, ideas and thoughts come unbidden to the mind that cannot be easily dismissed. Those that are dismissed often return again and again in a relentless, if irregular, irrevocable pattern. This tends to create in the mind of those affected, an undeniable urgency or need to rush connected with every living Moment. Symptoms and symptomatic periods come and go, rise and fall in strength, change with time and experience, and are exacerbated (made worse) by stress, intense emotional reactions, and fatigue.

When the OCS affected are focused on a given thing, thought, or idea, there is a tendency to be literally unable to conceive, receive, and/or hold in the mind another idea or thought at the same time. Thus, in the story about Joey's behavior, if OCS *is* involved, might have been that he was wolfing down his food, feeling the pressure to hurry so that he can get on to the next thing at the forefront of his mind. He similarly also could have been picking at his food, eating slowly and seeming to be lost in thought as his mind went over and over and over a specific idea. In either case, upon completion of his dinner, with his mind in such a state, it is easy to imagine that he could truly rise and leave the table without so much as an afterthought being given to the transporting of his personal eating implements over to the sink. Even though it had been an established family pattern and rule throughout his entire life to do this, the need to do, or go, or think sometimes overrules all else.

Obsessive thoughts and compulsions, whether in the mild-moderate or severe ranges, can interfere at different levels of intensity with any and all activities. Thus, as Joey races to fulfill the driving thought and is interrupted when he reaches the hall of his home, one can perhaps more easily begin to comprehend the reasons for his own frustrated reply to his Father of "What?" Depending on the symptom's strength and urgency, such an interruption can result in anything from mild irritation and resistance all the way up to unbelievable and unjustified emotional explosiveness. Without the OCS explanation of frequent and chronic over responsiveness and hypersensitive reactions, it simply does not make sense.

Responding to his Father's insistent request, Joey heads back towards the table. The obsession or compulsion pounds on in his head like a silent drum. His Father told him to put his dishes in the sink. Dishes in the sink. Pound . . . pound . . . pound. Dishes! Pound. Joey takes them to the sink. "Finally."

He then returns to his quest. Pound.

Upon being interrupted a second time, he is genuinely confused. Pound, pound, pound. "What now?" his thoughts scream out in protest. Pound. "There's more?"

Joey honestly can't think of anything else. He did what his Father asked. Pound. Why didn't his Father just say, "Take the dishes and the silverware?" The silverware never even entered his mind. Pound . . . pound . . . pound. All he saw was the dish that was keeping him from getting immediately to what he really wanted, needed, to be doing just then. Pound . . . pound . . . pound. Precious time was being lost. Pound . . . pound . . . pound.

Joey was getting angrier by the minute. His Father was now

yelling at him and placing the entire blame for the matter on him. But it clearly wasn't Joey's fault. It wasn't fair.

Pointing this out to his Father, however, that Joey was not to blame did not seem to be helping to settle the matter. His Dad kept screaming that his insolence would not be tolerated and to stop sassing and get his a— (rhymes with sass) in gear and blah, blah, blah.

"Okay! Okay!" Joey had to shout to be heard over his screaming Father. "I'm doin' it."

He headed back towards the kitchen.

Joey's Father left the room. Joey could still hear his voice though. He was talking loudly to Joey's Mother. He found him self wondering if his Father even knew how to speak softly. That voice usually carried all through the house no matter what room he might be in.

Joey glanced up at the air conditioner and heating vents. He decided it probably had to have something to do with the air ducts.

"Your son," Joey's Father was saying, "does that on purpose. He knows *very well* what will make me angry. He's a little . . ."

The last part seemed muffled. Joey could imagine his Mother placing her hand over his Father's mouth. He wished he could get away with something like that.

"Now James," Joey had heard his Mother's voice, "You don't know that. You can't be sure he's doing it just to make you mad . . ."

"Caroline! PAH-LEEEZE." The please was distended and had that familiar sarcastic twist people used so often to pound their point home. "Please, honey. C'mon you heard him. *You* didn't tell me to take the *silverware*, as if he didn't know. Is he really that *STUPID?*"

She must have shook her head.

"I don't think so either. So," he continued, "we both agree it's not stupidity, although I still sometimes wonder. If he's not dumb, what other reason could there be for such idiocy like we've just experienced right here in our house in front of our own eyes and ears?"

There was a short pause.

"I . . ." Joey's Mother began, "I don't know. I'm not sure. He does have an awful lot on his mind, you know."

"And *I* don't!" was his Father's curt retort.

They seemed to be taking a breather.

Joey carefully picked up his fork, spoon, knife, and napkin (even though his Father had neglected to tell him to dispose of the napkin). When the task was completed, Joey rinsed his hands, dried them on the dishtowel hanging from the handle of the refrigerator and directed him self, once again, towards the hallway and his bedroom.

As he passed his parents closed bedroom door, he heard his Father whispering. "So, he does know how to speak softly!" Joey thought.

"Caroline," he confessed, "I'm actually afraid to go back out there. What if he's taken the silverware, but left his napkin?"

Joey gave him self a mental high-five. He'd gotten the napkin.

"Or," his Father continued, "he's left the milk glass? I will go nuts! I'm afraid I'll hurt him or something. After all, how long has this been a rule in our house, anyway? We didn't just make it up. We've all been doing it for years."

Joey had just come down from patting him self on the back when his Father had mentioned the milk glass. He'd had to retrace a couple of steps to get a clear view of the kitchen table. The Moment he did, he slapped him self on the side of the head hard enough to cause him to involuntarily wince. "Stupid idiot!" Joey told him self. "If I'm not the dumbest jerk . . ." he raced to get back to the table. Just as Joey cleared the hallway, his Father also had stepped out of his bedroom and into the hallway for a recheck.

This type of circumstance is extremely common within the households of the OCS affected. It can happen from one, or just a few, to many times on a daily basis. That means there are usually several times throughout the course of a single day in which children, like Joey in the story, are getting in trouble. The parent/child relationship is weakened just a bit each time. It also means that the children in these situations are criticizing themselves many times daily with thoughts like, "I'm so stupid! What a jerk! Of all the good for nothing . . ." And so on.

Although common, OCS affected individuals don't always react quite so literally as Joey did in the example. Most of the time Joey would experience no problems whatsoever remembering to put plate away and accessories where they belong after having eaten. This fact, unfortunately, further complicates the problems associated with this behavior. Parents, teachers, and the like tend to feel that if a child has been capable of adequately demonstrating appropriate responses and behavior previously, they should be able to do so again at any time thereafter. They are, therefore, considered to be obviously choosing to act inappropriately. This, however, is simply not necessarily true. Although on the surface such an expectation does make sense, perhaps the following example will serve to dispel this heretofore sensible, but sometimes faulty, notion.

Jimmy is an excellent first baseman. He rarely misses a throw from a teammate and also has not missed a ball hit in his direction for the entire season, thus far. Similarly he is well rounded in the batting area too. He has not struck out yet this season, has the most RBI's of his team and the entire league, and has hit 13 home runs in his last 15 at bats.

At the start of the game his coach, with high expectations, has him bat in the cleanup position. Jimmy strikes out for the first time. After taking the field, Jimmy single-handedly allows six runs to be scored by the opposing team due to his errors at first base. Fans are booing. The coach is so astonished by these actions that his frustration is quite slow in coming. What happened? He pulls Jimmy from the game and demands an explanation

Jimmy, it turns out, had lost one of his contacts earlier in the day and then somehow misplaced the other. He'd told no one because it was the third pair he'd lost in a month and he didn't want his parents to find out. He thought he could get by without them at least until he could search his room just one more time a little more thoroughly.

Behaviors, responses, and reactions with his contacts on, that are typically not much more difficult for Jimmy than breathing became suddenly next to impossible as, unable to see the ball, he simply could not hit or catch it successfully.

Admittedly the example related above is clear, simple, direct, and easy to imagine. Of course, in many similar situations in which prior behavioral abilities and capabilities are being interfered with, the causative factors are nowhere near as direct or easy to see or at times to even believe.

Typically, when the OCS affected respond so undeviatingly to the "letter of the law" as did Joey at the dinner table, at least one or several other elements tend to be involved. Significant fatigue and/or stress, as well as emotional hyper-responsivity in any direction (positive or negative), is known to make all such symptoms worse. This heightening of symptoms can interfere with the fluidity of the mind and make focusing difficult and singular in nature.

Another factor, probably the most likely to interfere in just such a situation as this, involves competing thoughts, a single track mind, and/or what might be called "tunnel vision." During such an episode the OCS affected is already engaged in an idea or thought relating to something else and cannot let go of that thought (another common OCS happening).

When a persistent thought or idea is unrelentingly engaging the mind of the OCS affected, it becomes very difficult to attend to and/or hold in the mind any other ideas or thoughts. At the dinner table Joey, on this particular evening, may have been thinking of the video game he'd been playing when called to dinner. He may have experienced a constant increasing "need" to get back to his room in order to complete "the game." Throughout dinner he may have scarcely been able to think of anything else.

As a result, he ate fast and was ready to go before anyone else in the family had finished. He was then reprimanded and told he'd have to sit five more minutes at the table as a consequence, after the last family member was done. This only stressed and irritated him all the more while intensifying the incessant thought and need. As soon as his little brother Billy left the table, Joey started counting under his breath. His Mother set the cheap portable kitchen timer. The Moment the chime rang out his freedom,

Joey jumped up and dashed towards the hall leading to his room. "Finally," he may have been screaming out in his mind as he did so.

It is in the midst of such inner turmoil that his Father requests (yells) that he needs to come back and put his dishes in the sink.

In such a tormented state of mind with another thought occupying most of (if not all) his consciousness, he can only think "Dishes . . . Dishes." He grabs them and dumps them, plate and all (little did his Father know at the time, in the garbage) before returning to the unrelenting desire of his persistent, if not tortured, mind.

It is not always a "tortured" mind that pre-empts other information from entering and remaining therein. It may be simply a persistent thought, desire, or need that is taking up the conscious space to the point that incoming messages (if they get in at all) do not stay very long, nor do they have sufficient time to be processed to the extent that they normally would. The end result, therefore, when this occurs, tends to be very literal and concrete thinking with no extra frills or processing beyond just getting the thought and responding. Frankly, sometimes the information simply doesn't make it into the consciousness and therefore is unable to be considered even briefly.

The capriciousness of OCS/OCD symptomotology is well known although not well understood. Thus, on a given day, Joey may be, or seem, perfectly fine and capable of responding in a behaviorally appropriate manner no matter the situation. While the very next day he may be practically non-responsive and seem to be caught up in his own world, "a space cadet," for half the day or more (and/or less).

The tendencies described herein and dubbed "rigid" or "literal" thinking, when seen or demonstrated in another, can be symptomatic of mild-moderate OCS. As with other common symptoms, if OCS is truly present, the presence of (usually) a host of other signs and/or symptoms can also be observed if one seriously looks for them. Without such supportive symptomatic evidence, alternative hypotheses to OCS should be actively considered. Almost invariably these individuals are far from being blind, stupid, and/or deaf, although at any given Moment they may be accused of being one of these or even accused of all three.

Day-after-day . . . more of the same
It's depressing 'cause it seems like nothing's ever gonna change
Night after night . . . you pray it'll be all right
But you can't help feelin' somehow you're wastin' time

And it's nothing like the way that you once dreamed
When you were a mere child of thirteen
No handsome prince ever came to take you away
No frog to kiss . . . no dragons to slay

Year after year . . . you struggle with the fear
To the point of sometimes losing sleep and shedding tears
Time after time . . . when you thought you'd found the light
Someone would hit the switch and bring you back to the night

Day-after-day . . . you still get up anyway
You know it would only make it worse if in bed you stayed
Step after step . . . you'll go on until nothing's left
You may have a long search to find where the answers to dreams are kept

From the song "No Dragons to Slay" by Ron D. Kingsley

THE EMPTY BUCKET

(Hey . . . did you say *bucket* or sieve)

As I sat pondering what I was going to share about the specific focus of this particular article as it relates to the whole OCS picture, I searched my mind for an appropriate title. I was trying to come up with one that might help readers connect visually, and perhaps, emotionally with the common symptom that is to be the focus herein. In this exposé we are going to examine a symptom closely related to one that I've previously discussed in a paper entitled "Dissatisfaction . . . Guaranteed". In fact, this particular symptom may only be different in the way that it is expressed. It most assuredly stems from the same main theme of never quite being satisfied with anything. The focus this time, however, has shifted just a bit. Instead of continually being dissatisfied with the things that you actually do, the viewpoint herein is in not being satisfied with what others do or are willing to give. This would include developmental needs such as the need for security, love, attention, nourishment, friendship and the like.

No matter how much water you pour into a sink, unless the drain is plugged, it will never fill up. You could say it would remain forever thirsty. Efforts to fill the sink with water, even with the faucet continually running, would be met with complete failure. The visual image of some well meaning and serious individual desperately trying to fill a sink whose drain is operating at full capacity is equivalent to that of someone trying to meet the need, or needs, of the OCS driven. The OCS affected's needs, by the very nature of the problem, almost assuredly will not and cannot be met. Their drains seem (or truly are) never plugged. They cannot be filled, though they most desperately desire that they become just that. They are empty buckets with a hole in the bottom.

"Dad, will you do something with me?" a young boy asks.

The Father, who has just spent two-and-a-half hours playing football with the boy, sighs and says; "not right now, son, I need to rest a bit."

The youngster, hardly daunted, repeats his request not three minutes later.

"Not right now," his Father echoes

"But . . . Dad . . ."

"I said NOT NOW! Now, would you please leave me alone!"

The boy walks reluctantly away angrily muttering, "you *never* do anything with me."

There are several things happening in the scene above that are worth noting. The boy is demonstrating the *empty bucket* situation and he is also showing the *all or nothing* tendency so typical of the OCS population. The boy states, "You *never* do anything with me!"

He does this because the intensity of what he is experiencing at that very Moment is so overwhelming that this is how he truly feels. He wants what he wants *right now* and the two and a-half-hours of playing football are no longer a conscious thought in his mind. At any given Moment there is only one thought present to which the OCS individual is responsive. The satisfaction felt playing football with his Dad is gone. It's as if it had never happened because it is no longer a conscious experience. All the boy can think about is *the present*. Nothing else matters. He is locked in on a target and Momentarily unable to consider any other options. This, remember, is not an excuse; it is an explanation.

Depending on how strong or severe the OCS driven need is at a given Moment, the person's response to being prevented from obtaining the desired outcome varies considerably. In other words if the person wants something or wants to do something and the want is *very* strong (due to the influence of OCS), when the thing they want is prevented from happening their response tends to be *very* strong as well. Remember the strength of OCS symptoms go up and down frequently and can vary dramatically during even the course of a single day. This inconsistency makes it quite difficult for others to relate to them. When the OCS influence is weaker, the person's symptomatic responses are weaker too. Of course, knowing this doesn't necessarily make it that much easier to deal with at the actual time of occurrence (during the heat of the battle). Over time, however, this knowledge, along with having available some practical guidelines and strategies with which one might deal more effectively with these OCS driven over responders, can and does make a real difference. In time, relating to this chronically dissatisfied individual can get easier. Without the help of medication, though, quite honestly it may never become *easy.*

So, what can be done to make life with these *empty buckets* a little easier? Well, if you were actually attempting to fill an actual bucket with water and it wasn't filling up, chances are you would soon stop and either give up and walk away or try to find out what was the matter. You would then probably take action to correct the problem. If, however, you were unable to figure out what the problem was, taking action might not help at all. Without knowing what's wrong, specific actions that you take may not even come close to solving the problem and much effort and time may be wasted. When efforts and time are wasted, people tend to be less than happy about it. When a lot of effort and time, as well as materials and resources, are put into use and positive results are not forthcoming, people generally get frustrated and may eventually become very angry. This anger may be directed at the bucket (OCS affected child or adult). Sometimes buckets become damaged as a result of misdirected anger, and the initial *problem* may then develop into *problems*. When *problems* are present, things often become very complex and with this complexity comes, you've probably guessed it, more problems. When the bucket continually remains empty although you keep trying to fill it daily, it becomes a big problem. A way to make things better is to understand the problem as best you can and then with that understanding, manage the situation to enhance the positives and diminish the negatives. Believe it or not, sometimes this requires a shifting of perceptions and beliefs in order to make it work. For example, there will undoubtedly be times when you've simply got to quit trying to fill that bucket and accept that, at least for a time, it's going to remain empty. As the well known saying goes: "The grass isn't always greener on the other side."

The difference between walking away from an actual bucket that can't be filled and the OCS affected individual that can't be filled is monumental. The bucket isn't alive. It can't get up and follow you around. Furthermore, a bucket cannot ask, and eventually demand, again and again to be filled. Buckets don't whine. They don't cry, nor do they get angry, throw tantrums, scream, and lash out physically, or break stuff. This, of course, makes things a lot more complex and difficult to manage. The word manage is an excellent one for this and any situation involving those who are OCS affected. Symptoms are managed, not cured. The ability to successfully cope with OCS varies with time and is managed at some times better than others.

AWARENESS:

When parents, teachers, and others become informed and begin to truly understand OCS symptoms such as the one I've called, *The Empty Bucket,* this knowledge greatly enhances their ability to respond and deal with it. Patience tends to improve the same as tolerance, and the often-experienced negative thoughts others have regarding the affected one frequently diminish. Sometimes relationships between those who are symptomatic and others who are not do tend to get better without actual treatment. To honestly realize, however, that someone is not always entirely in control of their actions, thoughts, and behaviors is important for progression to occur. This, at times, enables those who *are* in control, or have better control, to openly consider alternative ways in which they can actually *help* the OCS affected one instead of silently (or verbally) criticizing them for their lack or weakness. A synonym for awareness is education. Education means learning about something. The more we know about a given thing the more comfortable we become around it. As we understand and learn about potentially effective strategies and interventions through education we are much more likely to put these strategies into practice.

If someone, including Doctors, Psychologists, Teachers, and Counselors, tells us to try interventions that we don't have an adequate understanding of or feel comfortable in using, or do not know why they should be implemented, it is unlikely that these interventions will be effective.

One of the most important things to keep in mind when dealing with the Empty Buckets of this world, especially children, relates to patience and the ability to withstand verbal onslaughts, tantrumming, and sometimes even death threats. When the OCS affected child is denied access to things, privileges, or related perceived "needs" and they are in the empty bucket mode, they will typically respond in a very dramatic manner. If the parent is able to withstand the barrage as it escalates and eventually runs its course, the involved child most often will come around and accept, at least Momentarily, that access has been denied. The resultant sulking behavior may last from just a few minutes to hours and even days. The older the individual is, the more likely the sulking will continue for longer periods of time. This appears to be related to thought patterns that are energized by the obsessive and compulsive symptomotology. Usually, though, when the process is complete, the individual will respond as if there never was a dispute at all. This tendency to totally *forget* that the incident ever occurred baffles and angers parents and others who must then sort through their own often bruised feelings and the emotional distress such behavior induces within themselves. The trick is to continually remind oneself during the empty bucket outburst that this is a symptom of a partially controllable biochemically induced underlying cause. This, of course, is easier said than done. Dr. Russell Barkley gives excellent advice in his book *Taking Charge of ADHD* when he reminds parents and others to work hard at trying not to take things personally. This adage also fits those with OCS. Try not to take what is said and done personally. Don't allow the child's responses to dictate how you feel about the incident in question. Situations such as these are not a race to be won. You don't have to win out over your child or force her to demonstrate her respect for you in order to appease your own inner needs. Much of the time it is so incredibly difficult to back away emotionally that many simply cannot do it. Keep trying. Never give up. This, however, is one of the reasons that medication to treat the underlying biochemical cause is often so important. When an individual responds to the medical treatment, these situations tend to quickly stop altogether or at least become so much less intense or in number that they don't create anywhere near the turmoil and distress that the untreated response generates.

When dealing with an older affected child in the late teenage years or with an adult, the picture is similar but usually much more intense and long lasting. Part of the problem is that these individuals typically have no idea that something is actually wrong with them. If they are in significant distress and truly want to change, educating them is actually quite rewarding and a fairly easy task. When symptomatic individuals in this age group are not in distress, it is nearly impossible to get them to see their behaviors as representative of an underlying biochemical cause. If, however, there is a motivational factor that is more powerful than the symptoms, progress can still be made. For example if a spouse says to the other, "get treatment or I'm leaving," and the affected spouse doesn't want this to happen, it can get them into treatment long enough to get some results and dramatically turn the picture around. If a teenager is faced with losing the privilege of driving the car, he may choose to attend treatment sessions instead. It is then up to the professional to achieve results that will then be likely to *sell* the affected one on treatment. Nothing works like positive results to keep someone in treatment long enough to make a real difference.

Often in the initial interviews and evaluation sessions, when OCS is the presenting factor, the Leyton Obsessional Inventory works like a charm to help those affected individuals believe that there truly is something that is identifiable and interferes in their life. As the questions are asked in a casual and non-threatening manner, the affected ones may begin to lean forward in their chairs and their eyes may begin to shine with interest. They often seem to feel that here, finally, is someone who really understands.

Without appropriate treatment and education, the empty buckets tend to eventually drain everyone they come in contact with. The strain this causes on relationships can be so overwhelming that parents may experience terrible guilt related to their dislike of being around their own child. Spouses shut down emotionally or become so embittered that anger becomes their constant companion. The affected ones sense these emotional changes in those around them, but typically do not understand any more than unaffected ones do why it is happening. Thus, they tend to feel rejected, unwanted, and unloved. This, of course, can fuel the emptiness already felt and impel them to even greater efforts at getting their buckets filled. The result is a circular downward spiral. Recognition and treatment are the answers.

I've never felt so all alone . . . as I do today
Been searching for the answers . . . yet still can't find a way
To take this yearning that I feel . . . and that I can't deny
And turn it into something . . . that will keep my hope alive

We're told just how we're supposed to feel . . . and all were supposed to need
But I'm not sure just what is real . . . or what I should believe
There's no room left to wonder . . . about life and the things we do
It's all preshrunk and prethunk to fit us so that we'll end up like we're expected to

But the world I see is not the same as the one other's must see
Those who look with their eyes but don't include the heart
And it's not that I . . . want to try . . . and see it differently
It's just that's the way it's been right from the start

No one knows what I'm thinking . . . there's no way that you can
And you can't feel what I'm feeling . . . and you don't know who I am
And though it seems you listen to me . . . at least until you think I'm through
Yet you don't hear what I'm saying . . . it might change your point of view

From the song "So All Alone" by Ron D. Kingsley

CONTROL:

(OR NOT!)

The issue of control is another major element that plays itself out symptomatically for many of those who truly have OCS (whether diagnosed or not). In my experience with those reacting to the influence of OCS, the accusation that they are "control freaks" or "control-aholics" virtually never describes adequately what is really going on. Admittedly their actions, reactions, and behaviors *do* appear to suggest an extreme need to control others and/or to control the environment and themselves but in the OCS driven case it is generally not truly an issue of control. As the familiar adage goes *"appearances can be deceiving,"* so it is with most of the OCS affected. As a result it becomes very important to understand the true dynamics behind this common misconception if one is to enhance the chances of unraveling the true symptom and eventually get a handle on dealing with it effectively. This is essential not just for the OCS affected individual but also for any others who must live with, work with, or spend much time with the one who has interfering OCS symptoms.

Typically tremendous anxiety and/or a sense of certain impending doom are constant companions of the OCS affected. When actively symptomatic, there are a host of *"needs"* experienced by those affected by OCS that simply *must be* adhered to, *"or else"*. When someone is perceived to be either interfering with, or ignoring, the parameters, or rules, associated with a specific *"need,"* the individual experiencing the need will make efforts to enforce these rules. Such efforts quite naturally *appear* manipulative and controlling as the affected individual tries to get everything to be done or to turn out like he feels it must. This, however, is not an effort to *control* the situation or the others involved. It is really an effort to protect the self from experiencing the overwhelming anticipated disaster that is believed will absolutely occur if unable to orchestrate things exactly the way he needs them to be. There is no argument that the behaviors engaged in to achieve this goal do indeed look like exercises to control, but they are not. This is why these individuals immediately bristle and adamantly deny such an accusation when so confronted. For them the issue is not at all one of control. For the OCS affected it is one of doing and getting things *right*. This occurs in order to avoid what they perceive as certain catastrophe or to insure that things are done right because often they perceive that it won't be done correctly if they aren't continually checking or doing it themselves. Are these individuals manipulative? You bet. The reasons, though, are not what others often perceive them to be.

It is true that almost invariably no catastrophe follows when things do not go exactly the way the affected one feels they should. That is to say no visible or tangible disaster occurs. The thoughts and emotions within the one with OCS, however, when things don't go right, tend to escalate in intensity and severity such that this individual may even seriously start to wonder if his own death is imminent. This can often create a frenzy of activity along with intense emotional outbursts. Anyone directly in the path, or near the path, is likely to be perceived as interfering and get *blasted*. A great deal of the anger that these individuals often display is none other than misdirected. This is caused by frustration, anxiety, and fear associated with the emotional build up of a host of seemingly silly and/or minor things experienced throughout the course of the day that didn't quite go the way they were supposed to have gone. Not, I reiterate, because she wanted or had to have *control,* but because there is an internal standard that it is felt must be met, sometimes, at all costs.

Once, in an attempt to explain this situation to someone else, an interesting question was raised. In response to the idea that much of the time the OCS affected are furiously working, not to have control but to keep from being controlled, this individual responded with, "So, what's the difference? You're either trying to control or trying not to be controlled. It's the same thing." In other words she seemed to be suggesting that when someone is in the process of working not to be controlled, his active engagement in efforts to keep from being controlled actually constitutes a form of trying to control. Thus, her argument was that they are controlling everything in an attempt to be free from control. This is an interesting argument that led to further conversation and thoughtful investigation.

The paragraph above would seem to indicate why so many observers of the OCS affected might be so quick to jump on the band wagon in a declaration that these are indeed individuals in need of controlling others and their environment. The key to unlocking the apparent paradox lies within the individual. It is their intent that is important. These individuals are locked into their intentions and cling to them with an intensity that is formidable, to say the least. Thus, because there is no intention whatsoever in relation to the actual controlling of others and/or the environment, these individuals are at a loss when confronted by what appears so clearly to others to constitute controlling behavior. The vehement denial they frequently display at these times relates to the fact that they perceive that another, or others, are describing them inaccurately. As you probably already know, for the OCS affected to perceive another as representing them falsely is not something that such an individual will be able to deal with very effectively.

Consider the following conversation that shows how easy it can be to see someone as controlling when in fact they are not. The underlying driving force is none other than OCS in disguise.

*　　*　　*

"How can you say that?" David whirled on his heel and confronted his wife.

Brenda was leaning back against the counter. Her arms were crossed. "Because it's true."

"TRUE?" David shouted. "True? Nothing could be further from the truth."

Brenda stood firm. "Face it, David. You are a control freak. You have to control everyone and everything around you."

"I DO NOT!" He clenched and unclenched his fists. His face began to redden. Finally he threw his arms into the air. "When!" David stammered. "When! Give me one example of when I try to control everyone and everything."

"How about this morning?"

"What about this morning?"

"You made me redo your eggs. They went fifteen seconds past the timer and *you* had to cook two new ones. You wouldn't even try the eggs that I already cooked."

"They were over cooked!" He threw his hands into the air. "You don't expect me to eat something that's over cooked, do you?"

"Fifteen seconds," she reiterated.

"Fifteen seconds is fifteen seconds," he returned.

"You see," Brenda stated, "it's control."

"That's not control," David was nearly shouting now, "it's basic common sense. Three and a half minute eggs aren't three and a half minute eggs unless they're cooked for three minutes and forty-five seconds, now, are they?"

"I'll bet," she said, "if you hadn't heard the timer, you wouldn't even know the difference between a three minute and thirty second or a three minute forty second egg."

"I would know!"

"Yeah, right!"

"Do I sense a bit of submerged hostility?" David began. "Could it be that your insidious inability to admit to your own inadequacy is surfacing in a vain attempt to place the blame on me by labeling it a *control* issue when in fact it is a mistake? A plain and simple personal mistake that you just can't own up to."

Brenda was nearly in tears. "Call it what you will, *David Johnas Wirthing,* but I know control when I see it." She took a deep breath. "I'm surprised you didn't say anything about your fork being on the wrong side and your napkin being folded incorrectly."

David twisted his head around so he could see her. "I was going there next," he informed her matter-of-factly.

"Ohhh . . ." Brenda threw up her hands and ran from the kitchen.

"Hey, where ya goin'," David called after her. "The eggs aren't done yet."

* * *

Was it really control? There was no doubt in Brenda's mind that it was. She felt like she couldn't do *anything* without having to revise and correct it the way that David wanted it done. He controlled her every move. She even confided once that she was sure her husband would try to control her breathing if it were possible.

Other counselors had told David that he would have to let go of his control if his marriage was going to survive. They might as well have been speaking to him in an alien tongue. He had no clue what they were talking about. They all seemed to take sides with his wife and believe her every word about him. None of them listened to him. Not a one believed him when he said he wasn't trying to control his wife, his children, or anything else for that matter. The consensus of his former counselors, and hence his wife as well, was that he was in denial, big time denial. Accordingly, progress could not be made therapeutically in their marriage until he recognized the denial and began to let go of and work through his issues of *control.* This, however, he simply could not do because there *were* no issues of control. Consider the following story:

Because humans, in general, are able to choose many of their actions, there is a natural tendency to believe that all actions, therefore, are chosen. This, however, is simply not true.

A blind man stands before a table upon which there are two

sandwiches. Each rests on its own paper plate. On each paper plate for all eyes to see are written either the word "*poisoned*" or the words "*safe to eat*". The blind man is then instructed to choose and eat one of the available sandwiches. He is fully informed ahead of time in regard to the writing upon each plate. If, then, the blind man picks the poisoned sandwich, can one argue that he chose, therefore, to die? Is he then responsible for his own death?

As far-fetched as the above stated example sounds, it is really not so very far from what actually happens to many people every day. There are a host of individuals who, for one reason or another that is not readily obvious to observers, may make choices that are harmful to them selves and/or to someone else. Furthermore, these individuals are then held responsible for their actions even though there was no awareness or intention involved. Frequently they are treated as if, not only the intent was present but also as if they knew exactly what they were doing as well. A lot of times those who place the blame have a very real need to see the individual's actions as purposeful. Doing so enables them to justify their own reactions and responses. People tend to feel that if certain behaviors are not paid for, justice is thwarted and when this happens behavioral change cannot ever occur. This is also not true.

In a reconstruction, once again, of the blind man choosing a sandwich, just one change may provide further insight and understanding into the point being explored herein. This time there is an observer involved. The watcher is placed in an adjacent room behind a two-way mirror. This person is told about the sandwiches and the messages clearly inscribed upon the paper plates. There are no outward visible signs of the subject's inability to see and the observer is not informed that the man is blind. The man's behavior in making the choice does not in any way suggest blindness, and therefore this fact remains unknown to the observing party. The watcher clearly sees the man appearing to gaze intently at the available choices. Since the subject's fingertips are already touching each of the plates, the choice he makes is smooth and sure. The consequence is witnessed. When interviewed afterwards, the observer is a bit hesitant in assigning responsibility. Questioning is, however, allowed at this time. First, the observer asks if the man was mentally or intellectually impaired. He was not. Second, the query is made as to whether or not the man could read. The answer to this question is *yes*, although no mention is made that he was only capable of reading Braille. Was he learning disabled? No. The observer fails to ask whether or not the man is able to see. This is because the watcher's own eyes perceived the man as a sighted individual, and information regarding this disabling characteristic was not freely provided. Since it had appeared to the observer that the man was perfectly able to see, he never thought to question this assumption. The observer therefore felt compelled to conclude that, indeed, the man *was* responsible for his own death.

What if the individual facing the sandwiches and the subsequent choice *is* sighted, and in fact, has 20/20 visual acuity but is severely depressed? Depression is not necessarily obvious during a brief or even an extended observational period. Such a man may see the poisoned sandwich as a way out of his misery. The only way out. Depressed individuals frequently do not think clearly. This is widely known.

*   *   *

In his own words, David put it like this:

> I never wanted to control anybody. Not ever! I honestly don't understand why people are always accusing me of this. In that famous *egg* example Brenda is always bringing up, I wasn't trying to *control her*. All I wanted was for my egg to be cooked for 3 and ½ minutes, no more, no less. Heck, I don't even mind cooking it myself. Not really. But Brenda is always trying to be the *best* wife and tells me over and over again that she wants to cook for me. If she doesn't do that, she feels like she's not being a good wife or something. Like she's not holding up her part of the marriage. I'm not trying to control her into making my egg a certain way. Eggs *need* to be a certain way, or they aren't *right!* Just like oatmeal needs just the right amount of water. Like the grass. It needs to be one and one-half inches tall and mowed

evenly. *Evenly.* Then there's the trimming. I just don't get it! Nobody in our family does things right but me. So, I have to do everything. Everything! Nothing is ever done right so I have to do it all. I can't do that any more. I just can't.

Something that the other counselors in David's life appeared to have missed was the fact that he wasn't in denial at all. In his mind, the problem was not one of him trying to control others; it was of him trying desperately to make everything *right*. If things weren't done in a certain way, the way he perceived they were supposed to be done, then the world was not right. David couldn't stand it when the world wasn't right, and since it was hardly ever right within the confines of his own little corner, he was frantic and miserable most of the time. His *control* issues were born of his inner need to get things right or correct, not to actually control.

The identification of what was truly at the heart of David's difficulties was extremely important in his therapy. Progress of a significant and lasting nature had not been made over the course of several years and several different therapists. As soon as the focus became the OCS symptom of needing things to be *right*, progress took a huge leap forward. Awareness and knowledge, combined with couples therapy relating to the varied dynamics common to the OCS affected and appropriate medication, enabled David for the first time to actually accept that a true problem did exist that was in need of intervention. Prior to this, he had been virtually incapable of acknowledging that a real problem was present. This marked the beginning of David and Brenda's journey into psychological and emotional health.

When OCS is present and a given individual is considered to have a problem in the area of control sufficient to require intervention, it is nearly always related to the OCS need for rightness in the world. It looks, smells, feels, and sounds like a control issue. No one in his or her right mind could argue that it doesn't look like control. It does seem like control is the issue. As soon as a shift in thinking (known as a paradigm shift) can be made, and the focus becomes the often hidden issue of an obsessive need to make things right in the world, true growth and change can occur. It may be a good idea to consider the OCS hypothesis or possibility whenever there is evidence suggesting issues of control in order to either rule in or out this very real possibility. If present, a radical shift in therapeutic focus will be needed. If OCS is not determined present, one can simply continue with therapeutic strategies to deal with real issues of control.

"You know I never needed anyone
Until you came and found me alone
Now at times it's not easy livin' with you
But I'll keep tryin' because I love you so

We both want so much to be always right
To have control and not appear the fool
It destroys some of the tender feelings in our hearts
And elicits bitter memories too

Playin' the fool . . . and lettin' it taint our lives
Playin' the fool . . . about bein' right
Playin' the fool . . . and lettin' it tear us apart
Playin' the fool . . . and breakin' our hearts . . ."

Excerpt from the song "Playin' the fool" by Ron D. Kingsley

Intimate Partner/Relationships:

How Could We Both Have It? Don't Opposites Attract?

The genetic link in OCS is speaking loudly and has been for a long time now. When a child is brought to me that manifests the OCS symptomotology invariably, within two sessions parents begin to utter, what has become, almost predictable phrases such as:

"Doesn't everybody have this? I mean . . . I do"

"Hey! I used to do that when I was his age too . . ."

"Do adults sometimes have this stuff too? . . ."

"Can this be treated in adults too . . . uh . . . like me?" and so on.

The tendency for parent and extended family members to demonstrate a variety of OCS, ADHD, and Tourette's symptoms has never been surprising to me, as it has been pretty much expected. What caught me off guard and did surprise me, in the beginning at least, were how many times, both, the Mother and the Father, as well as their extended families had significantly identifiable symptoms. Typically, as is common throughout the OCS affected population, parental symptoms would be manifested quite differently such that while one parent might easily recognize their own symptom picture, the other, often enough, might not (or at least it was much more difficult for them to do so). This may have something to do with marital power structures. When power in the partnership is unequal, it appears, thus far, that the more powerful member has the most difficulty recognizing symptomatic behavior. They often seem to feel there could not possibly be anything wrong with them. "Just look at how I'm doing. Who do you think is making this marriage work?" And so on.

Thus, as I began to see in my clinical practice the commonality of not just one, but two symptomatic parents, I initially started to wonder about the viability of the diagnosis. Soon thereafter, however, I began to interview these adults in an effort to determine why, if it is so, OCS individuals might have, perhaps, a predisposition to marry another similarly symptomatic individual. The following hypothesis, although surely not all-inclusive, represents the conglomeration of ideas melded into a framework that, to me, seems viable and also (perhaps more importantly) seems to make sense.

Much of what an individual learns and the resultant behaviors expressed over a life time are either directly or indirectly related to the "patterns" that occur. For me the term "patterns" refers to all experiences, behaviors, thoughts . . . etc., that for one reason or another have been consistently occurring enough that a part (or all) has become incorporated into the "self" and could be considered a part of "who that person is." Although simplified for the sake of understanding, I believe this definition catches the gist of what is intended. A few examples may further help to clarify the meaning.

A child who grows up in a family with two alcoholic parents tends to learn how to survive or "live" with alcoholic people. This, then results in a style of behaving, thinking, reacting . . . etc., that becomes one of the many "patterns" of life for the child and often is carried into adulthood as well.

An only child learns the pattern of living with adults and of always having the attention, and having to share the weight of the responsibility to be all that her parents expect her to be and so on. For an excellent discussion of this pattern of life and many others relating to birth order the reader is referred to two very good descriptive books on the subject by Kevin Leman. These are *Growing up First Born* and *The Birth Order Book*.

Our lives, therefore, are replete with complex combinations of "patterns" none of which stands alone. That is to say that any given pattern may affect other patterns and so on. The stronger the need is to adopt a given pattern, the more likely that specific pattern will reoccur and the less likely it is that other patterns will interfere or influence the stronger pattern as a whole. The strength of a "pattern" is also related to how often, or long, it has been needed and used, as well as to the physical well being of the individual. Some "patterns" are bioneurochemically induced and some result from disabilities, whether physical or mental and so on.

When a child grows up with one or more OCS affected parents, a rather significant "pattern" is created. This particular "pattern" is often twofold in nature. First, there is the part of the "pattern" created in response to the actions, reactions, and behavior of the OCS affected parent(s); and secondly, when the child has biochemically driven inherited symptoms, as well, this too becomes a part of the "pattern" of living in the OCS world.

Such a "pattern" as described above commonly becomes a powerful, or what might be called a core "pattern." The child typically lives in it, around it, and with it for 18 to 20 years. This "pattern," therefore, eventually tends to preempt and/or influence most other "patterns" and be interfered with and influenced by relatively few.

Now, if we take into consideration the fact that very often the OCS affected are not even remotely aware of the problems created by their own OCS, it becomes easy to see how this "pattern" is often experienced as a part of the "self." That's just who I am and so on.

Thus, when the undiagnosed and unaware child reaches the age wherein partners are sought for the purpose of intimate relationships, all the previously established "patterns" come into play. These become constantly consulted (if you will) in the attempts to find a partner.

Allow me to diverge Momentarily. It is not unusual for children with OCS who have parents with OCS to have quite stormy, and sometimes even abusive, relationships through the years the child is developing and growing into adulthood. Anger is often a factor, and quite commonly, the child is incredibly adamant that they are not going to grow up to be like Dad or Mom, or both. Without awareness, and sometimes treatment, they probably will become like their parents, but typically they seek to find a partner as far removed as possible from resemblance of either parent. And yet, the OCS "pattern" often interferes with this commitment, no matter how sure the individual is that such a "pattern" will not be repeated.

I believe that the young person (or later aged individuals, as well) who has grown up with the OCS "pattern" knows (by then almost instinctively) how to survive and get individual needs met when living with those who are OCS affected extremely well. They usually don't like what they have to do, but they can and have survived it. As a result, when the OCS "patterned" young person meets another young person who has also grown up with OCS affected parents, there is a sort of "celebrating of the souls," to give it a creative term. I believe they immediately feel comfortable with each other. Each has had years of experience in how to respond to the OCS affected; and they initially do so with each other nearly instinctively. Since neither one may not have a clue as to why they feel so incredibly good around each other, I think it becomes one of what must be many similar situations (when "patterns" meet) in which each begins to respond to the age old notion of "love at first sight."

Interestingly, even though these relationships so often can become quite "rocky" prior to a wedding date (which should act as a warning signal to the couple, but typically doesn't due to lack of awareness), these individuals do end up deciding to marry and go on with plans anyway. When this happens, I am fairly convinced the continuance of the relationship though stormy and reminiscent of Mom and Dads that hardly ever is there awareness of this now becomes related to the other part of the OCS "pattern." Once a relationship is initiated, the comfort and commonality of knowing how to live with the OCS affected becomes secondary, giving way to the more immediate individual symptoms of the OCS affected young person.

These can include an obsessive need to be with the intended partner or an obsessive fear of rejection (then "no one may ever want to be my partner"). There may also be an obsessive commitment to the partnership itself and an obsessive need to smooth things out. Similarly there could be an accompanying inability to admit to the possibility that the partnership might be a mistake; and many, many other variables and symptoms that are likely to come into play when such symptoms are active. Thus, the OCS pattern may very well be at the heart of the matter relative to those who initially suggested that children grow up and marry their Fathers or their Mothers.

There comes a time when we must
Pack up the bags and leave our inner child behind
So the signs say
There's a thing takes place
When we reach a certain age
Considered older
And suddenly it's sir
Hey
I never really wanted to grow up in a world like this
If I were to step right off
Do you think I might miss
Something
Well
Bring me a little sunshine oh yeah down my way
Sing me a little good times song I'm sad today
Yeah . . . I'm sad today

From the song "Reflections" by Ron D. Kingsley

(N ²)

NEGATIVITY SQUARED

Since Obsessions and Compulsions can surface in any area of human functioning, it should come as no surprise that an Obsessive Compulsive focus on the negative side of things can quite commonly be a problem worthy of intervention. When an individual already has the inclination for obsessing and becoming compulsive about things, the chances of becoming obsessively focused on the negative at some time during the course of their life time is very high. This is because the Western World Culture tends to generally do exactly the same thing. In school the focus is on how many questions you get wrong on a given test. In the media the focus is on the tragedies and bad things that occur in our environments. The focus is on what's wrong rather than on what's right. Thus we are constantly bombarded by potential "triggers" that could set the Obsessive Compulsive gun into action, firing down that road towards negativity.

One of the truly fascinating things about this symptom is the fact that the individual immersed in the negative behavior and reactions may not be able to perceive their own negativity. They frequently describe themselves as "realistic" and/or "honest". The feeling is that only "honest" individuals would openly admit to their own as well as others' faults. It is viewed as dishonest to emphasize the positive and ignore the negative. Yet, when there is a similar emphasis on the negative at the expense of ignoring the positive, this is frequently considered "honest". It is, however, an exact reverse of the other. If one viewpoint is dishonest, then they are both dishonest for the same reasons. This very fact demonstrates how deeply the focus on negative performance and mistakes is imbedded in the culture. The very idea that one focus would be considered honest and the other dishonest is a flagrant violation of reality or rational thought.

There was a ten year old boy I was working with whose Father was very symptomatic for OCS but also totally unaware of his own symptom laden behavior. The boy was being brought to counseling as the identified problem, but the problem in this case was truly the Father. The boy was considered to be one who never followed through on chores and essentially didn't do anything right even though he knew the right way things were to be done. Actually the Father had expectations that were so incredibly stringent and specific that it was simply impossible for the boy to meet them. In particular, one issue that was brought up as an example was the way the boy completed the job of upkeep on the family's lawn and landscape. The Father kept coming back to the fact that over time he had shown this boy again and again exactly the way the lawn should be taken care of. He would check the boy's work immediately after the boy had declared that the job was completed, which, the Father pointed out, it never was. This boy was only ten. He would cut the yard like a ten-year-old and not like a forty-seven-year-old. This is not surprising, given the boy's age. The Father would come out and check the yard, fire his negative comments telling the boy what was still wrong, and do this three or four times before he was "satisfied". Actually, even then the Father would not be satisfied because he was angry that he'd have to keep telling the boy what to do. Thus, when the boy finally had it right, it would still generate negative comments from the Father. The Father would complain to me that the boy could do the task the way it was supposed to be done due to the fact that each time the Father told him what to do, he could successfully carry out the task. The Father therefore would conclude angrily that the boy was perfectly able to complete the task the way it should be done. The fact that he continually was not doing so was evidence that he was choosing not to and was clearly not doing the job right just to get back at the Father and make him mad. The inability of the Father to say positive things to this boy was the problem. The man could only find fault at every turn. Unfortunately they did not stay long in therapy because as soon as it was pointed out to the Father that the boy had never really mowed the lawn at all because the boy was simply an instrument in the Father's hands, the Father did not bring him back. This, however, is an excellent example of what can happen when someone's focus is obsessively negative.

Another common problem when someone is over focused on negative outcomes and events is that they will also tend to be complainers. They complain about everything. My foot hurts. Nobody likes me. Do we have to eat *that* for dinner? You gave me too much. You gave me too little. Jimmy got more than me. There's nothing to eat! I hate my teachers. School sucks! There's nothing good on TV. School lunch sucks! Some of the complaints may be justified, but like the boy who cried wolf, these often get lost in the torrent of whining and griping that is compulsively driven from their mouths. I could go on and on but I won't. Suffice it to say that the complaints never seem to stop. Who among us wants to hang around with someone who is always complaining? Such people aren't fun to be around.

When another points out to the affected individual that their tendencies toward the negative are beyond the norm, the affected ones often react with total disbelief. Since they don't view themselves as being too negative, they may start to wonder if the accuser has some kind of an ulterior motive. This may cause undue suspicion, which is not necessarily healthy in its own right and may help to muddy the water. Denial is common and can itself become an obsessive symptom.

Remember, over responding emotionally to incidents and information is nearly a sure bet with someone who has significant OCS. As a result, when accused of being negative, sometimes the affected individual becomes very angry and may respond some-what paradoxically. " So, you think that's negative, do you?" The affected one might say. "Well, I'll just show you what negative is then!" What follows is an incredible barrage of super negative actions, thoughts, and behaviors. Often these individuals use such a reaction unconsciously to ward off any further attacks on their psyche or emotional well being. By pouring out even more negativity in a flagrant and melodramatic manner, the individual is in effect saying, "If you think I'm bad wait 'til you get a load of this." Another way to put this would be that the affected one in such an instance is trying to tell you to just shut up and let it be. Although they still haven't acknowledged that they are negative, they are essentially saying that things could be worse, much worse. So, leave it alone. This tactic of over responsiveness is more of a gut reaction than a thought-out planned thing. Usually it is so distressing to others that they shut down or retract their earlier statements made in relation to the affected individuals. Life goes on. The negativity continues.

Side effects of constant negativity tend to be difficult to live with as far as others are concerned. A focus on the negative sets one up to consistently expect to fail, or expect others to fail. The attitude of an excessively negatively focused individual can seem quite stern, sour, and even downright mean. Since the focus is on what's wrong rather than what is right, it can be very difficult for such a person to smile or be happy about much of anything. Constructive criticism is another term these individuals will frequently use to justify their negativity. Think about it. If someone is constantly engaged in criticism, be it constructive or otherwise, can they ever truly acknowledge an accomplishment? Will Billy be able to hear "good job, son" if it is followed with "but . . . you could have," or "you should have," or "if you just did this or that"? A critical comment such as this, whether it comes before or after a supposed positive remark, takes away or cancels whatever praise may be intended by the positive. The inability to compliment another without also adding *"constructive criticism"* can motivate others to stay away. The intent of a critical remark doesn't make it any less critical. This intent, however, does interfere with the ability of those manifesting this OCS tendency to label their actions or behavior as "*negative*". It is much more likely to be considered as "*helpful*" or "*needed*".

The sooner you catch this tendency in the OCS affected and work to understand and change it, the better the outcome for everyone. As individuals become older and even more set in their ways, the negative focus is embedded ever deeper into the core of their being. It can become such a way of life that others begin to see it as "*personality*" rather than a symptom. Negativity can become so entwined with every aspect of an individual's life that the extraction thereof would result in serious emotional decomposition.

First, you must somehow spell out exactly what "*being negative*" really means. If the affected one is aware and actively engaged in trying to change and can agree on a definition of negativity, it will be much easier to point it out or to use a cue to help them see when they are being that way. Most of the time, it is this definition of negativity that stands in the way of progress. If someone cannot be convinced that what they are doing is what you say or think it is (*negative*) then why in the world would they want to change it? Not only that but the old obsessive need for exactness and the literal meaning of a word makes it even more difficult for the individual who doesn't see actions and behaviors as negative to be able to suddenly see it from another perspective. Therefore a fight ensues. To be, or not to be "*negative*", that is the question. If a definition cannot be agreed upon, acknowledgement of the problem and progress towards correcting it or making it better will not occur.

Frequently other problems are so severe, those that the constant focus on the negative causes, that they (the other problems) become the main *target* of treatment. When these other problems are corrected or made less problematic, it is then that the affected individual may be led to see the insidious underlying difficulty of negativity. Because OCS is a biochemically driven dilemma, it often requires medical intervention (medication) for a period of time along with counseling/therapy, to truly get a handle on and make positive changes that will last.

As the negatively oriented individual progresses from childhood to adult, that tendency discussed earlier to justify or rationalize their negativity to escape fault or responsibility for the results or consequences of their negative behaviors can look like a personality disorder or flaw. "That's just the way I am," is a commonly heard statement. "I can't help how I look at the world" is yet another. Again, these individuals also imply that their openness and *honesty* in relation to this "so called *problem*" is actually a virtue that they have been cultivating over the course of their entire lives. What else could such an affected one think? They may have been taught to consider it thus by similarly affected parents or by a parent through modeling. Also, as stated previously, the various media we are bombarded with on a daily basis can be very influential in our developing a primarily negative focus on the world and on our personal views of life.

Sometimes the negative focus is so entrenched within the individual's being that there is a tremendous fear of what might happen if they were to lose this perspective. A large portion of their experienced "self" seems they often feel, dependent on this way of being in the world. There can be a dread or strong fear that to lose such a focus would be to lose themselves or the who-they-are. Since they have never really been able to look at the world in a different manner or through someone else's eyes, it is not surprising that such a fear might exist. The affected individual though, commonly, is either unable to or simply will not acknowledge that such a fear is present or ever could be present. This, of course, can complicate matters immensely.

For family members, friends, and supervisors or peers in the workplace, an awareness of a person's very real inability to be anything but negative or simply in the *very* negative range can be quite helpful. Understanding another's capacities as well as incapacity's allows you to better predict and prepare for their actions and reactions to environments, stressors, and situations. By being better prepared and aware, your own responses to the actions of such an individual can be moderated and mediated to the point that it is much easier to live around or be involved at times with these negatively focused OCS individuals.

With older individuals, many times there will have been prior attempts to change or moderate their negative behavior. Their very inability to successfully accomplish such a change can be so upsetting and/or depressing that hope is drained away from them. Even though they may have sought out professional help from counselors or psychologists and the like, if the underlying OCS was not recognized and treated, success tends to be very long in coming, if it comes at all. Think about it. If every time you tried to do something and you were met by failure, wouldn't you just stop trying? Why put forth the energy and effort if you can't succeed?

For those of you who must spend time daily with such an OCS affected individual, this article is an educational tool and gentle reminder that there are ways to effectively deal with another's negativity. Knowledge and awareness is the most essential tool as all other interventions depend on it. For those of you who might be getting a glimpse of yourselves in this article, it was written for you as well. There is hope. Change can occur. When OCS is the driving factor underlying a person's negativity, treatment is available and does bring about positive change. Trust me, as I speak from personal experience.

"If it's love you're looking for
Better just walk on by
'Cause I . . . don't want no more

Someone once said if it looks and feels like love
Then that's what it must be
And that's something for such a long-long time
I've really tried so hard to believe
They said . . . love will set you free
Yeah . . . right . . . maybe in your dreams

There are ghosts no one can see
Buried deep inside . . . but in time . . . they are set free
And you know I've heard we shouldn't be concerned
Because time heals all wounds
But I don't think . . . No . . . I don't think that's necessarily true
Look at me and you
Oh yeah . . . and all that we've been through . . ."

Excerpt from the song "If it's Love" by Ron D. Kingsley

PARADOXICAL INCLINATION

I conceived of the term Paradoxical Inclination in order to help explain a situation I recognized early on in my work with OCS. I noticed that for quite a few of the common symptoms relating to OCS, individuals would frequently report that, not only did they not have or experience some of these symptoms, but they in fact experienced the exact opposite. This was somewhat puzzling to me for a while. Many of the people with the greatest amount of reported symptoms present would have quite a few of these polar opposites. How could this be? Could someone have an actual compulsion not to be compulsive about some things?

In my search for answers, I began to realize that individuals with significant OCS had a common tendency to respond to the events and situations of life in an "all or nothing" "black or white" fashion. That is to say that if they were confident in their abilities in a given OCS area and continually achieved successes in that area, they would tend to go all-out most, if not all, of the time. If, however, they were insecure regarding their abilities in a given OCS area or were unable to meet, or come close enough, to the standards they felt they needed to reach, their appeared a strong tendency to simply give up and shut down. Others very often labeled this subsequent lack of effort (or trying) as laziness.

A common example of this dynamic is the symptom question from the Leyton Obsessional Inventory that goes something like this: "Are you very careful that your room, house, garage, etc., is always neat and clean?" There are a great many people who have OCS that would answer this question in what I considered at the time to be a completely unexpected way. They would say something like:

"Are you kidding? No way! My room is a disaster area 99% of the time."

Somehow in my work with this condition, I came to the realization that such a denial in an otherwise very symptomatic individual was very frequently misleading. In other words, whereas for a while I had taken this to mean that such a response suggested the absence of one of the particular symptoms in question, it really was nothing at all of the sort. Life for these OCS individuals often started out with the need for everything in their surrounding environments to be neat, clean, and orderly. The older a person became the more responsible they were expected to be and the harder it would be to keep one's space neat, clean, and in order. There are also a host of possible interfering factors that may make it difficult for such a *neat freak to* continue successfully to reach and remain at a given level of neatness and order. Those who, for any reason, are kept from performing this need at the level that they feel is necessary begin to exhibit a fair variety of secondary symptoms as a result. Anxiety is a common by-product related to the inability to achieve a given obsessive and/or compulsive need. So, also, is the tendency to become angry. This anger may show up as a continual and chronic underlying irritability, moodiness, over sensitivity, or quick-temperedness. It may also be manifested in explosive outbursts of incredible and frightening intensity whenever something or someone interferes with the OCS affected's ability to meet this need. Eventually the individual who is chronically unsuccessful can become so emotionally distraught that they either simply can't try anymore or adamantly refuse to subject themselves to further frequent and continual failure. The consequence is that the opposite occurs. Things aren't put away anymore or cleaned or put in order until the individual simply can't stand it anymore and experiences a sudden cleaning binge or shuts down to the point that simply no more effort can be put forth in this specific area at all, ever.

The funny thing is that I began to sense that those individuals reporting these polar opposites weren't exactly symptom free. In fact when probed and questioned in a certain manner, it would become clear that they remained symptomatic. Oh, they no longer engaged in that compulsive need to straighten, clean and order but the obsession (the thoughts telling and reminding them that things really *ought* to be neat, clean, and orderly) remained. Thus, a paradox ensued. These individuals still desired, wanted, and needed things to be neat and clean but the fact that something was interfering with their ability to make this happen had frustrated and exasperated them to the point that chronic failure had become their constant companion. Rather than invite and keep such a companion with them, they simply did the only thing they could think of which, was to give up and quit trying. Since the need was still there going round and round in their thoughts, there would often be a certain amount of sadness and remorse associated with such a response.

In pondering this particular situation and common dynamic of OCS, I felt a desire to find a good yet simple way to accurately describe what was going on. Thus, the term "Paradoxical Inclination" was born. The paradox seemed obvious. These people still felt the need for order, neatness, and cleanliness; yet were not demonstrating this in their lives, although they often may have in the past. Their inclination was for cleanliness, but the interference was too much for them to be able to cope with. It also seemed to me that for any given symptom wherein this was occurring, the product of such a situation for the individual might be what I called "a little pocket of depression". It seems to make sense that when enough of these "little pockets of depression" had come into being that a complication of this might just be a more pervasive depression. Although a given symptom by itself might not be obvious to others as an element of depression, if several had occurred it would most likely become more obvious and so on until the individual beset with such "pockets" might begin to demonstrate a truly clinically significant depression. Experience with the OCS affected over the past decade has seemed to confirm this hypothesis.

The concept of Paradoxical Inclination led me to rewrite several of the Leyton Inventory questions to automatically include this possibility in the initial query. Thus the question:

"Are you very careful that your room, house, garage and etc., are always neat and clean?"

Became the question:

"Are you very careful that your room, house, garage and etc., are always neat and clean. If not, would you really like them to be neat and clean, but you find it very hard to do, or too time consuming? As a result you just don't have the energy and/or the desire to complete the task and therefore you just keep right on putting it off? (Paradoxical Inclination)".

Another excellent example of this problem can be seen in the question;

"Are you very careful to have neat papers and neat handwriting"?

This was changed to the following:

"Are you very careful to have neat papers and neat handwriting, or, have you simply given up on neatness because it takes far too much time or when you do try, it never seems to be right, or good enough anyway? (Paradoxical Inclination)".

When the latter was the case, I would simply code the symptom as present and encircle the words *Paradoxical Inclination* in order to remember which direction the symptom leaned. The use of this concept has given depth and breadth to the diagnosis of OCS and helped make sense of what was a common symptomatic conundrum.

I believe that almost any specific symptom could theoretically exhibit a Paradoxical Inclination type of response. Thus, on even the questions that I have not included this conceptualization, I still remain poised to query for it if an individual's response suggests in any way this possibility. To me it makes a lot of sense that this paradoxical response could eventually lead to depression. If you have 30 or 40 specific obsessive and compulsive symptoms, even though only of mild or moderate intensity, the accumulation of a failure to achieve expected levels of competence on a given day or at any specific Moment has got to be depressing. Almost any single symptom when in the mild-moderate range by itself is not really that big a deal. When there are forty of them, though, that are going awry the outcome becomes an entirely different story. It's like the breaking of a single toothpick. Breaking one toothpick is not hard even for a very young and frail child. Put a rubber band, however, around forty of them and they suddenly become unbreakable by even the strongest of human hands.

There are times in our lives
When the Moment is right
And we're all sure we know where we're goin'
There's a look in our eyes
That can't be disguised
And it says . . . hey . . . I know what I'm knowin'

But it's cold . . . oh . . . so cold outside
I've been told . . . but I don't . . . don't remember why
If we're gonna go where we wanna go
It takes time

There are things we can't change
Like the wind and the rain
Yet at times we'll act . . . just as if we could
Oh . . . it's hard to maintain
Through the anger and pain
The belief . . . that we can become . . . all we would

And time isn't something that can be saved
It can't be bought or even rearranged
And whether or not we want it to . . . oh . . . it takes its toll
Ah . . . we can't ever be sure just where it goes
No one can ever be sure where it goes
And it's cold . . . oh so cold outside
I've been told . . . but I don't . . . don't remember why
If we're gonna go where we want to go
It takes time

From the song "It Takes Time" by Ron D. Kingsley

OCS AND TIME:

"I'm late, I'm late . . .

For a very important date . . ."

Individuals with significant OCS invariably have difficulties with time. Again, as is true in most other cases, there tends to be an all or nothing type of reaction to time issues. In other words these people may be very organized with a timetable and schedule, mapping out virtually every second of their day, or, they may be so severely disorganized in their management of time that the word *overwhelmed* becomes their constant companion. Regardless, however, of which "pole" one may lean towards the bottom line is that time is an issue that impacts social, familial, and even business relationships.

"I feel rushed all the time," is a frequently heard statement from the significantly OCS affected.

"There is *never* enough time to do everything that needs to be done."

This all-too-common feeling of being cheated by time results in some very problematic and misunderstood situations that should be clarified and explored. This clarification is not meant to excuse the affected one from the responsibility and subsequent consequences of their OCS driven actions, it is offered as an explanation. From this explanation can stem intervention techniques and awareness levels that may then allow the individual and significant others to interpret various actions and responses differently than they had previously been interpreted. In simpler terms, this means that your beliefs about why certain actions and behaviors may occur change. As a result of these changes you better understand why you feel the way you do and react differently. For example, once a parent learns that Jimmy's initial "*attitude*" whenever he is asked to do something really has nothing to do with his not wanting to do his part for the family, it is easier to manage the behavior of resistance when it does occur. And it will occur, many times. In fact, knowing this allows for a plan to be made to effectively deal with the reaction and make things better all around.

Invariably, when someone asks the one with OCS to do something unexpectedly, the initial response is one of resistance, sometimes in the extreme. As might be anticipated, this occurs most often within the context of the home setting. At any given Moment, affected individuals perceive themselves as busily engaged in whatever it is they may be doing. This tends to be true, even when it looks to others like the "activity" they are engaged in is literally that of doing *nothing*. They quite frequently feel put upon the Moment another tries to get them to do something other than that which they are, or are not, currently doing.

"I always have to do *everything* around here" is a commonly heard complaint.

Some instances are explainable, although such instances tend to rarely be explained. This may seem like it doesn't make sense, so, allow me to give an example of just what kind of situation the OCS driven often find themselves facing.

Billy is minding his own business. He is sitting on the panel-brown living room couch and staring at the ceiling tiles. He is busily counting the holes in each one to see if they are all the same.

Mother calls from the kitchen. "Billy!" she says. "Will you please come in here and take the garbage out? I've been canning peaches this afternoon and it's so full I can't get another thing in there."

Billy obliviously goes right on counting.

"Billy?" his Mother calls again. "Come take the garbage out, will you?"

"Two hundred and eighty-nine . . . Two hundred and ninety . . . Two hundred and . . ." Billy counts, keeping silent track inside of his head.

"BILLY?" His Mother is beginning to sound frustrated. ***"BILLY!"***

Finally her voice gets through and Billy replies, "Just a minute, Mom." Three hundred . . . Three hundred and one, three hundred and . . . .

The minutes tick on by.

Suddenly there is a jerk on Billy's arm.

"Ow," Billy complains. "What'd ya do that for? Now I got to start all over again."

"You're not starting anything, YOUNG MAN, until that garbage is taken out." She pulls him from his sitting position on the couch.

"I was gonna do it" he whines as she drags him out to the kitchen.

Now, in her anger, if Billy's Mother happens to say what may be on her mind, the problem could get much worse very quickly.

An argument would begin should she say something like, "no son, you weren't going to do it. If I hadn't come in here you would have let me do it and in fact that's probably what you hoped for anyway." In the scenario where OCS is present, this interpretation may seem accurate but it is not. Billy *was* planning to take out the garbage just as soon as he got done with counting that one square. Thus, if his Mother accused him of not being willing to take it out, he would undoubtedly feel obliged to argue the point with her. Then, if she also told him he was trying to get out of doing the task on purpose by putting it off until someone else did it for him, he would again feel compelled to deny that such a thing was true. The argument could get hotter and/or nastier. If then the parent listed all of the times in the past that Billy had said he was going to do something and yet there was no follow through, he would probably become defensive and try to justify and make excuses for every situation. In all likelihood Billy would not even remember the specific situations, but would nevertheless defend him self as if he did.

In the example given above, Billy could have just as easily exploded into an uncontrollable rage when his Mother grabbed his arm and forced his attention away from the group of dots on the ceiling that he was in the midst of counting. When an extreme over reaction to being interrupted occurs in those affected with OCS, time loss may be at the heart of the reaction. These individuals do not like repeating tasks under another's direction. Being asked to do something unexpectedly feels to them like a monumental request. Barbara describes it thus:

> When someone asks me to do something for them, I immediately get this empty feeling in the pit of my stomach. Even though it may take only five minutes of my time to complete the task, I have this sense of loss that is incredible. It's as if I can think of nothing else but the fact that there go five minutes of my life. Five minutes that would have otherwise been mine are going to be lost forever. I know this sounds silly but it's true. It's not that I don't want to do things for other people, because I do. It's just that it's a lot

easier if I have planned it and set aside a time for it. Does this sound selfish? I think it does. So, then I feel guilty. I'm such a self centered and selfish person. It's no wonder I'm miserable most of the time.

Actually, I'm miserable all of the time.

Barbara was miserable. She viewed herself as a loving and caring Mother, wife, and individual. She freely gave as much as 20 hours of service each week to her church and neighborhood community. The thought that she might resent unplanned intrusions on her time went against what she considered to be her true nature. She viewed such a state of being as tantamount to her actually being evil and simply could not accept that she would (or could) feel this way. The fact that she responded or reacted again and again in this manner caused her great distress and represents a form of what psychologists have called *Cognitive Dissonance.* In time with counseling, she was able to see the OCS pattern and eventually agreed to attempt medication even though she remained wary and somewhat anxious about it. Within two weeks she was feeling better and began to be able to recognize the many specific symptoms from the Leyton Obsessional Inventory that had gotten a little, or a lot, better in just that short period of time. She stopped thinking of herself as *"evil"* and began to see that she was indeed the loving and giving Mother that she always wanted to be. She began to focus on what did get done rather than what did not get done. She was no longer miserable. In fact, she came in to a session after about a month and a half and announced that for the first time in a very long time, she was actually *happy.*

*   *   *

Don, on the other hand, experienced difficulties relative to time loss a bit differently. For him it was a matter of never having enough time. He expressed it thus:

No matter where I am. No matter what I'm doing. I feel
rushed! If I'm heading to an appointment . . . I can't get
there fast enough. No dilly-dallying. No stopping to smell
the roses. Heck, I don't even notice when there are roses.
Every Moment in another Moment is gone . . . forever.
Forever. Think about it. Forever. That's a long time. So, no
Moment can be wasted. Before I'm finished what I'm doing
I'm already kicking myself for being late on the next project
or place that I need to be. Time is my enemy. It keeps me
from getting things done. What I really need is more time.
If I just had a little more of it. So, you can imagine how I
take it when someone wants me to do something outside of
my schedule. *NO WAY!*

For Don being interrupted was like getting in the way of
progress. Progress keeps moving forward and lets nothing stand in
its' way. If, however, someone was able to sneak through his barrier
of projects and appointments, Don's reaction was typically explosive as if to say, "*HOW DARE YOU INTRUDE ON MY TIME
AND SPACE*"! Then just as quickly, he would be off and running
on his chronic time chase. The wake he left behind was often an
emotional roller coaster ride for anyone who had to work closely
with him and especially so for those in his immediate family. He
seemed angry all the time. His wife indicated that she couldn't
talk to him at all. If she tried to simply have a conversation, she felt
that Don resented the time it took to do so. His body language
would suggest that he was annoyed. His responses would be short,
mostly one-word utterances, and the tone of his voice seemed to
imply boredom or a rising irritation. For his wife it was very dis-
heartening. If she, or any of the children, were to interrupt him for
any reason, Don would explode angrily and so intensely that they
would fear that he was going to physically harm them. This was in
spite of the fact that he had never hit any of them. Don's wife also
felt unable to ask him to do anything around the house or for the

children because invariably it would result in an angry outburst and, for her, it was simply not worth it. The possibility of a divorce finally motivated Don to get some help.

*   *   *

Daniel was experiencing difficulties while driving. Others traveling with him were often so frightened by his behavior that they would find excuses not to be in a car that he was driving. This luxury, however, was not always available to his wife and children. They were often terrified when going places with him in the car. His wife described it thus:

> I don't know what gets into him. When someone cuts him off or tries to pass him in another lane, it makes him mad. *Really mad.*
> He yells and curses and makes obscene gestures. He swerves in and out of traffic. Once he even chased another car going out of our way for five or six blocks after it had cut in front of us. Me and and the kids were all terrified. It's a good thing the guy in the other car didn't have a gun, I guess. It's almost like Dan just can't stand someone else to get ahead of him. My sister had a horse like that when I was little. That horse wouldn't allow another to get in the lead. Whenever another horse, urged on by its rider, would try to get in the lead my sister's would race ahead no matter what the rider wanted to do. I even fell off because of that once.

Daniel's response might have been a bit more complex than simply a time issue, but *time* was a major part of why he'd suddenly become so upset. He often reasoned that he was usually in a hurry (a part of this OCS symptom) and he'd catch him self thinking, "How *dare* that driver squeeze in front of me. He may be in a hurry but so am I. I was ahead of him. I was there first. He should have consideration for someone else." Other counselors had worked extensively with him on relaxation exercises and cognitive methods meant to enable him to learn how to control these thoughts and rages. The fact is that he knew he was over reacting, but once the reaction got started he felt helpless. He was in the grip of something that just *happened*. He didn't plan it. He didn't even want to react in that way. It just happened. Daniel was unable to talk him self out of it and completely unable to be soothed by anyone else while in the midst of the reaction. His awareness that many of his thoughts during such reactions were irrational and not worth risking his life or anyone else's could not be held in his mind long enough and persistently enough to make a difference. Relaxation was practically alien to his being to begin with, and apparently impossible when he was driving a car. The only reason he came to counseling was that it had been court ordered. He was cited for reckless driving and had been given the choice of a hefty fine or attending counseling sessions. After being diagnosed with OCS and beginning to understand the underlying reasons for his behavior Dan agreed to try a medication. After starting to use an SSRI (Zoloft in this case) things changed rather dramatically for Dan. He describes his experience thus:

> I was driving to work a few days after starting the medication and I was late. Normally I would have been tearing down the road weaving in and out of traffic and muttering under my breath, or even out loud. Suddenly I realized I was simply cruising along and thinking, 'I'm late . . . oh well. There's nothing I can do about it now'. This was incredible to me. I wasn't cursing. I wasn't driving recklessly. I wasn't angry. I couldn't believe it. I kept thinking, 'this is really different'. It was *GREAT!* I wasn't over reacting. This was something very new to me and I liked it. There had been nothing I could do about being late. It wasn't my fault. Still, in the past I would have been in a frenzy and nearly *crazy* about it. This time I was not upset. I was calm. *I was* calm. It was really weird. I kept thinking, 'I'm late', and it was no big deal. No big deal at all. This was the beginning of a HUGE change in my life for the better.

Daniel's wife agreed wholeheartedly with her husband's assessment of the situation. Although he still tended to go places early or on time, he no longer went "nuts" about it if he wasn't. She felt he was now *concerned*, whereas before he had been *obsessed*. Now he was *conscientious* as compared to *crazy*. Dan, she related, was easier to live with and he was a much safer driver.

When this time factor is present in the OCS affected, there is no stopping to smell the roses. Every Moment in another Moment is gone forever. They cannot slow down. They can see no good reason to do so. Often to get their attention, they must be on the verge of losing something that is very important like their freedom, job, spouse, or children. These are the motivators that tend to predispose them to seek out assistance. There is an old popular song that includes the lyrics "time . . . is on your side". For the OCS affected nothing could be farther from the truth. Time is their enemy and like the white rabbit in Alice in Wonderland, they are prone to continually moving about uttering the now infamous line, "I'm late, I'm late, for a very important date". We sense, however, that there is no real very important date, don't we?

You ask me why . . . but I don't know
You say I lie . . . but it's not so . . . it's not so
It's like something is always telling me
There's one and only one way things can be
And I can't let go of the need
Even though I've tried I can't get free . . . of the need
Some things can't be ignored . . . even if you try
And sometimes when there's a door . . . you still can't get inside

You ask me why . . . but I don't know
You say I lie . . . but it's not so . . . it's just not so
It's like someone is always reminding me
There's one and only one way things can be
And I can't let go of the need
Even though I try I can't pull free
And I don't really want to know what this might mean
That so often I just can't let go . . . of the need
Some things can't be ignored . . . no matter how hard you may try
Like the very fact that you and I were born
And some day . . . will just as surely die

You ask me why . . . but I don't know
You say I lie . . . but it's not so I tell ya it's not so
It's like something is always telling me
There's one and only one way things can be
And I can't let go of the need
Even though I try I can't get free . . . of the need
Some things can't be ignored . . . even though we may try
And sometimes though there's a door . . . we still can't get inside
You ask me why . . . but I don't know

From the song "The Need" by Ron D. Kingsley

THE DEVIL MADE ME DO IT:

AN ESSAY ON BEHAVIORAL CAUSATION

No one can force anyone to do anything. This I believe with all my heart. If we perform an action, it is because we are choosing to do it. We always have a choice when the actions are performed via our own will. You can't force another or cause them to do anything they don't want to do unless you are able to somehow take possession of their will. A simple example of this would be when a group of teenagers grab hold of a peer and then stick a needle in their arm, shooting into it heroine. In this type of a situation the teenager would be considered a victim. One can always argue that it might not have happened if the teenager hadn't been hanging around the "wrong" crowd, but such a statement is most definitely moot.

Fault, or blame, is an interesting concept. It is not always easy to determine. Let's say you are driving a car. You stop at an intersection for a red light. No cars are in front of you. The traffic light turns green and, just for safety's sake, you look left and then right before venturing out into the intersection. As you glance to the right, though, you notice a car hurtling towards the intersection at an incredible speed. You can't be absolutely certain, but you're pretty sure that there is no way that car is going to be able to stop in time. Your light has been green now for a few seconds and horns are starting to be blown behind you. So, you head on out into the intersection and "*WHAM!*" that vehicle you saw slams into the side of your car. He ran the red light. Who is at fault for that collision?

I am assuming that you might be thinking it was the other guy's fault. After all, he ran the red light. This is where it may seem a bit confusing. Although it is true that the individual that ran the red light will be cited and considered (by law) to be at fault, in reality it was your fault. You looked both ways. You saw the car screaming towards the intersection and you had the notion that it would not be able to stop in time. You went out into that intersection anyway. Never mind the drivers behind you were blowing their horns or the fact that the light was green. If you had chosen to wait because you saw the car coming, it would have raced through the red light and the intersection without hitting your car. The accident would be your fault, although legal responsibility for the crash and its results would be placed on the one who ran the red light. What if you had a passenger and the passenger was killed? You saw the car coming. You entered the intersection anyway. It doesn't matter that the other individual was breaking the law. Your passenger would be dead. This is a result that could not be compensated for by any amount of money or insurance. Now, if for some reason you hadn't seen the other car coming, then of course you become the victim and there is no blame or fault that could be placed upon you. Even though you had the right-of-way, wouldn't it be better to avoid the accident altogether if you could?

What if you are standing with another in the shadows between some buildings next to a busy street? Pedestrians and cars are constantly moving, loitering, and driving by. The other that you are with has a rifle and for fun, you decide to pretend to shoot various individuals that you imagine might be foreign spies or crooks on the lamb. You begin to sight the rifle on different targets, but you never pull the trigger. After all you are only imagining. What if one of the times when you sight out the spy, the other with you reaches over and pulls the trigger? Who would be at fault for shooting the innocent bystander? You could argue that it was the other, since you didn't actually pull the trigger and never intended to. He could argue that it was your fault because all he did was fire the weapon. It was you that had sighted it on a real person.

There are people who are locked up in prison for all types of crimes. Why are they locked up? This may seem like a silly question but think about it. Society, as a whole, has a set of rules. These rules have been agreed upon for the protection of individuals and the society. When someone breaks those rules, society takes action and locks her up. This is done to keep them from harming others or from continuing to break the law. Society, in effect, takes responsibility for these criminals and locks them up for protection. If this were not done, people would blame society for the wrongs that these individuals continued to commit. The real fault lies with the individual perpetrating the crime, but when society knows within a reasonable doubt that crimes will continue to be committed if these individuals aren't locked up, it is generally considered a fault of the society itself if the individuals are not locked up. In this way, societies disallow the criminal behavior to continue.

The same type of thing is done with individuals who are mentally ill. These individuals are locked up too. The difference, though, is that the mentally ill individuals are placed in hospitals where efforts are made to actively keep them from escaping. This is done to protect society at large and the individuals themselves. If society leaves the severely mentally disabled out on the street, the safety of others could be compromised.

Let's return to the scene previously discussed of two people standing in the shadows of a busy street. This time let's imagine that the individual with the rifle has told the other (let's imagine this is you) not to aim the gun at any objects or people while standing there because if the rifle is pointed anywhere, even for a Moment, he will pull the trigger. This is such an unbelievable statement that you simply refuse to take him seriously in spite of his having told you so several times. Thus, you aim the rifle anyway in pursuit of your fantasy game. *BANG!* Someone is wounded. It's his fault. He pulled the trigger. You aimed it, though. Is this not similar to the red light accident situation? What if you did not know what caused the rifle to shoot and you went right on aiming it toward things and people anyway? The act of not aiming the thing and instead putting it down (not entering the intersection) would stop the senseless destruction and pain, as well as render the instrument harmless, at least in relation to yourself. Your hands would be clean of all involvement and the question of your influence and/or fault would be lessened considerably and more than likely, not considered at all.

There are teachers who refuse to believe that there are some behaviors that children either cannot control or can only partially control. This is a travesty for the children involved as they are continually treated as if they were in total control of everything they do and say. In severe Tourette's Syndrome, there may be movements, noises, actions, and even words that are engaged in uncontrollably and/or that are only partially controllable. This is a bioneurochemical disorder that responds sometimes to triggers in the environment. In other words, there are environmental cues that, when experienced, tend to result in such behaviors occurring. Without medical treatment, some of these behaviors can be unstoppable. Let's pretend, for a Moment, that there is a student that has been diagnosed with Tourette's Syndrome and is not medically treated because parents cannot afford the cost. The teacher involved had been experiencing great difficulties with this student and the school evaluation team determined that there were a group of actions that the teacher engaged in that provoked many of the behaviors that she was having such a difficult time dealing with.

The team, therefore, asked her to alter and modify these actions in order to make it less likely that the student would respond with those disruptive behaviors that had been targeted. This teacher, however, believed that the student was in total control of the situation and that the implication the evaluation team had made that she was responsible for the student's actions was ridiculous. She refused to cooperate. She wasn't going to allow them to blame the student's actions on her. The disruptive behaviors, as a result, continue.

What if the teacher in the above example had been cooperative? What if, rather than take the team's suggestions as a personal affront and accusation, she merely began changing her actions as suggested? What if, in response, the student's disruptive behaviors diminished significantly? Neither of these teachers was at fault. The fault lies more in the disorder the student was afflicted with. The two situations described above were not imaginary. They were real. They occurred during the 17 years I spent in the public schools working as a School Psychologist. In fact, they did not occur just once, but did many times. Although the teachers were not at fault or to blame for these student's behavior, they were all capable of influencing the degree to which these behaviors occurred when it became known that such a diagnosis existed and the teacher's actions were compounding the problem. Those that respond by trying to accommodate such a student have no blame whatsoever, even when the suggested modifications did not result in dramatic behavioral changes for the student. Those that either refused to believe such a thing could be possible or simply did not follow through with the suggested interventions were at fault for the degree of the continuing disruptive behaviors even though they were not to blame for the behaviors themselves. The teachers who wouldn't try were sometimes not even able to consider that something they were doing might be a contributing factor to the student's behavior. These would personalize what was being suggested and end up feeling that if what they did could influence disruption (or cause it for those who couldn't break away from this idea), then that would mean they were not good teachers. Thus, they had to avoid even the hint that their own actions could be a contributing factor to a given student's disruptive behavior.

Finally, let's consider one more scenario in an attempt to understand how our own actions can affect those of another even though the behavior itself is not caused by us. In this situation you are driving down a two-lane highway. Suddenly you notice a car off in the distance that is driving somewhat erratically. When it gets to be about 100 yards from you, it suddenly swerves into your lane and keeps on coming straight at you. As the realization hits you that this car is going to smash into you—head-on, you quickly swerve to your right and end up in a ditch at the side of the road. Your actions (although not caused by the oncoming car) were, nevertheless, influenced by the individual driving that other vehicle. This is why there are efforts made to modify and amend the behavior of drivers on the road so they will not drive in such a way that others will react and end up having a collision or some other driving mishap as a result.

Our own behavior has an impact on all those with whom we come in contact. Sometimes that impact is negligible and sometimes it is so powerful that another individual will accuse us of causing their inappropriate behavior. This of course is simply not true, although it may seem true to the accuser. If someone holds a gun to your head and says, "sign this blank check or I'll shoot you," you are still free to tell him to "go jump in a lake". The act of holding the gun and threatening you cannot force you to sign that check. If you want to stay alive, though, you may choose to sign.

If you want to have less disruptive behaviors in a class that you teach, you may choose to alter or modify your own behavior. If you want to stay close to another in an intimate relationship, you may be willing to change some of your actions in order to enable the relationship to continue to grow and so on.

CHAPTER FOUR

OCS: CASE EXAMPLES

"It's said life is hard . . . though sometimes not
And we should be thankful . . . for all that we've got
Thankful . . . yeah . . . on that I agree
But satisfied . . . *NEVER!* . . . No one can force that on me . . ."

Excerpt from the song "Satisfied . . . Never" by Ron D. Kingsley

Three Case Examples

The following cases were chosen due to their comparability in relation to the OCS population as a whole. Nevertheless, each one has it's own unique specific twists and turns as well.

The initial case presented begins in story form in an effort to enable the reader to, perhaps, emotionally experience what it is like to have OCS as a child (although what happens to the child is also not uncommon *for* the OCS adult as well). All names have been changed to protect confidentiality and no times or dates used for the same reason.

The second case presented is one of an adult professional woman. There is a tendency for professionals who see adults with the types of presenting problems she came in with to spend a significant number of sessions and time with the individual thera-peutically and not make a lot of progress (when the problem is unrecognized OCS). Screening for adult OCS when certain signs or possibilities are present is a good therapeutic practice, as the biochemically driven kinds of symptoms do not typically respond well to traditional therapeutic efforts.

The third case represents an example of a misdiagnosis of a fairly serious category in regard to treatment planning and expected eventual outcome. It is also demonstrative of how strange symptoms can seem until they are understood from an OCS frame of reference.

Throughout this work I have provided examples from actual real life cases in which I have been involved within the last 10 years or so. There are so many variations in OCS symptoms among those affected, and the ways these symptoms become manifested are also so extremely varied that it is almost ridiculous to attempt to demonstrate all of them in a series of cases. Thus, a few have been presented, rather than many. The first case I present is a bit unusual. I wanted people who read it to feel what the young man I'm talking about felt in relation to his undiagnosed symptoms. I therefore wrote it like a fiction story so that the emotions involved might have a greater impact on the reader. The main focus symptom is very common and can be applied to all kinds of other situations. At the end of the story I analyze it a bit and share the outcome.

Case No. 1

"I used to think . . . if they could just see
The one I know that's really me
Then they . . . would surely understand . . ."

From the song "They Couldn't See into the Heart" by Ron D. Kingsley

Charlie's Dilemma

.He wanted to do it. He really did. Each time his parents, or another adult, got mad at him and told him to stop what he was doing, he meant to do what they said. The trouble was, no one believed it.

"If you really wanted to, Charlie," they'd say, shaking their heads, "you'd *do* it."

"You're just not trying," his Mother would tell him again and again. "You could do it if you tried."

His Father would shout, "If I have to tell you *ONE MORE TIME* I'll . . ." But his Father never seemed to finish that line, so Charlie didn't know (for sure) just what to expect if it were to happen that one more time. As a result, his mind was free to wander. And wander it did. He was *more* than just a bit worried about it.

Charlie's teachers seemed to like to write things on his report card. It wasn't fair! He knew other kids in his classes that never had much of anything written on their report cards.

"He's lazy!" Charlie had heard his Father say to his Mother late at night, time after time.

"I don't think he's lazy, Jim."

At least Charlie's Mother tried to be on his side more often than not.

"I just think . . . well . . ."

Charlie would hardly breathe. Sometimes the sound of his own breathing was louder than anything else, making it hard to hear.

His Mother would go on. "I'm not sure what I think."

And there it was. When he yearned for his Mother to say what was in his heart; when it was time to set things straight with his Dad; to tell him . . .

"Charlie's a good boy! He truly wants to mind. He wants to do what his teachers tell him to. He listens to us. He hears what we say. He tries. He feels bad when he doesn't do what we want him to."

Charlie's thoughts would slow. He wasn't sure what else he might want her to say. There might be more, though.

"Lazy." His Father would repeat. "Face it, Marge, he's lazy."

"Oh, Jim."

At about this time, in the continuing long term debate, Charlie would hear his Mother begin to get all-emotional. It was usually pretty hard to tell exactly what she was doing. Charlie's need to breathe would over-rule his desire to hear.

"Isn't that," his Father's voice would sound softer, "what his teachers at school have been saying all along, though?" Invariably there would be a pause. Then it would seem like his Dad was reading something.

"Charlie would do better, I'm sure, if the level of his effort matched the enthusiasm he has for certain other activities throughout the day."

Did his Mother cry harder then? He thought so.

His Father's words would become even softer, "isn't that what it sounds like to you, honey?"

Things would get mushy, then Charlie would begin to breathe normally and his thoughts would take over.

"Am I lazy?" He'd wonder. He didn't feel lazy. There were so many things that he wanted to do that it seemed to him there was never enough time to do any of them. Wasn't being lazy when someone didn't do anything? When they didn't want to do anything? Charlie wanted to do EVERYTHING.

Sometimes he would lie awake at night for hours just thinking. On these occasions he couldn't get to sleep even though he wanted to.

It *was* true, Charlie figured, there were *some* things he was supposed to do that he didn't do, but that was never because he was lazy. There were too many other things that needed to be done instead. Too many things on his mind.

Still . . . even when he'd try so very hard to do his chores and other stuff asked of him, he would often forget. He didn't want to forget. It seemed to him that it just happened. There were even times when he forgot about things that he really wanted to do. Like the time he was going to go to the state fair with his friend Winchell.

Winchell's family had decided to go to the fair practically at the last minute. After school on a Friday, they, out of the blue, had announced they were going to go that Saturday morning.

"Can I go, Mom, please?" Charlie was practically jumping up and down. The phone cord was slapping hard on the kitchen counter. Little bottles of pills went cascading about as it whacked them.

His Mother began to grab at the small plastic bottles trying to catch them before they rolled off the counter.

"Settle down," she said. "Now what's this all about?"

"Winchell!" Charlie nearly shouted. "He just asked me to go to the state fair with him tomorrow morning . . . Can I? Can I, Mom? Can I, huh? Please?" He knew by the look she was giving him that there was a problem of some kind. "Please, Mom?" He barely breathed.

"Well," she began "I'll have to talk it over with your Father . . ."

"Can you call him now?"

"He's at work now, Charlie-honey."

"Yeah, but Dad doesn't get home until 5:30 or 6:00 and Winchell said they need to know by five." They had actually said no such thing, but Charlie couldn't resist the little white lie. He needed to know *NOW!* "C'mon Mom, please?" He gave her his sad little "I'm-going-to-die" look and her eyes told him she was weakening. "Pretty please?" Now, had his Father been involved, he never would have gotten this far which is why he so desperately wanted her to call him. Now!

"Well" . . . Her voice wavered, "I suppose I could, just this once."

"YES!" Charlie shouted triumphantly, leaping and shaking his fists in the air. Unfortunately he'd forgotten he still held the telephone receiver in his hand.

Small brown bottles with white capped lids were swept off the counter in one stroke as the tightly wound phone cord responded to his upward motion. There was a Moment of complete silence that seemed to last forever, during which Charlie shouted in his mind, "That stupid cord! It was that stupid cord's fault! If we had a cordless phone this never would have happened!" Lucky for him he hadn't said it out loud.

Suddenly his Mother burst into laughter.

"What the . . ." he thought, and then started laughing too. He didn't know what they were laughing at but laughing, he knew, was a lot better than yelling. His Mother had a tendency to be weird like that. She could go from laughter to tears without a Moment's notice. And worst of all, most of the time there seemed to be no reason for the sudden change. Just then it was in his favor so, rather than question it; he simply went with it.

Charlie could see tears forming in her eyes; she was laughing so hard. He put the phone receiver back on the hook.

"I'll get them," he said and sidled around her to where the bulk of the plastic bottles lay on the floor. One of the caps must have been loose. Scattered around the brown cylinders were what looked to Charlie like hundreds of little blue capsules. He quickly found the empty container and began picking up the stray capsules one-by-one.

Charlie's Mother took a step backwards and away from the counter where she'd been leaning heavily on her elbow for support during her fit of laughter. As she did so, a loud crack marked the place where her foot came down.

Charlie jumped. Loud unexpected noises always freaked him out. The jumpiness made his Father angry and he'd usually yell, "*WILL YOU STOP THAT!* You over react to everything!"

Charlie wasn't sure if he was over reacting or not. It's just what always happened.

At the sound of the smashed pill bottle, his Mother started to laugh again.

"Charlie?" she managed to get out. "If you'll clean this up, I'll call your Father."

"Okay, Mom."

By the time Charlie had picked up the mess and placed them, once-again on the counter, his Mother was just hanging up the phone.

"**What'd he say?**" Charlie cried, "**What'd he say?**"

"Calm down, Charlie," she took his hands in hers and held them over the counter. "Calm down". His Mother glanced downward. "Your Father asked me what your room looked like."

Charlie groaned and tried to pull his hands away, but she wouldn't let go.

"I got him to agree to let you go," she said, "if your room was clean enough to pass his inspection."

Charlie groaned again. "HIS inspection," he thought." His Mother must have seen the effect this announcement had on him. She patted him on the shoulder.

"C'mon, Charlie," she soothed, "you can do it."

He looked at her with a doubtful frown.

"You *do want* to go to the fair, don't you?"

"The fair!" He had forgotten all about that! Yeah. He could do it. He *would* do it. Charlie started towards his room.

"Wait, honey," his Mother called after him. "That's not all."

He stopped and slowly turned to look at her. He should have known.

"Your Dad wants it done before he gets home tonight."

"Oh, great!" Thought Charlie. "So much for going to the fair."

"It's not so bad, Charlie-boy," she cut into his thoughts before they could go much farther. "He's going to be late tonight. He won't be home until around 8:00."

Charlie watched her standing there, acting like this was suppose to make him feel better. Clean his room good enough to pass his Father's inspection? He might as well grow wings and fly.

"C'mon, Charlie-boy, go on in there and show your Dad what you can do!" She was smiling.

He really did want to go to the fair. But his *room*! Why did it have to be his room? He glanced at the wall clock in the kitchen. It was four-thirty. That gave him, maybe, three-and-a-half-hours if he was lucky. Could it be done?

The phone rang.

"I'll get it," his Mother told him, "you go and get started on that room."

Charlie nodded. He turned and headed towards the hall. At the doorway of his room he heard his Mother's voice.

"Charlie!" she called. "The phone's for you."

He made his way back to the kitchen.

His Mother smiled. "Don't stay on too long, hon. Remember the room."

It was Winchell. "So Charlie, can you go?" he asked. Charlie told him about the situation.

"Why don't I come over and help you clean it?" he offered.

Charlie was genuinely surprised. "Sure," he said. "That sounds great." Then he felt guilty. He didn't think he'd be offering to help Winchell clean his room if the roles were reversed. "Uh . . . I better tell my Mom. Hang on." Something told him his Mom should be advised of the situation.

"I'm sorry, Charlie boy," his Mother patted him on the shoulder again. She did that a lot. "That was part of the deal. Your Dad was explicit. *No* help, he said. Of course, he *was* talking about me . . ." she let her sentence sort of trail off into the air.

"Yeah, okay, Mom. I get the picture." He told Winchell it was a no-go. Before he could hang up the phone, Winchell made him promise to call just as soon as his Dad came home, saw the room, and said it was okay for Charlie to go.

Charlie hung up the phone.

"Don't look so glum, Charlie-boy," his Mother commented. "You can do it. I know you can."

Once again he headed towards his room. He opened the door, walked inside, and then quickly closed it before actually looking at any thing.

Then he looked.

The situation was even worse than he'd imagined. There were clothes on the bed, the dresser, his desk, and in little piles all over the floor. Papers covered his desk and the nearby floor space. His collection of rocks had been tipped over and a whole assortment was scattered between the bed and his closet. N-64 games were, well, they were everywhere. Here and there, mounds of assorted junk were visible that were unrecognizable from where Charlie was standing. The bottom of his closet was hidden by at least two feet of stuff.

Charlie'd taken in enough.

He slumped onto the bed and then immediately jumped right back up. He grabbed the jumbled up quilt and lifted it. A fork was dislodged from the folds underneath and fell to the floor. He rubbed his left backside and counted him self lucky he hadn't sat down any harder than he did.

What a mess!

He slid his hand over the spot on the bed now uncovered with care and lay the quilt back on top of itself. His roving fingers found a peach pit, which he threw, towards the overfilled plastic waste-basket in the corner of the room. He'd put-up a tiny basketball hoop with net and backboard over the cylinder, using parts from a Nerf basketball set. The pit hit the rim and bounced away.

Again he sat on the bed. What the heck should he do first? He didn't know. He leaned over and picked up the fork. What had he been eating with this? He couldn't remember. He wasn't supposed to eat in his room. Lucky thing *he* was the one to find it in his room and not his Mom, or especially not his Dad. He could visu-alize his Father finding it.

"I've *told* you a thousand times," he'd shout. "When are you going to start listening!"

Since no food had been found with it, Charlie could also easily imagine his own impulsive response.

"I wasn't eating with it, Dad," He'd say. "I was doing an ex-periment . . . for school."

Charlie knew his Father valued school above all else. That was because he'd never had the chance to finish high school him self. When Charlie's Grandfather died at a fairly young age from *the croup* (whatever that was), his Father had been forced to go to work to help support his Mother and three little sisters. He regularly lectured Charlie about this whenever he got below a B in one of his classes at school. So, Charlie had gotten the lecture and heard the story at least once every quarter since he was in first grade. He knew it well.

It probably would have started in Kindergarten if they had actually given letter grades back then. During the lecture, If his Dad thought Charlie wasn't listening, he'd get mad and yell at him. Charlie hated it when his Dad yelled. He hated it so much that he'd almost rather do anything than be yelled at. He'd *even* lie. He hadn't been using the fork to eat with. Yeah, right.

Charlie took the utensil into the kitchen. His Mother was standing over the counter cutting potatoes into tiny squares. He grimaced. Potato soup, for sure. It wasn't all that bad, but it certainly wasn't his favorite.

"So . . . How's it going, Charlie boy? You getting a lot done?"

Charlie glanced at the fork in his hand. "Yeah, Mom," he said, "tons."

"Dinner should be ready in about 45 minutes," she announced. "Your Father can eat later."

"Yeah. Okay, Mom." Charlie didn't tell her he wasn't all that hungry. He returned to his room.

He started picking up clothes but had a hard time determining whether they were dirty or clean. Should they go into his drawer, be hung up in the closet, or put into his dirty clothesbasket? **What a pain!**

Maybe he ought to just put all the clothes in the basket, but wouldn't that upset his Mother? Besides, the basket wasn't nearly big enough for the hordes that still lay in scattered desperation throughout the course of his entire room. There was no *way* he'd ever get the mess into that tiny little basket.

Maybe he should do clothes last.

He'd have to do something with them, though, so that he could see what else still needed to be cleaned up. He decided the bed was in a good central location. He threw the T-shirt already in his hands onto the bed and began to do the same with the rest of his scattered wardrobe.

After about half the clothes in the room had been shifted to the bed, Charlie came upon an unusually large pile. Beneath a pair of his old pajamas, a shirt (that even he had no trouble seeing belonged in the dirty clothesbasket), and several pairs of pants, he found something he hadn't seen or even thought about for months. It was his partially built model replica of the *Titanic*.

Not long after his Mother and Father had seen the new movie with Leonardo DiCaprio, his Father had been walking down an aisle in a Target store and happened to see the model on sale. It was a *huge* model, and had about a billion pieces that all had to be glued in place. Right on the top of the box it said in big clear letters **"WARNING! NOT FOR BEGINNERS."** Charlie's Dad bought it for him anyway. He'd said it would be fun and educational. Fun? Not really. Educational? Charlie supposed so.

He hoped his Father had learned the lesson that you really ought to pay attention to label warnings and that his only son didn't really like model building.

There it lay on the floor, unfinished.

He wondered if the real *Titanic* had had as many pieces to it as the model, probably more. All that time it must have taken to build the incredible boat just to see it end up at the bottom of the ocean.

What a waste!

He was sure that the inhabitants of the ocean didn't think it was such a big deal.

Then, all the weeks he'd spent trying to follow the pages and pages of diagrams and directions just to have the model end up uncompleted on the floor of his bedroom underneath some dirty clothes.

What a waste!

He supposed it was fitting in some strange way that he couldn't really explain.

Charlie glanced once more around his room. He had no idea where to put the unfinished ship. It would never be completed, of that he was pretty sure. Perhaps he should just throw it away; but, then again, he couldn't do that either. After all, his Father had bought it for him. He'd have to figure out *some* place where it could go.

The box with the remaining pieces was sticking obtrusively out from under his bed. He pulled it the rest of the way out and dusted off the top.

He immediately sneezed, twice. Charlie always sneezed in twos.

He lifted the top off and peered inside. A three quarters-used tube of Testor's model glue and an old Exacto knife lay side-by-side on top of the instructions, which were opened to page thirty-three.

That had been all the farther he'd gotten.

Charlie felt he'd really let his Father down on this one.

Maybe he should just sit right down here and now and complete it. No wonder his Dad didn't trust him to finish anything. He hadn't finished this.

He pushed aside some socks that might have been worn several times without ever having seen the inside of a washer, and a few of his scattered rocks, to make a flat space on which he could work. He lifted the instruction booklet, glue, and the Exacto knife from the box and placed them directly in front of him on the floor.

He began to read page thirty-four.

As Charlie labored, he began to wonder what his Dad would think when he saw the ship was finished. Would he even remember giving it to him? Surely he would.

Surely he'd also be surprised that Charlie had actually followed through with its' completion.

Would he be proud? Of course he would. Why, the educational value of the task alone . . .

His Father would undoubtedly be speechless at first, and then would quickly congratulate him on a job well done. He would no longer doubt that Charlie could start a project and finish it. The proof would be there. No one could deny it. They wouldn't dare.

His Father would have to stop calling him lazy. He could see by the completed ship that he wasn't.

Charlie became so intensely focused on what he was doing that he never consciously heard his Mother call him to dinner. Nor was he aware that she had come to his bedroom door and engaged in a brief conversation with him.

"Charlie-boy," she'd called ever so softly, "don't you want to come out and eat? Dinner's ready."

Charlie was so intent on the task at hand that his answer was automatic. "Not now, Mom! I gotta finish this." He'd said it, but his tunnel vision focus on the *Titanic* kept him from ever recording in his mind that it had been said. At some level it *must* have registered in his brain though, because later, after being reminded, he knew that it had happened.

"Okay, honey," his Mother had replied through the closed bedroom door. "I understand. You go right ahead. I know how much this means to you. You can eat later, too."

Charlie was putting the final piece in place, a banner that said "*Titanic* the Unsinkable", when he heard a knock at his door. It made him jump. He dropped the banner and the tube of glue to the floor. "Just a minute," he called towards the door. "I'm almost finished."

He quickly retrieved the banner and the glue, completely ignoring the glob of cement that had ended up on his well-used carpet. Charlie dabbed the needed portions onto the proper places, put the tube down, and placed the banner over what must have been the . . . what's it called? The Bridge, maybe. Or was that just on *Star Trek*? Oh, well . . . anyway, it was the place where the captain stood over the steering wheel. Whatever it's name.

Another firm and insistent knock began at the door.

"Coming," he said. He let go of the banner. It stayed in place. Done! Charlie jumped up and flew towards the door. He quickly unlocked it and threw it open.

He felt like one of those magicians on TV who raise their hands into the air after a trick and invite everyone watching to take a look at what they've done.

"Charlie's been working in here all afternoon," his Mother was saying. "He didn't even want to come to din— . . ." her voice trailed off without finishing as she looked past Charlie into the room.

His Father's head had been initially turned away. As he brought it back around to face Charlie and the room, he froze.

Charlie gestured towards the completed *Titanic*. "So, what do you think?" he asked. When he didn't get the reaction he'd expected, he quickly glanced back at his Father.

Something was wrong.

His Father stood, hands clenching and unclenching at his sides. As Charlie watched, he saw the muscles in his Father's neck begin to tighten. The color of his face started looking sort of bluish-red. Suddenly, with a quickness and force that was frightening, the man turned and forced his way past Charlie's Mother and strode away, muttering. "Stupid, lazy, good-for-nothing . . ."

"What have you been doing?" his Mother asked.

"Working on the *Titanic*, Mom! I finished it. The *whole* thing! And Dad never even looked at it!"

Well . . ." she began.

"Well, what!" Charlie demanded.

Then it dawned on him. The fair. His room.

Suddenly he knew his Father wouldn't care a whit about the *Titanic*. He'd probably long ago given up on Charlie ever completing that.

It was the *room* he'd been interested in. That was what he'd come to the door to see.

Charlie couldn't figure out what had happened. He'd sincerely started out fully intending to clean his room.

Later that night he could hear his Dad telling his Mom (the walls of the house were thin). Charlie didn't care about going to the fair. If he did care . . . if he'd really wanted to go . . . he would have cleaned that room!" **Could it be true?** Was it possible that he actually didn't want to go to the fair? He didn't think so.

He'd almost cried over the phone when his Dad had forced him to call Winchell and tell his friend he couldn't go.

It was only with the utmost effort that Charlie'd kept the tears from falling. He didn't want to give his Father the satisfaction.

So, he went right on acting, as if what his Dad had thought actually *was* true.

He tried hard from that Moment on to convince him self and everyone else that he could've *cared less* about the stupid state fair.

It almost worked, too. He almost convinced him self. Almost.

"Why didn't you call me earlier?" Winchell had been clearly upset.

"My Dad didn't get home until 8:30," Charlie told his friend.

"What happened? Didn't you get your room done?"

"Not the way he wanted me to," Charlie was unable to tell his friend what had really happened. Winchell would probably conclude, just like his Father had, that he didn't want to go to the fair in the first place. Heck, it even seemed that way to him.

He was confused.

Something was wrong. There had to be something wrong. But what was it? What could it be? Charlie *just* didn't know. He wondered if he ever would.

THE END
(OR PERHAPS . . . THE BEGINNING)

There *was* something wrong with Charlie (not his real name, to protect confidentiality). After spending time with him and his family and evaluating Charlie, I found him to be demonstrating evidence of a number of characteristics consistent with a mild-moderate Obsessive Compulsive symptomatic picture. Evidence was gathered through clinical interview, Burks' Behavior Rating Scales (completed by his Mother, Father, and fourth grade teacher), a slightly modified version of the Leyton Obsessional Inventory for Children, and extended family history.

The Burks' Profile Sheet actually suggested the possibility of ADHD and/or OCS. The specific single item summary, however, leaned more towards primarily OCS related factors. Thus, the decision to administer the Leyton was made.

Charlie responded positively (he felt he had the symptoms) to 39 of the 45 queries made. Interestingly, when the results were shared with his parents, they questioned whether or not he actually had many of the symptoms he'd reported that he did (not an unusual occurrence), because they had never seen evidence of, nor had he spoken to them of such things before. The affected individual frequently tells no one about many of their experienced chronic thought patterns and the concomitant feelings they have that they "must" do certain things at practically any cost. It tends to be both embarrassing and there is also a lingering fear that others simply will not believe them and will get angry or make fun of them as a result. Unfortunately when the OCS affected individuals do tell the truth regarding symptomotology they quite often are not believed, peers do make fun of them or look at them in ways suggesting that they think the person might be crazy, and parents, along with well meaning teachers, do often become angry.

As the four of us explored the extended family history, parental eyes began to widen as they began to recognize various characteristics of OCS in their own siblings on both sides and in both sets of Charlie's grandparents as well.

Charlie's symptoms were not, of course, limited to those mentioned in his "story." These symptoms also included such things as a short temper, poorer school performance than he was capable of, peer relationship difficulties, inconsistent problems getting to sleep at night, a tendency to be irritable and slow getting ready for school in the morning, and frequent arguments with especially his Father.

A recommendation was made to Charlie's pediatrician to start him on Anafranil at 25 mg about one hour before bedtime. Given available evaluation data, the pediatrician agreed. Charlie's Mother brought him in on the first session after he had started this medication. She was obviously pleased with his response but was also slightly confused. Her pediatrician had informed her that it would probably be three to six weeks before she would likely see any benefit from the medication. Her perplexity came from the fact that the very morning after he had taken just one dose, Charlie had, for the first time in as long as she could remember, gotten up with his alarm. He then dressed and made him self ready for school, and was in the process of eating his breakfast before she'd even entered the kitchen to start up the coffee maker. She indicated she had been literally "amazed." This same occurrence had, however, continued every day since. Charlie's teacher had also sent home a note spontaneously congratulating him on his newly demonstrated efforts with a personal note that said, "You see, I told you could do it if you tried!" She had not been informed, as yet, that a medication had been started.

In further interview of a general nature, it was determined that Charlie him self, as well as his Mother, had noticed he seemed much calmer and less angry. He had finished all of his work at school since starting medication and, as a result, had only had one homework assignment, which he had completed easily. It usually took him hours to complete even a small amount of homework, and without his parents sitting next to him, it often would not be completed at all.

In a re-administration of the Leyton, Charlie reported 25 of his initial 39 positive symptoms as "better" (meaning, less intense, less noticeable, and/or fewer in number). He indicated that 5 of the remaining 14 were "gone" or hadn't been noticed anymore at all. Of the final 9 symptoms, there were several that actually might not be noticed one way or the other due to the type of symptom involved. For example the question relating to hoarding various odds and ends and objects had not changed, nor had the one regarding his unwillingness to eat certain foods "*no matter what*" and so on.

After about the fifth or sixth session Charlie's Father took me aside briefly as the others walked out of the session and whispered with some apparent consternation, "so, can adults take this medication too?" Eventually Charlie's Father was also diagnosed with mild-moderate OCS and treated with an SSRI to which he responded positively. I have found that it is not unusual for one and/or both parents to question the possibility of treatment for themselves after they see the positive results that have occurred with their children.

Case No. 2

"There are too many holes inside this heart
And the emptiness within's so hard to bear
You promised me forever right from the start
And though I look again and again
You're not there

I cannot think . . . I cannot see
I cannot feel . . . this heart inside of me
I want to know . . . and then I don't
I will decide . . . and then I won't
If it's not you . . . and it's not me
Who else could it be . . . oh . . . what can I do . . ."

From the song "You're not there" by Ron D. Kingsley

Judy

Judy was a young attorney when she initially came to see me. Her presenting problem was a bit vaguely stated but seemed to center on her perceived relationship with her relatively new husband. They had been married just shy of one year, and she had become increasingly concerned about the marriage as time went by. She was quick to point out that there were no real "major problems, just," she said, "a lot of little things." These little things, however, were causing her to worry and experience uncomfortable Moments of anxiety. She was of the opinion that she herself might be contributing a bit more than her share in the creation of these little problems. She therefore had come to see me with the goal in mind of initially working on her self in the hopes that this would be enough to straighten things out before they might really get out of hand.

As Judy described her perceived situation, at home and at work, as well as fragments from her past, a pattern began to emerge. She appeared hyper-concerned over what others might be thinking about her. As a result she tended to second-guess what certain comments, as well as the actions of others, meant, some of which, by her descriptions, may not have been directed at her. Thus she seemed to have a, perhaps, slightly distorted view of her own reality, based on what she "thought" others were thinking about her, often related to comments and actions meant for someone else entirely. Heightened anxiety and chronic worry were both partial results. These led to hyper-vigilance and subsequent irritability.

At work she was able to keep herself together although she experienced frequent inner bouts of perceived worthlessness that were difficult to withstand. Upon coming home after a long and tedious workday, she found herself much less able to "hold it all together" in relation to her husband. Consequently she would become openly upset with him, which would further heighten stress and bring out the hypersensitivity and over-responsivity even more, along with other characteristics frequently present when her underlying OCS was asserting itself.

Again, utilizing clinical interview, the Burks' Behavior Rating Scales, the modified Leyton Obsessional Inventory for Children (in spite of her status as an adult), and personal as well as extended family history, the provisional diagnosis of mild-moderate OCS was made.

Her husband completed the Burks' as he saw her now. Judy's Mother filled it out as she remembered her when she had been a child, and by Judy also as she viewed herself at this time in her life. Although the Burks' was created to behaviorally rate children and adolescents, I find it can be easily modified for use with adults as well. Having employed this instrument for more than 20 years now, there are a group of its descriptors that I have found particularly useful in determining the presence of OCS, whether rated with child, adolescent, or adult in mind. The results of all three raters were consistent with the OCS possibility.

The Leyton was then administered and Judy was positive for 43 of 45 symptom questions. The OCS diagnosis was then explored in depth, and extended family history was also thoroughly discussed.

Judy immediately recognized her own symptomatic responses, as well as those of several of her siblings (one of whom actually carried a diagnosis of OCD), her parents, and grandparents as well. Her genetic history seemed to make the diagnosis of OCS even more plausible, although it had never occurred to her previously. "Suddenly," she indicated in later sessions, "my whole life began to make sense."

Judy had married at a time, considered by the social community with whom she had grown up, and still belonged, rather late in life. Though she had actually been engaged several times before, something had always interfered in each case that brought about the cancellation of the culminating event. It was she who had called it off. She eventually found something wrong, that she felt she couldn't cope with, for each and every fiance she'd had. Now, with her new knowledge, she had gained a sense as to why this had been happening. One might wonder how she managed to finally marry. The man she married had OCS too.

As Judy came in for her first scheduled session after having started the prescribed medication, she was sporting a wide smile. She nearly skipped into the office and plopped herself down on the two-seater couch across from me. At the same time, she exclaimed, "It's amazing. Absolutely amazing!"

Judy went on to describe her week as being one of the "most terrific" of her life. The little things weren't bothering her anymore. She was not worrying every second about what others around her might be thinking in relation to her performance of the Moment and, hence, not second guessing and creating her own distortions either. She and her husband were getting along a lot better and the heretofore-chronic anxiety she felt around him had lessened to next-to-nothing. Judy became a believer. She even sent her parents and sisters and brothers copies of the OCS articles I had given her, talking to a couple of them at length on the phone as well. She seemed thrilled because now she knew. Her past and present were finally coming together and making sense.

Case No. 3

I want to go where I can be free to dream
I want to live where people care
I want to know things are exactly as they seem
I want to go . . . please take me there

Take me on a journey . . . 'round the sun . . . oh . . . and sing me a tune
I've got such a yearning . . . to run free . . . across the moon

I want to see the ocean way down deep where it's still clean
Take me to the rain forests . . . oh . . . oh . . . while they're still green

I know there are books that can help to see
And I . . . I can turn the TV on
But neither of those can take care of the need
To live life . . . before it's gone

I want to go where I can be free to dream
I want to live where people care
I want to know things are exactly as they seem
I want to go please take me there
I want to go please take me there
Take me there

From the song "Free to Dream" by Ron D. Kingsley

Randy

Randy had been diagnosed with ADHD long before he was brought by his Mother to see me. He had been taking Ritalin for a while, and it was reported to me that it had stopped working; and though other things had been tried, nothing much seemed to be helping. He had explosive episodes that were legendary at his school. Though only in the 4th grade, he was, in the eyes of the children, the terror of the school. No one messed with him. No one got in his face. No one disagreed with him. No one was his friend. He'd seen counselors and psychologists before. He knew about them. I was just another in the on going and lengthening list. His Mother had not liked the last one who'd added a diagnosis to the already present ADHD of Conduct Disorder. This professional had also apparently painted such a dismal picture of Randy's future as an ADHD Conduct Disordered individual that his Mother found herself experiencing feelings of utter hopelessness that seemingly intensified with each visit they had. Randy did not like him either. In fact, he later told me he hated him.

In our first session, it was rather obvious that Randy did not want to be there. He had informed his Mother prior to their coming that he wasn't going to talk. Randy, it seemed, was bound and determined to be a living example of my favorite psychologist joke.

Question: "How many psychologists does it take to change a light bulb?"
Answer: "Only one, but the light bulb *really* has to *want* to change."

This is my favorite joke because there's so much truth in it. So, there he was, arms folded tightly across his chest, legs one over the other and stretched out as far in front of him as they would go, glaring at me as if to say, "Go ahead, try and make me talk."

He knew I couldn't make him participate. I knew it too and that was my advantage. I didn't try to make him talk and it caught him off guard.

You can't change a conduct-disordered kid. Randy had learned that from the last professional. So, he figured, why even try.

I acknowledged him and his position and told him I knew I could not be of help to him if he didn't want me too, or if we couldn't get along and so on. Then, having told him this, I picked up my guitar, a staple in my office, and started playing a fairly up-tempo song I had written about the environment. Music can get through sometimes when nothing else can, and I had chosen a song that I thought was fairly linguistically and lyrically benign, yet one that I thought might also, perhaps, sustain his interest.

We ended up both being surprised. I was surprised because my "fairly benign" song turned out to be loaded in a way that had simply escaped my awareness prior to my singing it to Randy. And Randy was probably surprised because in the middle of the song during the third chorus, he suddenly burst into an emotional flood of tears. The lyrics of the chorus went:

> "I want to go where I can be free to dream
> I want to live where people care
> I want to know things are exactly as they seem
> I want to go, please take me there . . ."

You see, Randy had long ago become convinced that his Father didn't care that he was alive. It was the one person that he wanted to care about him more than anyone else in the world, although if asked point blank he would have denied it. He would have acted as if he him self couldn't care less what his Father did or didn't care about.

For Randy's entire life, he felt alienated from his Father (who had significant problems of his own). He so wanted his Father to show him he cared, that upon hearing the song lyrics, it hit him in a way that a direct question never could have.

After he came apart emotionally, we explored the relationship with his Father in great depth and had a good session. Randy and I developed a tenaciously held therapeutic bond, and he agreed to cooperate with my attempts to determine what might be going on and how things might be made better.

In the next session, Randy's Mother informed me about an incident that seemed the main reason the prior professional had additionally diagnosed her son with a conduct disorder. It was reported that one—day Randy's Mother began to notice fewer steak knives and knives in general in the kitchen, or so it seemed. She began asking various family members if they'd seen any of them, and each one told her that they had not. Then, on a day when the kids were at school, she happened to be in Randy's room looking for something when a glint caught her eye and as she moved towards the bookshelf; there, on the second row down, was her butcher knife. She described a "chill" briefly zipping along her spine as she picked up the rather large knife and began searching the room for some trace of the others, at the same time desperately hoping she wouldn't find them. She did find them, though. Randy had placed, or hidden, 16 knives in fairly diverse positions through-out his bedroom. He also kept an aluminum bat at the side of his bed.

Randy would not tell the previous professional the reason for this stashing of knives. The professional apparently interpreted this behavior as evidence that Randy might be planning to use the knives on a family member and/or whatever else may have been thought. Thus, a conduct disorder was brought into the picture.

I asked Randy what he'd planned to use the knives and the bat for. He replied simply, "for protection."

I believed him and told him so.

"You're the first," I remember him telling me. "All the others, including my parents, say something like, "now, why would you do that? There's no need for protection in your bedroom.' And I know they don't believe me."

"Well", I told him, maybe they can't conceive of a possible way that what you've been telling them could be true."

"And you can?"

"Yes."

I believe it may have been some movies Randy saw in the past that triggered his obsessive fear that someone would enter his room at night, and that he would have to be ready to protect him self in case it happened. The moderately persistent obsessive thought was, "someone is coming to get me at night in my room." The compulsion that led to a lessening of the anxiety he experienced was the stashing of knives throughout his room so they would be handy, and the placing of the baseball bat where he could instantly grab it were he awakened. With the "weapons" in place, Randy finally felt secure enough to sleep. He needed something in place for protection in order to sleep. Never mind that it may appear wildly irrational. The fear was real and unwavering.

There were other signs and symptoms of OCS beyond those already stated in regard to Randy. When Anafranil, and later Prozac, was added (to a lower dose of the Ritalin he was previously prescribed), he began to do better in his school work as well as socially and emotionally both at school and home. His Father though symptomatic him self (14 jobs in 15 years, among other things), never did come to a session nor did he recognize the OCS characteristics in him self. The stress this caused the family, and especially Randy, was tremendous and continued to have a negative impact on all of them.

CHAPTER FIVE

EDUCATIONAL IMPLICATIONS

If you really want to know how I feel
Oh . . . you got to open your eyes to what's real
If you want to understand what I say
Somehow you got to open your mind to today
But I don't even know that you can
You always swear you've heard it before
Yet you still don't know who I am
That's for sure

I want you to listen to the things that I say
If not . . . then I wish you'd just get out of the way
There's room enough for us both here
Even though we don't agree
The pressure's been building for so many years
Can't you see?

You tell me you want me to speak only the truth
But you don't like it . . . when I do
So . . . I've been telling you what you want to hear
I thought you knew

Looking at you it's like you think you're already there
You're the lion . . . and I'm just a mouse
But there's nothin' that you'll learn from a fairy tale
You're too proud

From the song "If you really want to know" by Ron D. Kingsley

OCS IN THE SCHOOLS

In my experience, and opinion, OCS (Obsessive Compulsive Symptoms: Mild-Moderate range) in the public and/or private school arena continues to be, perhaps, the most misrepresented and misunderstood problem in childhood and adolescence. Simple ignorance seems to be at the heart of this dilemma. This lack of awareness, however, is not only found in the schools. Many health care professionals are also unaware. In preparing to write this article, I have remained blocked (for a time) by all the many ways that OCS can show up both directly and indirectly in the schools. It has been very difficult to decide the best way to present the problem. Finally, I simply began writing following the popular and well known Nike advertisement's suggestion to "just do it!" I will begin with general issues and move towards the more specific symptoms that actually may, or may not, be present when working with a particular individual.

Anxiety:

In one form or another, worry and excessive anxiety are usually very common for those with OCS. The anxiety can be in all areas, but may also be very specific. Transitions from one activity to another or one environment to another often bring out this seemingly senseless anxiety.

"I don't want to go, mama," Jimmy wails.

"Here we go again," exclaims his frustrated Father. "Will you tell me please, Jean, why . . . no matter where we go, this son of yours never wants to go with us?"

Jean smiles just a bit before answering. "That's not true, Tim, and you know it."

"Yeah, but the only places he doesn't throw a fit about going are those that he's already been."

"There, you see," she said. "Does this tell you something?"

"Yeah, it tells me something all right. I've got a spoiled child. That's what it tells me. And he's running my life."

"No, Tim," Jean gently reprimanded him. "It tells you that he's worried. He's never been to these places and he is afraid of the unknown. Now, who else do you know that is afraid of the unknown?"

He grimaced. "I don't know."

"Sure you do," Jean smiled. "Your Mother comes to mind. And then, let's see . . . who else? Hmmm . . . Could it be *you?*"

He was looking down. "Not me," he whispered halfheartedly.

"Oh no, not you. Heck no. *You!* Who won't go anywhere without spending half the day studying every little detail, *you!* Who won't go at all if anything changes. And I mean anything!"

"Okay. Okay!" He batted the air with his hands. "Stop already."

There seems to be no hard rule regarding the how, when, and

where anxieties are expressed, at least not in general. There are those people who are anxious about everything, and those who are worried about only some things. One very important thing to keep in mind involves the amounts, or levels, of worry or anxiety that is present. Usually, for it to be OCS, it goes beyond the norm in how long it lasts and/or how intense, or severe, it appears to be. The cause of the anxiety may seem very clear, or it may seem to make no sense at all. There is, however, an unreasonable quality to its expression. As a result, teachers and other adult school staff members soon become annoyed with such a student. The irritation and annoyance tends to build over time. Tolerance levels may, as a result, diminish considerably.

Crystal approaches the teacher's desk slowly. She holds in her hand an assignment she's been working on. She really needs to ask a question before she can go on to the next problem.

"What is it *now,* Crystal?"

She holds the paper up so the teacher can see. "Teacher?" she whispers, "is . . . is this right?"

"You know, Crystal, if every student came up to my desk like you after every problem they complete, I'd never get any lessons planned or papers graded."

"Yes, Ma'am. But is it right?"

"Of course it's right. It's always right. You *must* know that by now."

"But teacher," Crystal persists, "you didn't check it."

"Oh for goodness' sakes." She grabs the paper from Crystal's outstretched hands, glances at it and then returns it.

Crystal remains standing passively by the desk.

"What now!" the teacher sighs.

"Is it okay? Did I do it right?"

"*YES!* Now don't you come back up here until you've finished every one of those problems." She smiles and adds; "do you understand?"

Crystal nods and returns to her desk. After finishing the very next problem, she stands and approaches the teacher's desk once again. There is a question she needs to ask before she can go on.

In the above scene, Crystal's anxiety and worry center on

whether or not she has completed a problem correctly. She needs to know this before starting on the next one. It doesn't matter that, as the teacher reminded her, she usually does them all correctly. She needs to know.

Teachers and parents frequently mistakenly identify this type of behavior as an exaggerated need for attention. Another common misinterpretation of such actions is the belief that the student is constantly seeking praise. When OCS is the cause, neither of these explanations is accurate. The real reason is usually something like an inner need to be absolutely sure a mistake has not been made. Thus the ultimate authority must be consulted.

Some common examples of how worry/anxiety may show up in the schools specific to an OCS affected student include the following:

Work Resistance and/or Refusal:

There are a host of plausible reasons why students may resist and refuse assignments. In fact, even when OCS is found to be the underlying cause, teachers often continue to blame the behavior on another, though possible, unrelated cause. This is one of the main reasons attempted interventions can be notoriously ineffective. Affected students either do not know why the resistance/refusal occurs or, similar to the teachers, mistakenly think the reason is due to something else when it is not. One begins to sense why confusion can run rampant in relation to OCS.

Resistance/refusal can result from an excessive fear of making a mistake and/or of failing. If the student is able to resist and refuse to complete an assignment, he can avoid even the possibility of doing it wrong. The student may not be able to openly admit that such a fear exists. He may not know. The tendency, when confronted by an adult about the reason for such resistance, is to reply with an "I don't know," which may or may not be the truth yet is practically always unacceptable. Frequently the adult or teacher persists, and may even begin to demand, an explanation for the inappropriate behavior.

They don't like, nor will they accept, an "I don't know" for an answer. Affected students often work very hard at finding a satisfactory reason for their behaviors that they can believe in or, at least, a reason that the teacher will accept. A commonly attempted response, which some are unable to let go of, is the statement, "I can't do it" and similar explanations such as, "it's too hard . . . I don't know how," and etc. Teachers typically interpret such comments as clear evidence of a student's "laziness," and may tell colleagues, counselors, or the School Psychologist things such as, "He just doesn't want to work, he doesn't care," and "he's just lazy." Although these beliefs certainly can be accurate and reflect the truth, in many instances, when OCS is driving the behavior, such comments and beliefs represent unfair and inadequate judgements. Judgements like this work to undermine (even if just a bit) the student teacher working relationship. Eventually they can negatively affect the student's educational progress.

Students are also subject to what has been described as a self-fulfilling prophecy. Essentially this suggests students will become what teachers and other responsible adults believe them to be. In truth, this OCS self-fulfilling prophecy is even more likely because the student who doesn't know, or seems unsure about the reasons for his/her reactions and behaviors, will often come to accept the most obvious probable cause. When this is the case, it makes the diagnosis of OCS even more difficult. Inappropriate interventions frequently result. As time moves on, the twists and turns multiply in response to the misperceptions, inaccurate judgements, and misguided discipline efforts. It becomes increasingly difficult for the school counselor/psychologist to disentangle the resulting mess. When the actual cause is identified as underlying OCS, it can appear to be totally absurd to the teacher and more like an explanation in fantasy rather than reality. If not approached with cautious and careful consideration, most teachers will flatly reject such an explanation as nonsense, which, once again, further complicates matters.

Work resistance and refusal can also arise from time-related anxieties and the intensely felt need for task completion. In this scenario students are given an assignment and a specific amount of time during class to work on a task.

"Mark," the teacher called from his desk, "see if you can stop day dreaming and start working. You've got 15 minutes to get as much done on this assignment as you can." Mr. Donaldson then addressed the entire class. "Most of you should be able to finish this in 10 minutes if you work hard. Remember, students, what you don't complete in this class period will be added to your homework tonight."

Several groans issued forth from the students. "Enough of that! Now get to work."

Mark looked at the clock on the wall. There was no way he'd ever be able to get that assignment done in 10 minutes. Maybe in 30 or 40 minutes, but no way in 10. Why, start the stupid thing if he was just going to have to take it home anyway. So, he began to look around the room instead. He imagined him self inventing something simple but useful. So useful, in fact, that everyone in the entire world would want one. After catching up with back orders, he'd be rich beyond his wildest dreams. Of course half of the money he'd give away to the needy and to his church. The headlines would read "Eleven year old billionaire makes good on his promise!" He'd be famous. Jay Leno would shake his hand on the "Tonight Show" and congratulate him on national TV.

There may or may not be sufficient time awarded for most students to complete the assignment, but typical instructions include a section directing the students who do not finish in the time allotted to take it home, do the rest, and turn it in the following day. For many OCS students, this situation can be a serious dilemma. The inexplicable need to finish a given task, once started, without interruption, can immediately trigger the engine of anxiety. If the OCS affected is a slow worker (usually the result of the extreme distractibility associated with the problem and/or the need to accomplish all tasks exactly right), there may be no decision to make, just a reaction. This is because the student knows there is no way the assignment will get done. The reaction can include, but is not limited to, the following: sighing, wailing, or negative language (aloud or just under the breath). It may include the initiation of an alternate activity (such as playing with bits of paper, things in the desk, and the hair of the girl sitting close by, or micro-machines smuggled in to school). There could be daydreaming or even sleeping. Reactions could also include attempts to explain themselves with excuses like those discussed earlier. Not uncommonly, angry outbursts can occur if the teacher persists in demanding that the student work, and actions develop that simulate a working student in a deceptive effort to keep the teacher from continued harassment.

If the OCS affected in the depicted scenario does not have the same kind of slowness problem in this particular assigned subject, the student may decide to simply rush through the designated material as quickly as possible (and often rashly, with little regard for accuracy, or, interestingly enough, penmanship). Remember, in order to start, this student must believe the task can be completed in its entirety in one setting. The student described in this paragraph may finish well before the allotted time limit because the speed is driven by the absolute need to get done. There is no pacing for this student.

Sometimes those with the milder OCS are actually unaware of this insistent, yet undeniable, urge for completion. When such is the case, the OCS student may innocently begin working. If time runs out on this student and the teacher attempts to effect a class transition to the next subject or activity, it pulls the trigger on the dormant anxiety. A host of reactions may be displayed by the student, including, but again not limited to, the following:

• The student may ignore the teacher and continue working on the assignment at hand. If the teacher does not see this or chooses not to interrupt or redirect, this tactic may work well for the student.

• She may resist for a period of time while mumbling under her breath, etc., and then finally give in.

• He might vehemently resist, become angry, explode emotionally, demonstrate verbal disrespect, burst into tears, brood, glower, gripe, or obstinately declare (in retaliation) that nothing else then, will be done either, and so on.

Excessive self-doubt:

The tendency towards self-doubt seems pervasive and invades the lives, in one way or another, of apparently all those affected by OCS. The students are inclined to be chronically unsure of everything and may rarely, if ever, offer personal opinions. If they do share their point of view, it is often done quite cautiously and is immediately retracted at the first hint of another's disagreement or even slight questioning. They cannot let go of the possibility that what they think, do, or say may not be accurate.

In the classroom, the student thus affected may never raise a hand to answer teacher directed questions. If the teacher, nevertheless, calls on this student, the most commonly heard response is, "I don't know." Even when the OCS student knows the answer, the internal workings of this problem cause them to doubt the veracity of this knowledge.

The student may have trouble completing assignments because they doubt all aspects of what they may do or needs to be done. Such a student may constantly badger the teacher regarding the accuracy of every completed step of every assignment in a desperate attempt to relieve this intolerable uncertainly. Teachers often interpret the outward signs of this symptom as "attention seeking behavior" when, in a case like this, it simply is not.

The excessive doubt results in significant difficulties with decision-making. These students typically defer to others when a decision must be made. The experienced intensive lack of confidence also makes them more-or-less hesitant to try new things, go places where they haven't been before, and negatively influences their ability to successfully handle several tasks at once. There is a strong tendency to be easily overwhelmed by more than one task at a time.

The hyper-incertitude also seems to influence the affected ability to prioritize. They have trouble figuring out which task (of many) or which part of a multiple-step assignment should be done first, which second, and so on. As a result, they can be very disorganized.

Hypersensitivity:

The OCS student responds to pain, whether physical or psychological, in an intense manner that is typically well out of proportion to the norm. Feelings, therefore, are way too easily hurt. Their heightened sensitivity may convince them, however inaccurately, that others don't like them, or that other students are picking on them. It also, however, can make them easy targets to actually be picked on and, therefore, some may take on a victim role.

This student may apologize excessively over trivial incidents that others hardly noticed and/or didn't notice at all. At times this can be an irritation to a teacher, manifested by the seeking of constant reassurance. The indecisiveness and super sensitivity often work together here. The student's anxiety and worry are set in motion and maintained by the smallest faux paux's or infractions, as well as those that they only perceive as maybe, possibly, or it just might have been, infractions. They are chronically unsure if what they've said or done has hurt or bothered another, and if they do not apologize, as they may not, the incident nevertheless will take its toll on their psyche. In such an instance, this student may experience an inner turmoil and emotional pain. There are even times that some feel so badly about their own words or actions that they may initiate a self-flagellation (punishment) in one of several possible forms. This can be the student who repeatedly pounds a palm to the fore, side, or back of their own head. It can be one who seems to have a desire or need to feel pain and self-mutilates. I have seen a few who will refuse to eat for two or three days in an effort to show their own bodies just who is in control, or as punishment for an infraction, whether perceived or real. Other self-inflicted punishments include often-vitriolic verbal defamation directed inwardly. Sometimes words can be said aloud in frustration, but more often these are silent statements and chastisements that may be repeated over and over again and cannot help but influence the overall emotional and social well being of the student. Specific kinds of verbalizations and/or thoughts related to this are as varied as words themselves, but commonly include things such as the following, "What an idiot!", "I'm so stupid."

"Boy, am I a jerk!" "I can't do nothin' right!" "What the heck do you think you're doing!" "Well, what do you expect from such a worthless fool as myself." "Why do I even try?" and more often than I care to believe, and yet cannot ignore, self-statements also occur along the lines of "I should just kill myself." This last pronouncement, at least in the initial or beginning stages, appears more an indication of just how intensely and badly those with OCS feel, rather than a true wish to actually commit suicide. When students make such serious comments, however, it is a good idea to consider the OCS possibility, and to always follow up on their intentions.

Over sensitivity, as does over-control, leads to over responsiveness. Thus, the OCS student is almost "set up" daily to over respond. They frequently work very hard to control this hyper responsivity. Some do this much better than others. In Moments when control is lost, however, resulting actions may appear impulsive and certainly are over reactions that often come as a complete surprise to others. The trend is for these episodes to flare up, burn for a time, and then die as quickly and mysteriously as they began. As the flare is burning, teachers and other students can intensify and prolong this OCS reaction inadvertently. Patterns this over responsiveness may take are extremely variable. Some of the more common patterns, though, include statements and reactions by students such as follows: "Teacher, she's looking at me!" "Nobody likes me," "Shut up! (And quit talking about me);" "He did that on purpose!" "Do what?" I can't do that!" "It's too hard," "Do we have to do *all* that!" "We'll *never* get done." The student may suddenly yell, push, or hit another student. The student may be very easily frustrated and prone to tearfulness throughout the school day.

For teachers, and at times students as well, the hypersensitivity of the OCS student acts as an incredible distraction and is similarly quite irritating. Over time, it can become more and more difficult for others to treat the OCS student kindly. In fact, these are some of the very dynamics that work to place an OCS student in the victim role. The situation, in this way, feeds on itself. The

OCS student "victim" may feel the teacher and other students are "against," or "out to get him," and with time, this can seem very nearly the truth. Hypersensitive students, especially those with evidence of sensitivity issues that appear problematic, are very good candidates to screen for possible underlying OCS. When present, if not identified and treated for what it is (the underlying precipitator), all other interventions are like using a Band-Aid to treat a bruise. They are simply ineffective.

Perseverative Thoughts/Behaviors:

Essentially this refers to the propensity to obsess on ideas, needs, or wants. It also relates to the accompanying drives, or compulsions, that so often work to ease, or lessen, the intensity of the anxiety created by the obsessions. A simple example may help to clarify the relationship between the obsession (thought) and the concomitant compulsion (action). The student in the middle of a test who perceives (thinks) there's a need to sharpen his pencil (and is OCS driven) will not experience relief from this thought until able to get it sharpened. If he asks and the teacher refuses permission, the perception that it must be sharpened will persist and gradually intensify. Depending on the strength of the student's OCS at the time, this delineated scenario may, or may not, result in a happy end. If not too powerful, the student may make it to the end of the test, or period, without seriously losing control, and thereafter go and sharpen the pencil. Although this relentless thought probably will have interfered with the student's performance for the parts of that test while the obsession "was in process," this student won't be in any immediate trouble for defiance of authority. When the OCS driven obsession *is* too strong a variety of responses are possible, but whatever form taken, they tend to be more intense than in the situation previously described. Typical reactions can include arguments with the teacher, ignoring the teacher's directive and going to sharpen the pencil anyway. Such a student may announcing in a huff something like "that's just fine by me, then I won't have to finish this stupid test" (followed by a stubborn discontinuance of work), and so on.

The above related incident is a real life excerpt from several case histories and is meant to act as a springboard from which to reframe and process other classroom behavioral episodes with similar dynamics. This inability to let go of ideas, thoughts, and needs often greatly interferes with the OCS student's capacity to work well with classmates or in-groups within the classroom setting. When the OCS student begins to tackle an assignment in cooperation with another, or several students, obsessive locks tend to occur regarding the way things should be done, who should do them, or any other of a number of possible obsessions. As this happens, connected compulsions frequently cause havoc within the normal group process. The affected student may become obnoxiously bossy and, to any observer, appear to have an overzealous need for control. The need, however, is not truly for *control* it is a need to follow the inner demands dictated by the capricious workings of the OCS biochemical deficiency.

In time the OCS student may gravitate away from working in-groups and appear to teachers and others to prefer working alone. They can appear to have no interest whatsoever in the class work of others and often will seem completely unwilling (or unable) to accept suggestions from anyone else in regard to their own work. Teachers may hear comments such as, "They won't do it right!" "They don't care if it's right or wrong!" "But it's gotta be done like this!" and so on. Depending on the strength of this symptom's picture, the comments can be more or less intense, and the language (again depending) can become very colorful as well.

Competition is another factor that tends to be highly influenced by the inability to let go of ideas and the resulting behavioral urges. The OCS student may (and frequently does) experience a perseverative need to be first or the best at everything, i.e., first in line, first to start, first to be done, first in a race (and they can perceive everything as a race), and etc. In all these instances of needing to be first, they may push, shove, hit, scream, cry, or throw tantrums in an attempt to get these needs met, or when the urge has been thwarted. When sitting in a small group and another child is praised by the teacher for her efforts, the OCS child sitting nearby can, and sometimes does, experience this as a threat and feel slighted as if the praise of another somehow lessens his own status in relation to the teacher. As a result he may immediately act to achieve the same, or similar attention. This is attention-seeking behavior but, interestingly, not for the sake of getting the attention as much as it is an actual need for the OCS student to "stay ahead" on the scoreboard, or, at least, get an equal amount so that all this is evenly balanced.

Within this competition arena in relation to games (sports or otherwise), OCS students usually gravitate toward one or the other of two poles. They either tend to shy away from the game completely or they play and experience a very powerful urge to dominate and to win, often at all costs. In this intense and highly emotional setting, the OCS affected may come down hard, verbally or otherwise, on any player of his own team that makes even a small mistake or that is perceived as not playing hard or trying. If the OCS student's team begins to fall behind, one of several commonly seen responses may occur. Almost certainly this student would start to complain, gripe, and whine about things such as the teams not being fair, calls not going their way, getting fouled, and the other team's players not playing fairly. The OCS student, as things become more intense, may start criticizing the weaker players on his own team and scream and yell over incidents that don't really matter. This driven student, if the opportunity presents itself, may actively and aggressively cheat even if the student would normally never stoop to such actions. Fights may break out. On board games, the fighting typically consists of yelling accusatorily, screaming, and perhaps, the throwing of game pieces. In either of these situations, interesting things can happen if the OCS affected senses he will, or simply perceives that, he might lose. As a result he may leave the game under many possible guises like, suddenly becoming injured badly enough to be unable to continue. Of course, this one doesn't usually work for the board games.

He may accuse the other players of cheating and stomp off in protest or announce (as the bell rings) loudly that his team, and especially him self, had not been trying or that they were just "playing around." Statements like this are usually followed by comments further meant to essentially "save face" such as, "If we had been trying, your team would have been vaporized," and "As it was, we felt sorry for you and let you win."

The OCS student also often strains under the anxiety associated with constantly feeling pressure and the obsessive need to "prove" him self Moment by Moment, as well as over and over again. As a result prior accomplishments and successes mean nothing in the heat of the Moment. This can be why a young child who just received 3 hours of parental attention can seem like a bottomless pit. What has already happened simply does not mollify or appease the normal childhood needs for attention, because it is not attention that the child is really seeking. It is a biochemically driven obsession or compulsion that merely mimics, or appears exactly like crying out for attention. All the parental attention in the world will not change the intensity of a biochemically driven urge. On those occasions where it appears to do so it is not the parental providing of attention that lowers the symptom intensity, even if the parent thinks it is. It is the fact that the parent has, however consciously or unconsciously, enabled the child in some way to satisfy his obsessive and/or compulsively driven desires.

The hypersensitive nature of the OCS student sets them up for getting locked into (not being able to let go of) and experiencing many fears. Included in this area are a group of reactions that resemble fear responses and are therefore frequently categorized as such but, experience over time has suggested to me that, these are more a function of the extreme sensitivity commonly experienced by those with OCS.

The sensitivity also tends to extend to all of the five senses common to human beings. An extreme startle response is not unusual. Such a response can be triggered by an unexpected touch, sharp or loud sound; or noxiously experienced smell (whether intense or not it may be experienced as such). Over reactions can also occur from an unpleasant, bitter, sour, sickly sweet, or surprising taste; and/or a visual element, which typically consists of some-thing moving quickly in front of the eyes.

The over response to a touch is most often a quick, sometimes frantic, jerking away or a tightening of the body's muscles in a rigid, or stiff, display that can leave the one who touches thinking, sometimes, quite suspicious thoughts. These thoughts typically center on concerns of possible physical abuse. Such reactions re-ally can be indistinguishable from abuse in-and-of themselves. If OCS, however, is the underlying driving force a clinical interview along with certain specific screening instruments will reveal the presence of many other signs and characteristics of OCS that are not typical to patterns of abuse. A case of abuse alone would not necessarily have evidence of significant OCS signs and symptoms. This is not to suggest that an OCS student could not have been abused. It is shared to offer a possible clear alternative option (that does occur in real life) other than that of immediately jumping to the conclusion of abuse, when abuse may not be a factor.

Another intense reaction relative to touch can occur in rela-tion to food and its perceived consistency in the mouth. How it feels in the mouth of certain OCS students will dictate whether or not it can be swallowed and may result in a gag reflex, followed by, in the worst-case scenario, a "losing of one's cookies" or throwing up. Some of the OCS affected, for very similar reasons, will be virtually unable to swallow even the tiniest of pills.

The over reaction to sound is similar to that of touch. There tends to be an immediate startle reaction much like those seen with infants when an unexpected, loud, or sharp noise occurs. Typically the OCS student will inadvertently "jump" and turn towards, or shy away from, the sound's source. A very important point to remember in relation to the OCS student is that the sound initiating the startle response may not even be noticed by classmates nearby. When the OCS student experiences these reac-tions in the classroom or school environment, serious ridicule and/or teasing, especially on those occasions when no one else is react-ing similarly, can be forthcoming. This is one of the many ways in which the OCS affected student can pick up the reputation for being a little strange, weird, silly and/or "out to lunch." It also can contribute heavily to the general impression, or perception that others may develop (or pick up on) that can often suggest the OCS affected student is an "easy mark," or a "target."

When over responding to taste the probable worst case response would be the immediate spitting out of whatever had been put into the mouth. The most common reaction, though, seems to involve a variety of expressive language verbalizations that, once again, are undoubtedly over responses and yet do accurately reflect the Momentary intensity experienced by the OCS affected within the personal confines of their life situation. The OCS reactor, in a case like this, may inadvertently offend others by the sheer intensity of their response. This is particularly likely when tasting food that has been prepared by another who is also present at the time.

In relation to the sense of smell, the OCS student may have extreme difficulties. Problems may be encountered concentrating and completing work if sitting near another who is wearing strong cologne or perfume (especially if the smell is less than pleasing to them). This can also happen when sitting near another student who may have less than adequate hygiene (i.e., significant body odor), and/or if the OCS student is hungry and the odor of lunch being prepared for the day is silently wafting though the air around her. This particular sense, like that of the taste, often creates seemingly silly, and yet very real, problems in association with food. If a specific food item is not perceived as having a pleasing smell, and especially if perceived as unpleasant, getting the OCS affected to eat, or even take a taste, may be nigh unto impossible. Attempting to force this issue invariably will cause a commotion that, again depending on the strength of the biochemical driving force, may not be worth the fight. This can, at times, severely affect the diet and eating habits of those with OCS, and eventually can interfere with the biophysical nutritional balance and chemistry as well. The students, in relation to smell, may also have great difficulty not reacting physically, emotionally and/or verbally to a sudden overwhelmingly noxious odor unexpectedly affronting the senses, as can occur when another student is experiencing the effects of significant flatulence, and so on.

Relative to visual hyper responsiveness are the OCS affected's reactions to others movements within a fairly close proximity to themselves. Any perceived threatening action on the part of another (such as unexpectedly quick movements, approaches, a raising of an arm, and so on) can result in an obvious flinch, startle, or heightened fearful-seeming response. Again, as discussed in regard to similar reactions previously, this can easily lead to another's perception of possible physical abuse, even though such may not be the case. Honestly, though, the question of abuse can, and does, go both ways. Thus, caution is advised in both suspecting and/or too quickly rejecting the abuse hypothesis. The OCS student may also be prone toward over responding to any graphically explicit visually presented materials whatsoever. This may be true whether in the form of drawings, photographs, and/or films. Typically these heightened reactions will mostly be comprised of emotionally laden verbal expressions such as, "*Yuck*, eeeuw! Do they have to show that?" And there will be relatively few overwrought physical reactions. Responses, however, such as feeling ill, faint, and even actual on the spot regurgitation's have occurred in reaction to hyper-perceived visual images.

All the of the above related sensorial responses that the OCS affected are predisposed to experience come together in one specific activity that warrants some attention and a few words of caution. Movies, videos, and television all have, experience suggests a much more powerful potential impact and/or degree of influence on the OCS child/adolescent/adult than they do on their same-aged non-affected counterparts. Movies, and the like, have a limited amount of time in which to present their stories, and they tend to do so by manipulating time and varying both visual and auditory intensities in a typically extremely exaggerated manner. Since the OCS affected already experience things in a highly amplified fashion, the manipulated intensities used to make a movie work can be completely overwhelming and leave them, essentially, in a state of literal shock. If intensely exciting, the OCS affected may carry elements of that excitement with them for days and even weeks. For a time it may be difficult to settle down and get to sleep at night, and the actions of movie characters may be played out in both the imagination and real life simulations again and again for days, weeks, and months at a time. There may also be a seemingly insatiable desire to see, or re-experience the movie over and over again. Actually that part undoubtedly makes the actors, producers, and etc., of the movie very happy, as well as very rich.

If the viewed movie is frightening, an entire army of new fears and anxieties may be born in the OCS affected's mind and unwillingly harbored there over time. The same unmistakable manipulation of time and intensities are prevalent in horror movies as well. However, there does appear to be an additional influential factor also manipulated by intensities. This incredibly sensitive and yet powerful feature is the imagination. Similar to the other movie type already discussed, the horror-filled film's effects may persist for a very long time after the movie has been experienced. In my clinical practice I have recorded notes on many of my OCS clients that have suggested specific movies as initial precipitators of fears and behaviors whose influence and effects have been sustained for many years, and some for an entire life time.

Remember, anything presented to, and capable of being perceived by, the five senses that is subject to the, if you will, sixth sense (the imagination) can get locked into place for an extended ride. Over the years as I have worked with OCS affected students, adults, and families, one of the apparently important and recurring elements involving many facets of this problem involves levels of intensity. We also know that, like in ADHD, OCD, and Tourettes, stressors of any kind, fatigue, and highly emotionally charged experiences, or situations, tend to significantly exacerbate (make worse) characteristics of OCS. Movies, TV shows, and even commercials are working hard through the use of several senses (if we include the imagination) to achieve just such a reaction. It may not seem too surprising that I am suggesting that these fluctuating intensities working on several of the senses at once are responsible for the lasting effects created by the locking in of ideas, thoughts, and perceived needs. In other words, the more intensely experienced a thing is, the more likely it is that it will become a long time resident, or fixture, in the OCS mind.

Adapting to the Difference:

Some OCS students will begin to openly embrace their weirdness. They have no explanation why they can't seem to get control of these tendencies to over respond and over focus. No one else seems quite so picky about food, clothes, and how things need to be done. Why does everything seem to matter so much? These things get in the way. They embarrass him. Others make fun of him. They call him names. In an effort to survive amid so much confusion, stress, and growing emotional pain, the OCS student may literally start to take pride in her own seemingly random, and yet chronic, strange and noticeably different behaviors. In this scenario, the OCS student proceeds to actively take credit for all symptoms (both direct and indirect) the Moment awareness dawns that someone else has noticed, or when confronted by another in regard to why a given odd behavior may have occurred. The typical reply goes something like this: "I wanted to do that. I like acting like that, because it's fun. I want to be different. I don't want to be just like everyone else," and so on. At some point, still working to survive, the OCS student can actually begin to behave purposefully in obviously strange and different ways that are not OCS driven. This works as an effective smokescreen whose purpose is to make it easier for others to believe the student's OCS driven symptoms and subsequent actions are deliberate and intentionally off beat, peculiar, and downright bizarre. I am aware of an adult who in the experiencing of this had developed what I thought at the time was a unique compensatory strategy. Whenever introducing him self to others, and especially to the individual's in-groups he would shake hands and/or wave as appropriate, and say "Hi! I'm Dave Crenshaw" (not his real name) after which he would pause, raise the corner of his mouth in a sly smile and add, "I'm weird." During the process of therapeutic discovery and work, we were able to determine that this rather odd introductory style was unconsciously created to protect a long standing battered self-esteem and quite a fragile ego. We came to realize that after Mr. Crenshaw had introduced him self to others in this unusual manner, if future interactive sequences gave rise to symptomatic behavioral and/or verbal oddities (as eventually they might), he would be emotionally protected. If an observer approached him (and he had related that this particular incident had actually occurred) with a confrontational demeanor and said, "Mr. Crenshaw, you're weird." his ego would be spared. His actual reported response of, "I told you so," accompanied by a smile, would literally act to neutralize the negative potential associated with such a statement, as well as lessen its power to inflict psycho-emotional pain. In simpler terms, the comment wouldn't hurt as much as it otherwise might.

The OCS tendency to present one's behavioral idiosyncrasies as intentionally chosen acts in order to demonstrate personal individuality is usually very well done. As an approach to the exposed problem, it also has an inherently very powerful, yet subtle, component that practically guarantees its success: (that is, that others will accept the evidence suggesting actual symptoms are truly self-directed and intentional). In the schools, and ultimately the classroom, this insidious influencing of the teacher's and others' acceptance can be described. It is undoubtedly a whole lot easier for a teacher to believe that the OCS student's strange and irritating actions, reactions, and verbalizations are planned and purposeful rather than the OCS biochemically driven truth. When lies are easier to believe than the truth, the truth is not welcome.

Born Liars:

Another way of saying what this title is suggesting, "born liars" might be as follows: "born actors." Both descriptions are synonymous when said in reference to individuals who, for whatever reasons, present themselves in ways meant to induce others into accepting them as someone else by their actions. Born liars are excellent actors. Similarly (at the risk of a serious over-generalization), many of the best actors were, born liars. Often the OCS student's only easily available tool that can adequately explain to a teacher, principal, or parent what each and every one of them seem to desperately want to know, which is, "why" is a lie. Again, as mentioned elsewhere in this book, the actual honest answer to this question is almost always, "I don't know." Since this response is so often considered unacceptable to teachers, and usually to most adults, many of the OCS affected learn, early on, to stop answering the question "why?" with "I don't know." They also can frequently come to accept, and even actually believe themselves, whatever most of the involved adults seem to think the reasons for their behavior must be. The major problem in relation to this is that, although much of the time a teacher's perceptions as to why certain actions, behaviors, and responses occur may be quite accurate, when the underlying behavior or actions in question are biochemically driven, they are not. Most of the perceived reasons and explanations offered by naïve observers to OCS are either completely false or are misperceptions with a semblance of accuracy that are nevertheless still incomplete as explanations. The OCS student may experience an inner sense that seems to indicate adults' expressed reasons for their actions, or lack thereof, are definitely inaccurate, but, having no reasonable explanation for such behavior him self, remain passive in regard to these false notions. Teachers and adults often interpret this lack of assertion as clear evidence in favor of their own conclusions.

There are, furthermore, numerous occasions in which to save face or to deflect almost certain ridicule from others, as well as forestall and possibly avoid punishment altogether, the OCS student will embellish, fabricate, and/or lie. Sometimes they will rationalize to themselves that it's not much of a lie since, they so often have no reasonable explanation for their actions anyway. They surmise that any reason they might suggest actually *could* be true. The explanations offered to adults in these situations tend to reflect what the OCS student thinks, or knows, the adult will believe. The OCS affected, therefore, often benefit greatly over time from their early job training experience that can be translated later in life into theatrical careers and other careers in the field of acting. Who better to try and make you believe they're someone that they're not, other than one whom is obsessed with doing so? No one is more believable in a role than an intensely hyper-focused individual with OCS.

Depression and Depressive Characteristics:

OCS affected students often have a can't-quite-put-your-finger-on-it pervasive sense of sadness about them that teachers rarely fail to notice. They'll describe it in tentative and questioning-like tones, saying things like, "well, she's not like this all of the time, but she just doesn't seem happy." The OCS student, at any given Moment throughout the course of the day, may be functioning in a state of overload. On top of that so very much of what they try to do doesn't go right by their own standards, or the way they feel that it should have. Chronically misunderstood and shunned by nearly everyone, is it any surprise that the OCS student appears unhappy, sad at times, and even depressed? They may be angry with themselves for their own behavior and perceived lack of success. They may also be angry with almost everyone else for the very same reason. There also may be areas in the realms of the intellect, physical self, social and/or emotional performance areas that remain relatively intact and continue to function adequately. These working elements, however, may be surrounded by, what I like to refer to as, "pockets of depression." This, I believe, is why so many of the OCS students have that sort of vague seeming, maybe or maybe not, noticeable sadness.

Distractibility:

This can be a primary component that complicates and interferes with the learning process of the OCS student. Ponder, with me, the following setting for a Moment.

The hyper vigilant, unbelievably sensitive, and over responsive OCS student is sitting at his desk surrounded by other students similarly seated (usually somewhere between 28 to 36 students per class). A movement is perceived out of the corner of his left eye. He furtively glances in that direction, nothing. Was there a movement? He's not sure. If there was, his mind suggests, it was probably that Bobby Fenton who sits just to his left. Bobby is always looking at him. Yeah, that must've been it. Bobby looked at him again.

The OCS student begins to focus on catching his tormentor in the act. He narrows his eyes, squeezes them down into very thin slits. Then he slyly moves his gaze from the back of Nancy's green sweater slowly and surely to the left. His eyes leave Nancy's back and move on.

There's the teacher, Mrs. Westgate, gesticulating animatedly at the front of the class. Bobby! His eyes shift a tiny bit more. Mrs. Westgate's mouth is opening and closing like the clown's mouth on hole fourteen at Horton's Miniature Golf and Games. He wonders briefly what Mrs. Westgate might be saying,

"Students, I want you to take notice . . ."

The OCS student does take notice. He notices everything. He noticed Bobby.

Goofy-golf, old man Horton should change the name of the place. Goofy-golf sounded more fun than . . . Hey, maybe Disneyland would loan Goofy to old Mr. Horton.

Bobby was still looking toward the front of the class.

Class rhymes with glass.

Another movement brought his eyes back. Bobby still wasn't looking at him. He must be looking only at times in between glances. Suddenly a flurry of movement is perceived. The OCS student's eyes dart back to where his nemesis is sitting. The movements continue.

What the heck is he doing? Is this some kind of a ruse meant to lure him into glancing away? Well, it isn't going to work! Bobby's just fiddling with that book to make everyone else think he's working and not looking this way. But he hasn't been working. He isn't going to work now. He's waiting for my eyes to wander away so he can look.

At about this point, we might expect this OCS student's teacher to intervene by calling on him to inquire why he is not following instructions and getting out his social studies' book. She may have to call his name several times before he'll respond. She may be miffed at his complete lack of awareness regarding, her painstakingly clear directions. Will the teacher repeat the instructions again? It's hard to say.

The OCS student is distracted principally by the inner workings of his own mind. Any event, or circumstance, occurring externally can precipitate a given train of thought. It is the mind, however, that takes that initial intrusive incident and carries it on "to where no *mind* has gone before."

The OCS mind seems perpetually in motion. Other than the times it is obsessively locked onto an idea, or thought, it tends to roam the entire universe and beyond. If a student's most commonly heard response to an unexpected direct question happens to be, "huh?", then, perhaps, OCS is the reason why. The preceding comment is meant to be illustrative only and is not, therefore, considered to be an actual diagnostic characteristic. Hopefully, though, a valuable point has been made.

A constant battle is being fought within the context of the OCS mind in regard to the purposeful direction of thought. The intensity with which specific words are associated with emotional experiences can make the act of reading an incredibly difficult and painstakingly slow process. The Moment a word with powerful emotional connections is read, the OCS mind may thoroughly embrace those connections and follow them into oblivion while the eyes alone read on. This OCS related dynamic wreaks havoc on the comprehension aspect of what is read. A sentence, paragraph, or page may need several readings before the gist of what is being said is adequately understood. As a result of the extreme effort OCS students with this symptom must put forth in order to comprehend what they are reading, they frequently dislike and actively avoid books and reading whenever they possibly can.

There is an OCS pattern, however, that in some ways is an almost paradoxical exception to that which was described above. This exception occurs when a given OCS symptom package includes a biochemically driven urge (Obsessive Compulsive need) to devour the written word, or more simply put, to read. Interestingly, when this symptom is present, there may be a very specific genre of books that are obsessively sought and compulsively read. For example, I have had clients that will only voraciously read science fiction, or romance novels, or westerns, or how-to books, or nonfiction biographies, and so on. When reading books in a specific category that is OCS driven, there are typically no comprehension problems whatsoever. The Moment, however, the OCS driven (only science fiction) student is forced to read something by way of a school related assignment, or, given a book that is not SCI-FI the aforementioned comprehension problem often reveals it's ugly interfering face. This same student who devours science fiction books at the rate of one to, sometimes, two in a single day, may take weeks to plod through "The Westing Game," a late-child, early-teen directed mystery novel. The OCS student may, also, not be able to get through the book at all.

The apparent stubborn nature of the OCS student in relation to the types of books that will, or will not be read, is exemplified by an incident that happened to one high school OCS student, as the result of an English assignment. This particular student was obsessed and read compulsively only science fiction novels and stories. His English teacher, apparently in an effort to widen the depth and breadth of what he read, assigned a book report with the specific guidelines that it must be fiction of any other genre than fantasy and/or science fiction. This young man was livid. He ranted and raved to anyone who would listen about this horrible teacher who was trying to dictate to him what he could or could not read. How dare she! He wasn't about to read anything he didn't want to. No one could force him to read something if he didn't want to read it, they never had, and never would.

Of course, this OCS teenager was over responding just a bit, but the intensities of his OCS and the surrounding dynamics kept him from seeing his behavior as over reactive at the time. He carried on for about a week, verbally blasting this teacher everywhere he went before settling down to wallowing in mostly his own thoughts. Things like, "she can't make me. No one can and no one will." The teacher had a lever though, which was his grade. For this young man, it was a nasty dilemma. It had developed into a matter of principle. If he gave in he felt he'd never be able to look into a mirror at his own face again. He would be a traitor to him self.

The teacher had no clue what this student was going through. To her, he was just a stubborn and obstinate teenager whom she felt needed to expand his horizons and grow up. She had already put up with him far too long. This teacher, it seemed, had taken it upon herself to enlarge her student's very narrow field of vision and develop additional interests, which would thereby enhance his existence. She was not going to budge.

The OCS teen was able to sense that his teacher had put her feet down in a hole and filled the hole immediately with quick drying cement. He was determined as well that he would not act, as he saw it, in a way that would be untrue to him self. He was not going to budge either.

It is situations like this one currently unfolding before you (the reader) that allow the OCS affected to reach beyond commonly held boundaries and take a stab at doing something very different. If this particular OCS teen had not actually been quite fond of his English teacher, they both would have ended up the losers. As it was, because of this affection, the young man was really in a predicament. You see, he also had an obsessive need not to let anyone down that meant something to him. It was Catch 22. If he let her down, he would be devastated. If he let him self down, his "whole life would be like a useless piece of garbage" (his very words). What could he do? He focused on this predicament with the kind of Herculean intensity that it seems perhaps only the OCS affected posses. It finally came to him. He knew exactly what he had to do to satisfy both of these obsessive needs. It was a lucky thing for the teacher that this young man cared about her, because she also cared about him, and he couldn't have cared less about a grade. What he finally did do was done in order not to disappoint her. There was no other motivator. Necessity *is*, after all, the Mother of invention.

This OCS teen did the only thing he could think of. He knew that students in the past had done reports based only on the vague descriptions of a book provided on the inside cover flaps. At least sometimes, though, he was aware that these students had gotten nailed. He knew that if he did that and got caught, it would let this teacher down just as much as not the report at all. He wasn't stupid. So, he thought up his own title, created what he thought was a decent sounding author's name, and then literally wrote a very credible book report summarizing a purportedly non-fiction novel that, in all reality, did not exist. He had reasoned in his mind that, if she tried to check up on him and confronted him with the fact that there was no such book in the school library, he would casually inform her that he'd gotten this particular book at the main library in downtown Phoenix. He didn't think she'd go all the way into Phoenix just to check up on one book. It was a good thing, for him, she did not check up on him. He was not aware, at the time, of the reference volumes carrying the title, "Books in Print."

The teacher had been thrilled, believing she had broadened this student's world even if only a tiny bit. He was similarly quite ecstatic because he had remained true to him self (or his OCS). He hadn't read something he did not want to read, nor, had he let his teacher down. She gave him an A. He couldn't have cared less. On the very same day she handed it back to him, he threw it away. Naturally he didn't toss it out right there where she might see. As he left the class that day, he dropped it into the first circular file he came across. The real reward had been received the Moment he'd handed her that book report.

Black or White; All or Nothing Responding:

This apparent anomaly materializes often enough in every aspect of OCS that it warrants a brief analysis of its own. An over response or no response at all is very common. When symptoms are active, that's pretty much what you get. Hyper responsivity can essentially lean in one or two directions. In one, reactions can appear to be invariably focussed on the negative side of things. The OCS student thus preoccupied is often difficult to be around because she seemed to be incessantly complaining about anything and everything. The most innocuous of events can be impugned with such ferocious intensity and critical litany that even the most patient, kindhearted, and caring among us can become exhausted and seriously frustrated. The OCS student manifesting this tendency typically views things as either good or bad. There is no in between. Neutral does not exist. As a concept it cannot be conceived. You either win or you lose. There is no second place. Things are either exactly right, or they're not right. If they're not right, they're wrong. Many more of the OCS affected who manifest this dichotomous focus tend to do so in a negative vein.

The other seemingly perpetual focus is an unremitting orientation towards the positive. Although experience suggests this OCS group is numerically much less well represented than its counterpart, it is quite possible that such an assumption has been based on an under representative sample seeking therapeutic assistance. Very few of the OCS affected on this side of the coin are capable of viewing what they are currently experiencing as a "problem" in any sense of the word. Although they can also irritate others at times with a, sometimes preposterous, positive outlook, they are nevertheless much more easily tolerated by others than the predominantly negatively focused group. In this group everything is viewed as good. The OCS affected who manifest this chronic positive symptom picture can find, even in the most catastrophic and horrible of situations, something they can focus and comment upon that is good. Others tend to value and praise this as virtuous, but realistically it is often beyond virtuous and way past the popularized ideal of "finding the silver lining" or the "making of lemonade when given lemons." The all or nothing factor tends to leave this group incapable of even considering a negative thought of any kind. Those I have come in contact with in this, both professionally as well as socially, appear to be what might be called "the silently depressed." The face this symptom predisposes them to show the world is just too positive. They cannot truly accept or admit to weakness in any form, let alone consider the existence of something like depression. Thus, they suffer silently, hiding reality even from themselves. Though members of this group infrequently seek out therapeutic assistance, in my opinion, they are sometimes the saddest ones of all.

OCS IN THE SCHOOLS:
WHAT TO DO ABOUT IT

Make it known. Education is, without a doubt, ultimately the most potent and essential ingredient of all the possible interventions for OCS. Knowledge opens the door to understanding. Whether or not someone walks through the door or slams it shut and runs the other way remains a variable that is yet as unpredictable as it is uncontrollable. One cannot force understanding any more than a horse can be forced to drink. It is the physically experienced crisis of thirst that motivates the horse to drink.

Without adequate knowledge and subsequent understanding, appropriate adjustments cannot be made. When a competent teacher is given knowledge about a condition such as OCS, the level of awareness and understanding works to eradicate previously held faulty beliefs. Education also frees the teacher from unintentional misperceptions that may have been primarily instrumental in bringing about disruptive classroom confrontations. With new awareness will come, also, at least some elements of predictability. When teachers can at least anticipate some reactions accurately, this information can then be used to better manage the incidents as they occur. Knowledge applied by the teacher can also reduce even further both the intensity and frequency of a student's inappropriate behaviors, actions, and reactions.

Remember at all times: **OCS is an explanation, not an excuse.** Do not let sympathy, in the guise of empathy, interfere with appropriate disciplinary measures. Flexibility, though, when teaching the OCS population, is required in order to establish a true working/learning relationship. Rigidity, or inflexible routines, in teaching the OCS is like a set-up for confrontation and war. Think about the example of the young man in high school. His teacher was actually quite flexible, which is why he did so well in her class and had developed an emotional tie with her. When, however, she put her foot down, so to speak, a battle raged. If that young man had been a little less intellectually endowed and not as creative, or had a specific learning disability in written expression, or simply had no emotional tie of any consequence to his teacher, the outcome of that particular situation would have undoubtedly been quite different. Teachers, especially in a war with an OCS affected student, are fighting in a "no-win" situation. The teacher with the OCS teen and the book report issue lost the war, she just didn't know it. Does this mean I am suggesting that teachers should never assign an OCS student a task that they seem biochemically influenced to resist? Of course not! It just means that in those circumstances where the teacher feels the need for strict and unyielding authoritative measures on a given assignment, that said teacher had better be prepared (i.e., understand and predict) for war. By being prepared, the teacher typically can be more effective in not getting too emotionally involved in the struggle. The student may verbally rail against the assignment in front of the class. If so, surely there are established class, or school, discipline procedures for such occasions. The teacher needs to calmly follow through with them.

Finally, when aware of OCS and the most common symptomatic responses it takes, teachers should be much more able to withstand the student's over reactions. They should also be less likely to misinterpret the student's verbalizations and subsequent behaviors, as personal affronts to their authority as a teacher, *Above all, do not let this transpire.* Keep foremost in your mind that you are dealing with a student who, at times, is unavoidably going to be acting in concert with an, honest-to-goodness biochemically induced problem. The OCS student in such a situation is not vying for attention, in spite of how it may seem. This student is not being manipulative because of an inherent laziness. He may manipulate, but when OCS is the precipitating factor, the manipulation is not to get what he wants as much as it is to avoid doing what the inner workings of this problem have convinced his mind he simply must not do. To the OCS student, this experience is akin to a life-and-death situation, his own. The tremendous anxiety the OCS student experiences is exaggerated to the extreme, but not by choice. These exaggerated feelings are not created on purpose or with some insidious goal in mind. Teachers need to know this. Therefore, follow through with discipline calmly and with as little emotional attachment as possible.

Some OCS students, and eventually even those that carry on or make a scene, will simply shutdown. Don't take it personally. Understand. Fail them when they do this in relation to a specific assignment. Teachers should not allow their emotional reactions, whether observable or not, to influence the OCS student's grades on other assignments for which no symptomatic struggles ensued. Emotions of the Moment must not be allowed to cloud the judgement of a teacher about the performance of the OCS student as a whole. During obstinate shutdown periods, as long as the student is not disrupting the performance of others, let her be. Sometimes the strength of a particular OCS driven decision will fade, especially if there is no initial confrontation. Teachers who have been successful in following the above-related suggestions have reported that in some instances, they have observed students spontaneously begin an assignment on which they had originally experienced shutdown and sometimes not. Fail them on the assignment should this occur. An OCS driven war is neither worth the effort nor the potential casualties. It's usually a no-win situation.

Unfortunately a given situation with an OCS student is not often quite so simple as that described above. That's why flexibility is such an important concept to have a good handle on. If she balks on a particular aspect of an assignment, consider the following: Is remaining firm necessary? If it is, remain firm, and be prepared. Think. A true OCS affected student is not trying to usurp your authority as a teacher. Ponder. There are many possible ways to travel to a neighborhood grocery store. Most might agree that a few of these paths are probably "better" than others may be. This is often true for school assignments as well. You, as a teacher, may have assigned the path that you know, by way of experience, is the best one to take. What if, though, the agreed upon "best" path to the neighborhood store happens to go over curbs inaccessible to wheel chair riders, and includes a stretch with no sidewalk where the street's shoulder is made up of tiny rocks two inches thick followed by an irrigation ditch? Isn't it possible that the better route for the disabled wheel chair-bound individual may be quite different than what is considered the 'best' route for most others? It may take longer, but be significantly less dangerous. If the goal is to arrive safely, then it doesn't really matter what route is taken to achieve that goal.

OCS is a condition that is managed, not cured. As a result of the natural fluctuations of symptoms and intensities throughout the course of a day, a week, or a year, there will commonly be periods, sometimes even extended periods, during which no observable interference is apparent. Teachers must work to keep from interpreting these remission or asymptomatic periods as evidence that the student is in complete control and, therefore, the symptomatic periods must be backed by a purpose and intentional.

When, as a teacher, you begin to get a sense that a specific student's reactions and behaviors have that certain "OCS flavor," the philosophies already discussed herein may help much like a Band-Aid can help a cut or sore to heal. The actual healing process itself has nothing at all to do with the Band-Aid, and yet the Band-Aid remains a useful aid to the process. Discussing the student and situation with an OCS aware school counselor and/or psychologist, who may then interview the student and parents to gather further information, is an appropriate action.

Depending on the frequency and intensity levels of the student's symptoms, the counselor or School Psychologist should offer to share gathered data that is demonstrative of OCS with the family physician and/or pediatrician. Sometimes it is necessary to educate the physician, just a bit, in regard to OCS (See sample generic letter in appendix.) This is okay. It's why the letter was written in the first place. There are times these physicians may not feel comfortable prescribing certain medications such as Anafranil or one of the Specific (Selective) Serotonin Reuptake Inhibitors (SSRI) unless they understand specifically what the target symptoms are, along with a general description of the anticipated responses to such a treatment.

The School Psychologist/counselor can assist physicians by interviewing teachers and parents after the initiation of a psychopharmacological agent (medication) to determine perceptions of the child's responsiveness. At times the School Psychologist/counselor can readminister behavior inventories such as the Burks' to parents and teachers. They can also interview the child/adolescent involved in order to get firsthand personal perceptions of responsiveness. It has been my experience that the most appropriate way in which to complete follow up interviews is to start with the general and then move towards the specific.

There are essentially two main reasons for starting a personal interview with the general. One is to determine how much, when left to their own devices, of a change (if any) they perceive without specific cueing. It is not unusual in the initial follow up, about one week or so after medication has been started, for the OCS student to report no difference, or only slight improvements. Typical slight improvements reported personally may include feeling calmer; not getting into as many fights with siblings, parents, teachers, or other students. Typical initial improvements reported by teachers and parents tend to be similar and may include: easier to get along with; less intense about everything; when upset it doesn't last as long; doesn't seem as irritating as before; and, perhaps, a bit more on task than previously.

The second main reason for commencing the personal interview with general questioning has to do with personal insight and education in relation to the problem of OCS. There are specific symptoms that, once treated medically, tend to improve which thereafter result in the general types of progress noted in the previous paragraph. Experience has suggested that the OCS student's common inability to cite specific symptoms that have gotten better as a result of medication is quite understandable. When a symptom has improved, it is not on the student's mind nearly as often as it may have been prior to a medicational trial. A positive response to medication results in fewer episodes of persistent thoughts and therefore fewer compulsively experienced actions and/or urges. This very fact makes it unlikely that a given specific symptom, even though it has improved, will be identified by the student as such simply because it is no longer significantly interfering in their daily functioning. The thought to consider it, therefore, as a symptom that has improved does not even cross the OCS student's mind. When, however, the Leyton inventory is readministered, the student is brought face-to-face with each positively identified symptom from the pre-medicational administration. If parents and/or teachers (regardless of the student's general impressions of little or no response) have identified a positive response, it is important to re-administer the Leyton. It is not unusual for the OCS student, upon a re-administration of the Leyton, to realize that as many as ¼ to ¾ of the specific items originally identified (45 symptom questions) have become less frequent, less intense, better, and/or are no longer present. Their response is usually good enough that they can definitely state that many symptoms are "better" than they had been prior to the onset of medication. The term "better" typically refers to one or more of the following descriptors, depending upon the item in question:

1. The symptom is less intense when it does occur.
2. Problems are less frequent than they had been previously.
3. The symptom's presence does not persist as long as it once did.
4. Once the symptom does occur it is easier to calm down than it was and another person may be able to intervene as a calming influence rather than such an intervention, making things worse and/or more intense.

Typical comments made by OCS students when reminded of the specific Leyton symptoms can include the following: "Oh yeah . . . You know I haven't done that in a while," "Now that I think about it . . . you're right! That's not the same anymore," "I haven't even thought of that one . . ." and so on. It is also not unusual for the OCS student to remain fairly cautious and respond with something like, "Well, yeah, that's a little better, maybe," which seems related to the tremendous self-doubt and persistent tendency to be unsure of most, if not all, opinion and decision oriented questions. They will also typically report a group of symptoms as relatively the "same." These tend to be the stronger of the original presenting symptoms. The strength of these tends to be related to the habits, reinforcers, and social acceptability often associated with, and therefore acting as a support for, a given symptom in addition to the actual biochemically driven aspect of its originating source. As a result, such symptoms do not simply fade away (as many others do) as Serotonin levels increase in the brain. The strategies for working with, managing, and attempting to further ameliorate these stronger, or more persistent symptoms will be discussed in more detail later.

The educational importance and benefit derived from a follow up administration of the Leyton comes from the insight and awareness gained by the OCS student. Later on the parents and even teachers can benefit from information in regard to the specific symptoms that are improving as a direct result of medical intervention (i.e., a medication). This information tends to make believers out of those who previously were not quite able to buy the idea of a biochemical origin. As those who are skeptical and suspicious of biochemical causation begin to see the relationships and connections between the improving symptoms, the student's observable behavior, and newly found emotional stability, (simply in response to a psychopharmacological agent), it becomes very difficult to retain a skeptical attitude. Parents, teachers, family members, and the OCS affected often begin to learn about the underlying symptoms. This often newfound awareness can then enable all involved to appropriately utilize, when warranted, the only behavior modification technique demonstrated by long standing research to be effective in the treatment of OCD (although not always effective), which is the technique known as "exposure and response prevention." Symptom awareness can enable the OCS affected and others as well to recognize a resurgence of the specific precipitating characteristics early enough to indicate the therapeutic response to a medication may have leveled off. When this has occurred, it suggests a dosage change is warranted and/or that a medication may need to be reinstated.

What if medication, for some reason or another, cannot be tolerated, is not effective, or parents are unwilling or unable to follow through with medically related interventions and/or treatments? What if everyone involved is putting forth good and honest effort in attempts to treat the problem; but the correct diagnosis is not, or does not seem to be, forthcoming? What if the problem is not quite severe enough to be easily recognizable, and yet does interfere with a student's quality of life and education? What if, as a result, the subtle, camouflaged, and misperceived nature of the OCS keeps many others from even being able to consider that an actual real problem exists?

The answer to each above-related question centers on one shared but highly variable component, intensity. Levels of intensity essentially dictate what typically is or is not effective when faced with trying to educate (or deal with in any other way) an untreated or ineffectively treated OCS student. The moderately affected untreated OCS student whose symptoms are at fairly intense levels may need special education services. When they do need such services, they tend to be identified, or considered eligible (as defined educationally) as a student with an emotional disability, or handicap. These OCS students can fall under one or several of the descriptors used to make this educational diagnosis, or determination. Often, OCS symptomotology leads to significant depression, and this is one of the categories whereby a student can be considered emotionally disabled (ED). OCS students at moderate levels also tend to have great difficulties making and/or keeping friends and often struggle similarly in getting along with teachers. As a result they may also be eligible as emotionally disabled due to a manifested inability to build and maintain satisfactory interpersonal relationships with peers and teachers. Another descriptor relating to possible eligibility under the ED category that OCS students may demonstrate is that of having inappropriate types of behavior and/or feelings under "normal" or typical circumstances. As already discussed, many of the observed OCS symptoms do not seem to make much sense when compared to other students in similar, or the same environments (hence, as pointed out before in the title of this book). One other descriptor relating to ED eligibility that could also be considered valid for the OCS student, which has not previously been comprehensively discussed, is the tendency to develop physical symptoms associated with personal or school problems. The incredible hypersensitivity of the OCS student can become overly focused on physical health and/or concerns. When this happens, the OCS student will tend to have a highly inordinate number of visits to the school nurses' office when compared to the average for most students. They may also have a significant number of absences from school.

Although this particular chapter, and the comprehensive work as a whole, is not intended as a treatise on special educational requirements and the law, there are a few more important points relating to special education services that should be known to all and, therefore, need to be considered herein. A student may clearly demonstrate evidence of one, or any combination, of the ED descriptors discussed in the previous paragraph and yet still not be eligible for special education services as defined by the law. If the designated impairment is not adversely affecting a student's educational performance in a clear and identifiable manner, then, they are not eligible for, or in need of, special education services as defined by law. The adverse effects of the impairment on educational performance must also be considered not correctable without special education. Typically these adverse effects are determined by a comprehensive psycho-educational team evaluation that enables the evaluating time to rule out other possible reasons for academic/ school related problems. There must be a discrepancy of significance between measured potential (usually indicated by some form of standardized intellectual measurement) and actual achievement (typically represented by scores on formal standardized achievement tests). A discrepancy such as the one stated above is actually essential for eligibility in some special education categories. One other required component is also necessary for eligibility and can be stated in one simple word, and that word is *failure*. Although the actual evaluating team is responsible for making the determination regarding academic failure, a ball park figure for general use would be grades, for a consistent period of time, of D's or below, along with the evidence that the student is potentially capable of significantly better performance. Yet another component to rule out involves what is called "social maladjustment." In brief, this means the measured potential/achievement discrepancy cannot be due to intentional disregard or purposeful subversion. Similarly, poor grades must not result from a determined lack of effort. If social maladjustment is identified as primarily responsible for the poor school performance, the student is not eligible for special education services.

So where does that leave the teachers who must, day in and day out, handle, work with, educate, put up with, and somehow survive the OCS student? Right back to the beginning of this section of the chapter entitled, "what to do."

I am convinced that regardless of medical treatment or any kind of treatment, the teacher or parent who understands the OCS student can have a very positive influence. Those who acknowledge his or her limitations, and genuinely work to enable the student to succeed through firm, yet compassionate reality—based structure, will be doing what's best for the student. In doing what is best for the student, teachers also do what is best for them. It is not an easy task to live with, teach, or even be a friend to the true OCS affected student/individual. Remember: just like the presence of a wheel chair typically signifies a disabled situation (usually the inability to walk) with its concomitant needed environmental modifications and etc. (i.e., wider doors and so on), OCS signifies a disability too. However, like the wheel chair bound paraplegic . . . OCS is an explanation . . . not an excuse. Teachers and all others, including those so affected, need to work hard not to let it be an excuse. Knowledge sets us free from the chains of uncertainty.

No article, or book, can substitute for actual real life experience with its myriad of genuine complexities and subtleties. It is my sincere hope that the information herein enables the reader to get a solid enough glimpse of what the OCS affected are experiencing so that knowledge and insight are achieved. Perhaps the insight and knowledge gained will be sufficient to enable better and more positive working relationships with all those who are, or may yet be diagnosed as OCS affected.

CHAPTER SIX

"You can see it in the air
As you travel down the city streets and highways
You can close your eyes but it will still be there
Nothing's easy even breathing's getting hard
And today your life is in your hands just walking down a boulevard
And though you may not need me to I'll say it over and over again
It's not easy
Nothing's easy . . ."

Excerpt from the song "Nothing's easy" by Ron D. Kingsley

Treatment:

OCS – Mild to Moderate Range

It is essential to point out right up front in this article that many of the treatment recommendations to be shared herein represent an accumulation of strategies and interventions that clinical experience, over the last 9 or 10 years, has suggested can be effective. Some of what will be discussed has been culled from available research and literature intended to offer treatment options for other disorders that may be dynamically inter-related with OCS. Sometimes such a strategy has been effective with OCS by reframing reference points and/or the specifics of certain target symptoms, or even treatment goals.

The discussion of psychopharmacological interventions undoubtedly will be experienced by some readers as perhaps naïve, simple minded, or simplistic, and maybe even inaccurate and potentially misleading (or at least misguided). Such may very well be the case, although I don't think so. It seems to me that individuals who could adopt such a position might be those with medical backgrounds, experience, and/or training. I have purposely refrained from engaging in additional research beyond that which I've already completed in the natural course of being involved in the discovery, treatment, and identification of boundaries for the condition I refer to as OCS. Thus, my frame of reference has not necessarily been one of determining what ought to be done based on what has been done, or rigidly adhering to already determined standards. My clinical degree did include classes in psychopharmacology and, since graduation, I attend seminars and read literature each year in order to remain as current as possible in the area. I am first to admit I am not a medical doctor and in my practice I must, of a necessity, defer to those who are. However, I have been fortunate over the years in my many associations with medical practitioners whom have been open minded and played the role of equal partners in the planning stages and subsequent treatment provided to and for our mutual clients. Their willingness to hear me out and conscientiously work with me towards the goal of improving, or enhancing, the psychological well being of our mutual clients has been instrumental. It has enabled to formulate and discover many of the insights into OCS that have resulted in, what I think, are useful and sound conclusions. For my lack of sophisticated and specific knowledge regarding psychoactive pharmacological agents, I do not feel the need to apologize. Perhaps, had I been thus trained, my ability to insightfully consider OCS interventions would not have been as likely to occur. I intend to present what I have learned and offer my perspective. This is not a cookbook manual to be consulted in the treatment of OCS. It is hypothetical and will hopefully provide insight and direction in the on going process of discovery and treatment of this insidiously unspoken of and unrecognized epidemic. An epidemic that is responsible for so much psychological and emotional anguish, in so very many unsuspecting individuals irrespective of age and apparently gender every day of every year of their lives.

In the early years of my practice in Psychology both in the public schools and in private practice, I am convinced I did a disservice to surely more individuals and families than I'd want to admit. This was not because of ineptness or purposeful misdirection on my part. Simply stated, it was pure ignorance. The psychological framework of my training just did not include the idea of mild-to-moderate Obsessive Compulsive symptoms that, when present, would influence nearly all of an individual's behaviors and reactions in a relatively inconsistent yet persistent (over time) manner. Nor was I made privy to the idea that this condition would also wreak havoc with, and often render impotent, many of the most powerful, well known, and widely practiced behavioral modification techniques available. But, at times, I sincerely believe it did. With no frame of reference for the interference, it was usually thought to have been the result of several possible factors such as inconsistent parental, or teacher, implementation of the model. It was also often thought to be due to a lack of sufficient environmental control or even a conscious (or unconscious) effort on the part of a parent/teacher to sabotage the designed Behavior Modification Program, and etc. Never, to the best of my knowledge, did I think a specific as yet, essentially, undiscovered biochemical insufficiency might be responsible for the undermining of such sound and solid intervention techniques. I haven't pondered this idea I'm about to share long enough or hard enough to feel secure in it's presentation, but I have played it out in my mind, just a bit. Is it possible, it has occurred to me, that B.F. Skinner's, and a host of other strict *behaviorist's* notion of "negative reinforcement" is actually none other than a bit of OCS in action? Also, the idea that "punishment" can be reinforcing may, in time, be laid to rest. Why do people continue to do things in spite of punishment? Experience has led me to believe it is because they are obsessed, and/or the repeated offensive behavior is a compulsion.

I could honestly rock my head back-and-forth over my shoulders and scratch my crown in wonder, confusion, and eventual frustration along with parents in those early years when design after design of behavior modification failed to bring about anticipated changes or significant progress. Fortunately a large percentage of the time there were some improvements, but I have to admit this may have been from the placebo effect or the result of the strength of the established therapeutic relationship. This is not to suggest behavior modification is a worthless strategy with OCS because that is not necessarily true. When the appropriate techniques are applied under the right conditions, along with an understanding of persistent specific actual severe OCD target symptoms, it can be very effective. In fact, other than psychopharmaco-logical interventions, the behavior modification technique of "exposure and response prevention" is the only other method demonstrated in research to be effective in the treatment of Obsessive—Compulsive Disorder. It is only a small step from OCD to OCS, and so reason would dictate that the same technique would also prove effective for OCS. Clinical experience has suggested several problems in the application of exposure and response prevention with the OCS affected; although with awareness of these problems, exposure and response prevention can be applied effectively to OCS as well.

Not long after ADHD was thrust into the public mind and became the popular diagnosis in the child and adolescent arena that it continues to be, even today, I began to have children and adolescents brought to my private practice with an interesting conundrum. They had previously been diagnosed with ADHD, and either the stimulants were considered ineffective or they had been effective for a time, and then, seemingly all-of-a-sudden, they were no more.

These cases actually marked the beginning of a rather long journey into my awareness of OCS. In the interest of sparing you, the reader, the sometimes-boring details of this journey, I will share what I perceive as the pivotal Moments or experiences of this trek.

Working with physicians I found that the combination of Tofranil (Imiprimine) and one of the stimulants would work synergistically for those that, for all intents and purposes, had appeared to have lost the therapeutic effect of a stimulant. Often those with whom the stimulants had not seemed effective from the start tended to show some improvement on Tofranil as well. The positive effect on both these groups, in my experience and from my perspective, seemed to be in the areas of mood, or emotionality.

Although this improvement in mood is nothing to sneer at, especially for the family members of those being treated, there remained an unidentifiable "something" that suggested to me (over time) there had to be more that was not yet understood going on in these situations.

Today I believe those individuals described above either had predominantly OCS (for which the stimulants are not effective), or had ADHD with concomitant OCS that was at a level intense enough to eventually require direct intervention to reach an overall positive outcome.

When both ADHD/and OCS are present and are of significant intensity to interfere in a persons daily functioning and only ADHD has been identified and treated, I believe a typical pattern emerges. Symptoms of both of these conditions are usually exacerbated, or made worse, by stress, fatigue and intense emotional states. Therefore, when an individual has both conditions and is treated medically for one of them with some measure of success, the stress etc . . . . that has been dynamically tied to the treated condition is relieved. As a result of this reduction in stress the untreated condition's symptoms often may improve, or be reduced, as well for a time. These symptoms, however, remain potentially as strong an interference as they ever were.

Thus, if ADHD responds to a stimulant such as Ritalin or Adderall, the co-morbid OCS may initially improve as well for a while. Eventually stressors unrelated to the successfully treated ADHD are bound to occur. When this does happen, the untreated OCS re-enters the picture and symptoms reappear and once again interfere with the individual's day-to-day functioning. Since so many symptoms of OCS and ADHD result in behavioral problems that look exactly the same, parents, teachers, counselors, and physicians who observe this conclude that the stimulant is no longer working. Parents sometimes, in frustration, simply stop giving their child the stimulant medication, believing that it wasn't helping anyway. Dosages are raised and lowered or a change from one stimulant to another may be instituted. Diagnoses may be rethought and changed. Different medications may be tried.

The time, effort, and money it takes to do this can take its toll on parents as well as the affected individual. Doubt often begins to intrude on individual and parent/guardian enthusiasm, and hope that initially may have been quite strong may diminish considerably. Old patterns tend to return and the struggle goes on.

The ADHD literature began to suggest that sometimes ADHD responded positively to the, what were at the time, newly FDA approved medications, Specific (or Selective) Serotonin Reuptake Inhibitors, otherwise referred to as SSRI. For some reason there seemed to be a group of those diagnosed with ADHD for whom an SSRI had no identifiable positive effect. There also seemed to be an identified ADHD group that, when treated with only an SSRI, demonstrated significant symptom amelioration such that a stimulant was not considered necessary. Yet another group responded optimally only when an SSRI and a stimulant were used in conjunction with each other.

My research, experience, and continuing education with a focus on Tourette's Syndrome taught me much about OCD, a common co-morbid condition of Tourette's. The fact that Anafranil, a medication affecting primarily Serotonin levels in the brain, could significantly reduce symptoms of OCD led researchers and the medical front line to try the SSRI for OCD and Tourette's patients as well. Quite often these were found effective and had significantly fewer side effects.

It seems to me only a small step to have made the connection between ADHD and its surprising response, for some people, to the SSRI and OCD and the symptoms that were so familiar and yet could not, by currently available definitions, be diagnosed as OCD. Those I now refer to as OCS.

OCD/OCS symptoms tend to vary with time, fluctuate in intensity, and appear to even have significant periods of remission. Undoubtedly, then, this may play a role in the effectiveness or ineffectiveness stimulants seem to have on ADHD.

Experience suggests to me that once a stimulant has been titrated appropriately for symptom reduction in ADHD, it does not suddenly stop working. Over time dosages may need to be adjusted due to height, weight and growth, but otherwise when a therapeutic dose is reached, it remains therapeutic.

To the untrained observer the distractibility, inattention, and many other behavioral similarities that occur also with the OCS affected can be associated only with ADHD. Their ignorance regarding OCS disallows alternative conclusions. Professionals, parents, and teachers continue to treat, view, and conclude that ADHD is the problem. Often such cases are eventually considered "treatment resistant".

Within the context of the initial article I wrote entitled "Making Sense of the Senseless," towards the end, I listed a group of symptoms that, to the untrained (and sometimes even to the trained) observer, are frequently mistaken as obvious signs of ADHD when they are not. This is because the behavioral manifestations of these particular symptoms are shared and, from observation alone, often cannot be discriminated with any level of certainty to be due either to ADHD or OCS and many times are directly or indirectly related to both conditions. Thus, whenever ADHD, OCS, or Tourette's are a client's single presenting problem, it has become a routine practice of mine to screen for the other related conditions as well, which often can have important treatment implications

TREATMENT IS A JOURNEY, NOT A DESTINATION

The combination of literature reviews and experience over the last 10 years has suggested three primary methods as being those that are the most effective, and perhaps the only strategies effective, in the long term treatment of mild-moderate OCS as I have been describing it. For the rest of this article all three will be discussed, hopefully in enough detail that the interested reader can gain a working understanding of each one. The purpose, though, is not to delineate a specific instruction manual for treatment, rather, it is an attempt to foster a higher level of awareness.

The first, and most essential component related to the effective treatment of OCS, is accurate knowledge, awareness, or education. Once the insidious and subtle behavioral manifestations begin to be understood, social and family dynamics can, and often are affected dramatically. In fact, the intent and goal of this article and others I have written is just that, to inform and educate the reader in regard to this widely prevalent, yet still largely unidentified and misconceived, biochemically driven behavioral, social, cognitive, and emotional problem.

Parental reactions, as well as teachers, siblings, and even friends, tend to change when true understanding is achieved. It is not uncommon for others to perceive the OCS affected individual's behavior as a personal, purposeful, affront directed at them. Indeed, as has been suggested in another article, the camouflage tends to be so thick around the true nature and origin of the symptoms source that even the OCS affected agree (on the surface) that the actions under scrutiny must have been purposeful. Once, however, the problematic behaviors are identified as originating, either directly, or indirectly, from the biochemically driven OCS, a new perspective usually comes forth.

A seventeen-year-old client said it in his own words:

"It's like," he shared, "I'm seeing everything from another point of view . . . like I'm seeing things for the first time from someone else's eyes."

When understanding truly sinks in, parents are often relieved and sometimes even thrilled to discover (as their gut instincts seemed to be screaming all along) that there really is something exceptional and unusual about the long standing behaviors and responses of the affected child. The parents' imaginations have not been "running wild" and they haven't been "embellishing" or exaggerating their experience, with this preternaturally difficult child. Parents begin to realize the child's responsiveness is not primarily due to them having been overly permissive and/or lacking in discipline, as others often may have hinted at, and even blatantly declared. They begin to have, some for the first time, real hope that the child's problems were not caused by "bad" or incompetent parenting (or poor skills as a husband or wife).

Relationships improve and the journey towards healing these previous typically stormy and painful emotional ties commences. This tends to be a slow process that varies greatly. For some there is an initial burst of tremendous growth and progress, followed by a slow down. For others it may be slow going all the way, and still others may experience Moments of insight and improvement that are interspersed between lags, or periods of seeming stagnation (or slower progress). Whatever the pattern of progress, however, therapeutic assistance can be beneficial in the continuing process of uncovering symptoms and dynamics of the previously undiscovered OCS related factors.

At this point in time, from what I can tell, there is no "body" of literature and/or a knowledge base specific to OCS (mild-moderate) as defined within the pages of my work. Hence, the writing thereof. There is, however, a fairly extensive literature base for what I consider the severe form of this problem identified in DSM IV under the title of Obsessive Compulsive Disorder (OCD). It is often useful for clients and parents to peruse this available literature in search of a more comprehensive understanding of the entire spectrum that includes this severe end of the problem. Generally speaking, what works in the treatment of OCD can also work for the milder version of OCS (often, at lower levels of intensity, medicational dosages, and etc.). There are several books that, although certainly not all inclusive for the disorder, this author has consistently found useful in this vein as reference tools and to gain depth of knowledge. They are as follows:

The Boy Who couldn't Stop Washing, Judith Rapaport M.D.
Brain Lock, Jeffrey M. Schwartz M.D.
Getting Control, Lee Baer Ph.D.
Obsessive Compulsive Disorders, Fred Penzel Ph.D.

The therapeutic strategy of education and gaining knowledge is an on going, and essentially, never-ending process, or as someone has stated most eloquently; "it is a journey, not a destination." It is essential, during the therapeutic process, to instill within the minds and hearts of our clients and their significant others one very important concept. The concept goes something like this: OCS (or any other diagnosis or potential interfering factor) is an EXPLANATION; NOT AN EXCUSE. Individuals must be held responsible for their actions, whether pre-planned and purposeful, bioneurochemically driven, under the influence of voluntarily ingested substances (legal or illegal), or whether simply due to an accident. Otherwise chaos would eventually reign personally, within the family unit, and within society as a whole. Working phrases such as the following reflect the importance of the above-related concept;

"Okay, you may have done that, (problem, action or behavior), because you have OCS. So, now what are we going to do about it?" If reparations are warranted, they need to be followed through on; plans and strategies should be processed to attempt to prevent similar occurrences in the future, or to at least diminish the intensity of the next response.

Another component in relation to the successful treatment of OCS involves the consideration of psychopharmacological interventions. In simpler terms, this is the use of medication. Accumulated evidence implicates insufficient levels of the brain chemical Serotonin as an underlying (apparently causative) factor in the emergence of OCD. It is only a short step to hypothesize the same component for OCS as well, thus it makes sense (when we have the capability) to try and regulate these levels medically. Experience with the OCS population has strongly suggested that the medications which inhibit the re-uptake of Serotonin can dramatically diminish mild-moderate obsessive and compulsive symptoms (OCS) as they do for OCD, but at significantly lower dosages than typically required to ameliorate the severe OCD symptomotology, or, the actual disorder. Obviously, this also makes sense. The conclusive hypothesis, then, is that the mild-moderate symptoms result from levels of Serotonin that are summarily "less deficient" or "less severe" than those occurring in relation to OCD, hence, if this is true, it follows that OCS would respond to lower medicational dosages than those required for OCD. In fact, this is what it does seem to do. Less medication is directly related to fewer side effects. Fewer side effects contribute to a greater willingness to follow and continue psychopharmacological treatment, which then relates to a greater success rate when medication is used.

As suggested in the OCD literature, the medications that seem the most potent and useful include the antidepressant Anafranil (or Clomiprimine); and the Specific (or Selective) Serotonin Reuptake Inhibitors; most often delineated by the abbreviation "SSRIs". These, include Prozac (Fluoxetine); Zoloft (Sertraline),

Paxil (Paroxetine); Luvox (Fluvoxamine), Celexa (Citalopram), and sometimes the atypical antidepressants Serzone (Nefazodone), Remeron (Mirtazapine), Effexor (Venlafaxine), and Welbutrin (Bupropion). Clinical experience, over time, has demonstrated in my practice at least one case in which each of the preceding listed medications has effectively ameliorated the symptoms of OCS, although some seem to do so more consistently than others. It is important to be aware that all seem to have the potential for positive therapeutic benefit. Thus far, research and clinical experience suggest that, for some as yet unknown reason, the most effective agent in reducing obsessive and compulsive symptoms appears to be Anafranil, followed by Prozac. Of course it is possible that they are only considered more effective because they have been around the longest and, therefore, used more frequently. As stated, however, somewhat limited clinical experience seems to lend support to this notion.

Although Anafranil seems to have the most positive effect on target symptomotology, it is also well known for its many uncomfortable and not-well-tolerated side effects when treating OCD. This is because the effective treatment of OCD usually requires much higher dosages than those typically used to treat target depressive symptoms. Such is also true for the SSRI. Prozac, for example, is most often effective with depressive target symptoms at 20 mg per day, while 40 to 80 mg are usually needed in the treatment of OCD. Medical practitioners have therefore shied away from using Anafranil in favor of the sometimes less effective SSRIs which have fewer side effects. In my experience OCS responds best to about 20-60 mg when Prozac is the medication used. This seems to make perfect sense.

Another option reported in the literature is the effectiveness of the combination of Prozac and Anafranil. There is growing evidence that this particular combination is actually more effective in the reduction and amelioration of symptoms than either agent used alone, and at significantly lower dosages than needed when prescribed alone. As a result the side effects (especially those associated with Anafranil) are also greatly diminished to the point of being sometimes considered non-problematic.

Since OCS does not approach the severity levels associated with OCD and medication is effective at lower strengths, or dosages, it stands to reason that fewer side effects would also be experienced, since side effects are typically dose related. It also stands to reason that the more effective Anafranil might be a good initial agent of choice in the treatment of OCS as side effects tend to be minimal at the lower doses used to treat the OCS.

Clinical experience with the OCS population has supported the Anafranil hypothesis. The OCS affected individuals do respond positively to doses of Anafranil from 25 mg to 100 mg per day with significantly fewer apparent negative side effects reported than for OCD which typically requires dose ranges from 200mg to 400mg to reach therapeutic levels. Experience also gives evidence that, not unlike OCD, OCS too may respond with greater symptom amelioration and reduction when treated concomitantly with low doses of both Anafranil and Prozac. Limited experience also supports an enhanced effectiveness with the combinations of Anafranil and Zoloft as well as Anafranil and Paxil. Other combinations may yet be shown similarly effective.

Interestingly, as I initially began to propose to medical practitioners the use of Anafranil with my OCS affected clients significant resistance to such an approach was common, along with numerous blatant refusals to treat with the notorious, Anafranil. When such has been the case, I have always deferred to the doctors of medicine who were usually willing to at least treat with an SSRI.

There have been, however, medical doctors who were willing to treat with Anafranil as suggested. Some of these have become believers in not only OCS but its treatment as well. I am grateful these doctors have been around.

In the process of discovering the uses of the SSRIs and Anafranil, I have pondered at length what the literature has reported about these medications. In so doing I have come face-to-face with data that did not seem to make sense. For instance, prescribing physicians were nearly always informing the OCS client, upon the initiation of a psychopharmacological intervention, not to expect results and/or improvement for at least 3 to 6 weeks or more. When treating OCS, however, the reality has been that, when the agent was appropriate and well tolerated, noticeable and fairly predictable positive responses occurred the very next day, or within just a few days.

It appears to me that the tendency to expect a 3-6 week delay before improvement occurs is directly related to the treatment of depression which typically does not show demonstrable change for about that period of time. As I pondered this information (why no delay occurs when targeting OCS and yet a documented delay does occur when depressive symptoms are the target), I believe I experienced an epiphany. This could also be considered a type of paradigm shift, in regard to the depressions that respond with positive therapeutic benefit to Anafranil and the SSRI.

The research literature on OCD demonstrates equilaterally a relationship between OCD and the often co-morbid condition of depression. Clinical experience suggests a similar relationship between mild-moderate OCS, and depressive episodes, as well as serious depression. I believe when OCS or OCD are identified, along with co-morbid depression, the OCS/OCD symptoms nearly always predate the depressions. In fact it appears to me that the depressions that respond positively to this (SSRI) group of medications are secondary to, or caused by, untreated and often unrecognized OCS and/or OCD. If this is true, as it appears to be in my clinical experience, it suddenly makes sense that the depressive symptoms may take a longer time period for a positive response.

Allow me to diverge for a Moment in an attempt to explain: (also, see the article entitled, "OCS-An alternative Hypothesis"). What I am suggesting is that the OCS symptomotology, over time, tends to result in depressive episodes and serious depression too. Since mild-moderate OCS is so often camouflaged to the extent that it is difficult to see, let alone diagnose, it makes sense that the initial hint of problems needing serious intervention could be secondary to the OCS itself. As stated elsewhere, these secondary problems are not limited to depression (although depression seems to be associated more often, perhaps, than any other), but also include anxiety, panic reactions and states, explosive outbursts, chronic anger, chronic negativism, and etc.

There appear to be many pathways into depression from OCS.

These include, but almost certainly are not limited to the following:

1.) The tendency to need things to be 'just so' or 'just right' in relation to one's personal perceptions quite often leads, eventually, to situations in which many of these "needs" begin to be consistently unmet. Whenever an OCS driven "need" is thwarted, the affected individual typically experiences tremendous emotional upheaval and serious cognitive dissonance. Commonly, thoughts essentially conclude with something like: "either I do it the right way (and I am therefore a "good person", "competent", "worthy to live", and so on) or, it isn't right (and I am "worthless", "stupid", "incompetent", "a jerk", "ought to be shot", or "should just kill myself)". These tend to be "thoughts for the moment" occurring at the moment of frustration and typically do not reflect true, deep, and well thought out feelings. Even so, several such experiences every day, in time, can wear down even the strongest psyche. And, let's face it failing several times a day (even if only in the affected individual's perceptions) can be depressing. Self-esteem withers, previously practiced tasks and activities are avoided, new activities and challenges fail to motivate and are rarely even attempted due to the expectation of certain failure should they be tried; in short, depression sets in.

2.) Another pathway involves the common OCS tendency to be prone to extreme and excessive hypersensitivity to virtually anything and, at times, everything. Usually each over reaction (whether via action or reaction) is accompanied by serious and heartfelt guilt experienced (also in the extreme), sometimes immediately, but often at some time thereafter when emotions have settled down and the individual is in a calmer state. Constant and chronic anger at the self for these unjustified uncontrollable actions is not uncommon, nor is the proclivity of directing this anger at others. Again, over sensitivity can wear on the individual's emotional well being and cognitive equilibrium. These affected individuals "get down on themselves" as do significant others as well. To avoid "over reacting" and hurting others and/or the self, the individual may withdraw from interacting with people. Their constant reproachful thought processes can lead to a conclusion of their own worthlessness and so on. Thus, down the path they go.

Still other paths can primarily involve the dynamics surrounding and accompanying the common OCS symptom relating to the inability to focus, or the symptom of the perceived need to do everything and help everyone (which can eventually lead to a constant sense of being overwhelmed), and many possible others.

No matter which path is taken (usually several are involved anyway), there are accompanying dynamics and thoughts, as well as behavioral patterns that are learned and manifested that are not direct OCS symptoms. Rather, these develop adjacent to, and in response to, the primary symptom and are, therefore, not directly biochemically driven. Hence, when an effective psychopharmacological agent is introduced the more indirect patterns, thought processes, and/or actions are not initially affected. The primary symptom may significantly diminish in strength very quickly and, eventually, the other symptoms will also diminish in strength. They may also fall away altogether because the symptom they originated in response to, is no longer a present driving force, but this process is not strictly biochemical and so, takes a longer time period to therapeutically respond.

This mechanism of action, I am suggesting (or something quite similar) appears to be responsible for the research documented 3 to 6 week (or so) delay when "depression" therapeutically responds to those agents being discussed herein. If true, it stands to reason that, clinicians should be able to predict which "depressions" are likely to respond positively to these medications. If a screening for OCS via an instrument like the Leyton Obsessional Inventory reveals a preponderance of positive indicators, although depression is the only perceived initial referring problem, it may signify the depressive symptomotology is secondary to a Serotonin deficiency and OCS. This hypothesis may explain why so many of those who are "responders" to Prozac report feeling better after just the first dose. The "feeling better" corresponds with the symptom improvement I have documented in clinical practice that immediately follows the OCS responders to Anafranil and the SSRI. Although such an hypothesis as I have presented here has yet to be demonstrated and supported by sufficient and appropriate research, based on years of clinical experience and a culling and gathering of apparent related patterns, reasons, and (sometimes) a lack thereof, it simply makes sense.

As a part of the diagnostic process, a slightly modified version of the Leyton Obsessional Inventory for Children, the instrument I prefer over others available, for several reasons (see Assessment chapter) is administered and later used to track responsiveness to medication and progress in general. Since I code the Leyton with a plus (+) when the individual reports a symptom's presence, and a minus (-) when reportedly not present, the re-administration of the Leyton and monitoring of progress involves specific qualitative questioning. The individual in treatment is asked, usually in regard to only those symptoms previously responded to positively, if the specific symptom seems better (B), the same (S), gone (0), and/or worse (W). Sometimes individuals will respond even more specifically with variations of the above such as, "it's a lot better" or "just a little better" and so on. When this happens I code it in whatever way I feel will help me to remember each such response. Through the use of this instrument, progress reports are made to prescribing medical practitioners and recommendations are generated regarding the effectiveness of current psychopharmacological dosage levels and the advisability of raising and/or lowering a given dose. In clinical practice, this has proven to be a useful barometer of a medication's effectiveness, as well as an important tool in the pursuit of the OCS "knowledge" or "education" base. Through the re-administration of the Leyton, affected individuals learn which symptoms are truly biochemically generated. As symptoms respond (diminish in intensity) and behavior/thoughts change, sometimes quite dramatically, the individual begins to recognize how comprehensively their lives have been influenced by this insidious chemical insufficiency.

The goal of psychopharmacological intervention is multifaceted and includes symptom reduction, amelioration, and cessation (whether directly and/or secondarily related to the chemical deficiency). Also a part of this is education, knowledge, or understanding in relation to the true biochemical nature of this problem. Changes in negative family, social, school, and/or job related dynamics tend to greatly improve, given a sufficient period of time (due to the typically secondary and tertiary nature of the problems occurring in these areas). The recognition and/or identification of specific directly biochemically driven symptoms which, once recorded or documented, can later be referenced therapeutically as medication levels are reduced and withdrawn completely. This enables the determination of the individual's ability to now manage direct symptoms and refrain from re-establishing previously ineffectual secondary and tertiary patterns of thought and behavior. It also better enables the affected individual to utilize various cognitive/behavioral management techniques often needed when psychopharmacological interventions are no longer in use, cannot be used, or are not quite as effective as hoped for. There do not appear to be strict guidelines available that indicate the appropriate length of time psychopharmacological interventions should be applied. Given experience and related literature, six to 18 months seems a reasonable ballpark figure to apply. The important thing to remember, however, is that the treatment goal of medical intervention as stated above, and utilize the time frame required for a given individual to meet, in-as-much-as-is-possible, the goal. Depending on the severity of the underlying biochemical deficiency successful withdrawal of a given medication and concomitant successful management of returning symptomotology may take more, or less, time and be managed with varying levels of efficiency and efficacy.

Clinical experience has suggested to me fairly typical response patterns to psychopharmacological interventions that, at this time, research has yet to be completed before these ideas and practices can be, with some degree of certainty, recommended for use. With this in mind, current perceptions I have developed in regard to experiences in the treatment of OCS via the medicational route will be introduced. Perhaps these ideas will enable some to open their minds to further thoughts and possibilities not yet even considered, or may provide valuable hints into OCS the writer has yet to consider, and/or some may be considered, or found to be, inaccurate. Nevertheless, the sharing of these possibilities, therefore, in my opinion is warranted.

Anafranil is well known for it's common and powerful side effect of sedation.

Although the sedative effect typically wanes significantly in a week or two, for most people it is, nevertheless, the reason initial doses are recommended at night, about 30 to 45 minutes prior to the desired bedtime. For the individual with OCS, this side effect is often a real boon. This is because most of those affected by OCS have significant, to the extent that it is bothersome, difficulties getting to sleep at night. Hypersensitive as they tend to be to everything, the most insignificant seeming noises, smells (i.e., someone cooking popcorn), and changes in lighting or temperature can keep them awake as can repetitive thoughts engendered by fear, excitement, anger, or perceived emotions of any kind. They are also inclined to have difficulty simply shutting down the conglomeration of thoughts and ideas churning constantly in their minds, especially when forced into sedentary modes such as lying in a bed silently awaiting the sandman that, it seems, will never come. The initiation of Anafranil, even at its lowest available dose, frequently enables the OCS affected to get to sleep more quickly and easily than ever before. This works to the advantage of all, but an added benefit generally encountered in the treatment of young people is the direct emotional, psychological, and sometimes physical effects the young person's sudden facility in going to sleep has on the parents. This is often the first of many positive dynamic family transformations yet to come. The frustration and ultimate familial contention experienced by parents who must nightly face a battle, especially with younger children, trying to get the child to adhere to a given bedtime wreaks havoc on the bonding process and parent/child relationships. With this no longer an issue, the emotional atmosphere of the home becomes a lot less intense and its members much less on edge, making room for more positive and healthier interactions.

Another interesting and apparent side effect, associated with the use of Anafranil involves the affected individual's early morning behavior. It is not unusual for parents to describe their children with OCS as extremely moody, difficult, and exceptional pains to have to deal with in the mornings. These children often seem to passionately resist waking up, earnestly struggle against getting dressed and ready for school, have to be cajoled and/or threatened every inch of the way. All the while they grimace and groan, are sullen and angry, and generally contribute heavily in the making of each and every school day morning a miserable experience for parents and siblings alike who are forced to witness and play a part in this daily emotionally taxing display. The emotional wounds inflicted during these too frequent morning onslaughts can sometimes negatively impact a person's entire day and certainly do nothing to foster positive interactions and feelings within the family unit. When such a morning problem exists and Anafranil is begun, the typical Armageddon experience of the mornings is usually dramatically altered the very next day.

The range of positive responses varies with the individual but usually involves significantly less difficulty waking and getting up; little, if any, resistance to getting dressed and/or ready; virtually no grumbling or groaning; no sullen behavior or displays of anger; no real coaxing; and certainly no threats.

Gathered evidence from clinical experience strongly suggests, in particular with children and adolescents, that when the OCS affected do not receive an adequate amount of sleep, whatever that may be (as it varies tremendously from person to person) they tend to become difficult, moody, and quite emotionally labile (or hypersensitive). This is especially likely toward the afternoon and evening of the next day when the accumulation of these experiences impinge upon them, making them even more fatigued. Of course stress, fatigue, and extreme emotional states exacerbate obsessive and compulsive symptoms, as well as making this individual very difficult to live with on the day after not getting enough sleep. Given that the above related information is true, it seems sensible to postulate that the administration of Anafranil may enable the individual to sleep longer, and perhaps better, which then results in significantly less early morning fatigue and thereby less irritability and so on. The relief parents and family members experience, related to such a morning change, is often tremendous and tends to have a positive impact on commonly ailing family relationships that center around the affected individual.

Clinical experience suggests Anafranil is sufficiently effective in the treatment of' mild-moderate OCS (for children and adults) at levels ranging from 25mg to about *150*mg per day. This is why, even when participating in the treatment of adults, I typically suggest to the prescribing medical doctor, an initial starting dose when using Anafranil of 25mg, which I then help monitor weekly for therapeutic response and any evidence indicating a higher dose may be warranted. Similarly the SSRI often are quite effective at lower doses than might typically be expected.

It has not been unusual for those with OCS to respond quite favorably to the initial dose of Anafranil or one of the SSRI, and then experience what appears to be a loss of therapeutic effect after a few days or a week or two, and sometimes even longer. Exactly what is happening when this occurs is not currently known, although the most prevalent hypothesis seems to be the idea that tolerance sets in, requiring a higher dose to achieve the same initial therapeutic effect. In clinical practice, this has not seemed to be the case (that is, the idea of tolerance). What appears to be going on, although research remains needed to formalize support for this hypothesis is that the initial dose acts somewhat like a surprise, or a shock to the system. That is to say, it, as a newly introduced chemical, creates sort of an over response (not unlike many of the transient side effects that occur at times with all medications) that does not last as the body adjusts to this intrusive situation. In such a case it seems a true therapeutic dose has not yet been achieved and so the positive effects "level off". Re-administrations of the Leyton Inventory suggest that this "leveling-*off*" does not consist of a complete return of previous symptoms, or symptom intensities, but rather there is evidence of continued positive response that is not yet sufficient. Although prior symptom re-emergence is once again problematic, the strength of many of the symptoms seems somewhat less intense and the length of time emotional outbursts and losses of control last appear shorter in duration and less intense as well. This suggests optimal therapeutic levels have yet to be reached and the medication is still working, but levels are insufficient for the individual's needs. A raise to the next dose often results in improvements once again that, in time, may similarly level off. As doses get higher, there seems to be a less "dramatic" improvement with each adjustment upwards, and the leveling off seems to reintroduce fewer problematic symptoms as well.

The various unwelcome side effects of the OCS responding psychopharmacological agents tend to be dose related. As a result when reaching upwards to determine the individual's optimum therapeutic dose, a side effect may appear that contraindicates, remaining at the new dosage level wherein the side effect appeared, or raising the dose any higher. Typically the suggestion is made to return to the dose just prior to the arrival of the unwanted side effects. Thereafter an assessment is completed to determine whether or not the progress (or positive effects) achieved thus far are sufficient to be adequately managed at that truncated level, or if a trial on the combination, or one of the other OCS responding agents, seems warranted. If a change appears necessarily, it often seems due to the individual's inability to tolerate the particular dose needed to reach his or her manageable or therapeutic level sans significant side effect interference. Although there seem to be no guarantees that another agent in this group won't do the same thing; there is also no guarantee that it will. This is also another reason to consider one of the combinations discussed earlier, which, as suggested, can be more effective anyway, at dose levels that are lower and less likely to result in intolerable side effects.

Yet another very interesting observation which may be true for only special groups and/or in certain isolated cases involves what appears to be a type of an accumulative effect over time. In other words, once a therapeutic level has been reached and treatment continues over an extended time period (it seems anywhere from six months to a year-and-a-half) some individuals appear to develop what might be best described as an extreme "laissez faire" attitude towards things. Whereas prior to treatment they were hypersensitive to, and cared way too much about everything no matter how insignificant it may have seemed to others, when this apparent accumulative effect occurs they no longer seem to react as if anything mattered at all. If, as suggested elsewhere (see Alternative Hypothesis chapter), the Serotonin deficiency directly results in over responsiveness and hypersensitivity to all things, it seems tenable that an accumulation over time that creates, perhaps, an overabundance of Serotonin just might do the opposite. Whatever the mechanism of action, a withdrawing of the medication (always done under a medical doctor's supervision) each time this has occurred re-establishes once again the apparent diminished motivation. In this situation it makes sense to postulate that an overabundance, or excess, of Serotonin might be due to natural fluctuations in the individual's Serotonin levels over time. Research on OCD is consistent in reporting great symptom fluctuations over time that, according to hypotheses in the literature, include even periods of remission. Although clinical experience causes me to seriously doubt complete remissions, there is no doubt that symptoms of both OCS and OCD do indeed wax and wane over time. This inconsistency can include extended periods in which mild symptoms remain present but no longer significantly interfere with day-to-day functioning as they once did, or, have done in the past. Perhaps the Serotonin itself is the fluctuating factor. If so, the hypothesis suggested above may explain this observed behavioral manifestation I have called the "laissez-faire attitude."

The bottom line when working to ameliorate OCS symptomotology with psychopharmacological agents seems to be to "start low and increase slow." Typically I suggest the lowest dose available of the medication to be tried and monitor responses weekly with the Leyton, suggesting thereafter further adjustments based on the monitoring instrument, as well as clinical interviews with the individual, spouse, and/or teachers and parents if the client is a child.

As treatment progresses, and symptom fluctuations are consistently monitored, awareness of the often insidious interplay this condition has on the affected individual's day-to-day life activities and events is usually heightened dramatically. With this enhanced sensitivity to OCS and it's influence (whether positive and/or negative) comes a similarly enhanced capacity to utilize the only other method backed by the research literature as effective in the treatment of obsessive and compulsive symptoms. This is the behavior modification technique of "exposure and response prevention."

It is beyond the scope of this work to trace the long standing historical perspective relating to this well-established treatment method for OCD. The interested reader is referred to an excellent source for this information in a book by Lee Baer titled, *"Getting Control"*. In this comprehensive work, Dr. Baer presents what I consider to be currently the best available description of exposure and response prevention with practical and detailed applications of its use in the treatment of OCD (Obsessive Compulsive disorder). In fact, I frequently recommend to my OCS clients that they purchase Dr. Baer's book to be used as a reference tool specifically for its excellent coverage of the exposure and response prevention technique, including explanation, history, and step-by-step procedures in the where, when, and how of its use.

In brief, the exposure component of this behavior treatment method consists of essentially confronting a situation, fear, etc., as it occurs, or, at times, it is actually sought out (i.e., becoming exposed or exposing one's self to the threat). Thus, rather than avoiding all such situations, fears, and etc. The component of "response prevention" comes into play with each and every exposure experience. It is put into practice when, upon being exposed, the affected individual prevents the "typical" responses from occurring, whether they be compulsive rituals or the carrying out of an obsessively experienced need, both of which when acted on or completed, work to significantly reduce anxiety, tension, and stress. The persistent and frequent exposures in conjunction with the successful inhibition of the time consuming, or in other ways devastating, compulsions over time (usually 2 to 6 weeks) will diminish symptom strength as well as accompanying anxiety. For this

method to be successful, it often requires close work with a practiced behavior therapist, a knowledgeable coach and/or helper,
psychopharmacological interventions, and a very strong personal
desire to be free of symptoms on the part of the affected. In my
experience, however, an OCS or OCD affected's working knowledge of exposure and response prevention in relation to how, when,
what it's used for, and why it is used is important. It has almost
universally seemed clearly beneficial as an integral part of the overall treatment process and future maintenance of positive gains.
This is because once accurate and adequate knowledge of exposure
and response prevention is achieved, it is much like riding a bike
or playing the piano. These things, once learned, even after years
of disuse and neglect, may be "rusty," but the skills are hardly
forgotten and can be readily accessed when the need and/or desire
arises.

The information related in the above paragraph is of particular consequence to those individuals for whom this work is intended, the OCS mild-moderate population. The reason this is
true goes back to the fundamental differences and levels of intensity between OCS (mild-moderate) and OCD symptomotology.
Complete symptom awareness tends to be harder to come by and/
or determine in OCS, which makes it more difficult to apply exposure and response prevention with the exact specificity and op-
erational definition needed to adequately affect true and lasting
behavioral change. Even though only at mild to moderate symptom levels of intensity, in OCS there tends to be many more potentially interfering symptoms that the OCS affected are confronted
with on a daily basis, whether aware or not. These symptoms are
also inclined to come and go, wax and wane, much more rapidly
than the more severe OCD, and often similarly do so on a daily
basis.

Clearly the factors discussed above would make it difficult,
though certainly not impossible, to effectively apply previously
presented behavioral principles in the treatment of OCS. Clinical
experience with OCS affected children strongly supports the notion that this population, in particular, do not respond well when
treated solely by exposure/response prevention methods, although

they seem to do slightly better when this behavioral technique is used in conjunction with medical, or psychopharmacological, interventions.

Though Dr. Baer reports, also, more problems and less positive results in the treatment of OCD affected children, he nevertheless indicates some promising results when, and if, several fairly specific factors (that seemed to relate to treatment success) are also present.

The position seemingly taken by Dr. Baer in regard to the treatment of children does not seem notably different from my own. The element that appears to be singularly the most crucial to a positive behavioral treatment response for both OCS/OCD, that is quite commonly deficient in children, is motivation and/or incentive. A child's willingness and/or ability to submit to and endure the intense levels of anxiety and perceived serious assaults on their emotional well being required for extended periods of time to achieve significant symptom reduction via behavioral treatment methods is hampered in many ways. A child is not in danger of losing his job if symptom reduction is not achieved. His family won't *divorce* him.

Usually the dependent nature of a child's familial, as well as expected community relationships, are such that the child is not likely to become seriously invested in any proposed behavioral changes that are truly difficult and/or require long term and formidable efforts to achieve on their part. Thus, telling oneself that what one sincerely believes must be done does not really have to be done when one feels task incompletion is tantamount (or at least close to, the world coming to an end) is useless without sufficient motivation. To do so, thus, the personal motivation needed for exposure and response prevention to be successful tends to be severely lacking in the childhood population. It is true that those with the most "control" over children can set up the environment and/or respond to a given situation in relation to the affected child in such a way as to essentially force exposure and response prevention principles into action. In fact, the initial step (exposure) naturally occurs off-and-on, and even quite frequently, throughout the course of a day. The other component of this method (response prevention) is also nearly always, at least, attempted.

Attempted is a good word to describe what parents (in such a Moment) intend to accomplish and yet, when an OCS affected child is involved, all too often fail to do. The typical child often responds to parental directives in the immediacy of the Moment much like those with OCS, and can persist in their inappropriate reactions for some time. The difference, though, between even a child who has experienced extensive intermittent reinforcement schedules and one who is biochemically driven by OCS (and probably some intermittent reinforcement scheduling as well) tends to be dramatic in comparison. The biochemically driven individual will normally persist far beyond (much, much longer) than those primarily persisting on the sole basis of a behavioral reinforcement paradigm. These individuals also seem to eventually let go of, not just the inappropriate response (or behavior), but, in addition, they let go of even the thought and/or desire connected with responding in such a way. Experience in clinical practice has suggested to me that, although the response or behavior will eventually change, the related desires and/or thoughts of those who are OCS affected continue with varying degrees of diminished intensity with that typical waxing and waning pattern expected of OCS/OCD. Thus, in spite of significant and positive behavioral change, the OCS affected can experience a persistent lingering of related thoughts and desires that at times can act like a form of chronic mental distress, irritation, and/or torment is not that unusual.

Another important difference between those affected and those who are not lies in the intensities with which the behavioral responses are manifested. The OCS affected tend to respond in absolutes and extremes when things do not seem to go the way it is perceived they "need" to. This tendency to "over respond" to stimuli has been discussed elsewhere in this work. It is essential, however, to keep this in mind when working with the OCS population as their over reactions often seem unjustified and don't make much sense given the readily available identified precipitating factors and events. Knowledge of this allows a frame of reference to be used that, when OCS is involved, can bring meaning and sense to otherwise apparent senseless acts, reactions and situational events. Making sense of the senseless is what this work is all about.

CHAPTER SEVEN

YOU'RE IN GOOD COMPANY

I'm at the end of the road and there's no place left to go
But I will search out every track
Until I find the right path

It's a fool's dream
What do I know what can it mean
It's a fool's dream
The idea that I can lead myself down the road
It's a fool's dream

Patience wears thin at the edge . . . one more step over the ledge
So afraid to go on . . . yet I struggle along
Pretending . . . nothing is wrong

It's a fool's dream . . . what do I know . . . what can it mean
It's a fool's dream to think I'm so good I don't need anyone
It's a fool's dream . . . a fool's dream . . . a foolish dream

Each night I get down on my knees and pray for another day
Just to live my life
Each time I go over mistakes that I've made there's no better way
To clear my mind
And get it right . . . in time
I'll get it right . . . in time . . . yes in time

From the song "A Fool's Dream" by Ron D. Kingsley

OCS ON THE POSITIVE SIDE
ARTIST, MUSICIAN, WRITER, AND ACTOR

I feel absolutely confident in suggesting that nearly every great inventor, artist, musician, writer, and actor (and perhaps all of them) has had, one or both of what I refer to today as significant ADHD/OCS. ADHD tended to provide them with an abundance of energy. Thomas Edison is a good example of this as history records he needed very little sleep. The OCS did several things for them as well. First, and perhaps foremost, it allowed an afflicted individual to focus on a given subject, desire, problem, or need, with such intensity that nothing could get in the way with the obtaining of whatever happened to be the sought after object, desire, etc. Secondly, OCS made them hypersensitive well beyond the norm such that they tended to over respond to literally everything. Many situations and "facts of life" that others seemed perfectly capable of, and maybe even happy, ignoring these individuals could not.

Regarding Beethoven, history records when he was a child: "soon his Mother noticed that Ludwig wasn't quite like other little boys. He heard things that most children never noticed."

It is certain that many, if not all people, can become irritated with chores and tasks that are considered difficult. This irritation, however, tends to be far from sufficient to motivate them into thoughts and actions of change. Most don't spend extra time and energy in a search for a better way, or to try and make something easier as a result. The old or established way things work is just fine and the idea that it could be done differently and more easily probably doesn't even enter their minds, and if it does they typically do not act upon it. This is not so for those with OCS. These individuals, as has already been suggested, tend to be bothered to an intolerable degree or level by things that most others can simply "shrug off." Thus they go on to create, invent, and do things that have never before been thought of or done by others.

It is also not unusual for these individuals to spend more time and/or energy, trying to get out of doing something than would have been needed to accomplish the task or chore in the first place. This often prompts teachers, parents, and the like to shake their heads in dismay and disbelief. Forthcoming comments frequently include things such as:

"I just don't understand what the problem is," "I wish she'd put as much effort into accomplishing the task as she does in avoiding it," "He's making a mountain out of a molehill," "What's the big deal!" and so on.

The exact "problem" can be difficult to determine and similarly difficult to accept as credible. The identified "problem" can seem to be such a minor part of a given task that others simply refuse to believe, or are unable to fathom, such a possibility.

As has been previously discussed, what to most individuals may be incredibly insignificant can seem of "life-and-death" type of importance to those with OCS. Is it really a life-and-death matter? No. Do they believe that it is? Yes.

Question: Why do inventors invent?
Answer: Because things "bug" them.

There was a young girl, 16 years of age. She was a basketball player and quite a good one. The second game of her sophomore season she sustained a knee injury that kept her from playing the rest of the year. Undaunted she followed through on the prescribed regimen of physical therapy to get her knee back into shape for her junior year. Part of the reason for her specific injury, it was determined, was that her kneecap had an unusual smaller percentage of depth (or something along those lines) than the "*normal*" knee had. This made it somehow more likely that such an injury as she'd had would not only have occurred the first time, but also would now be much more likely to reoccur. Thus, to prevent this from happening again, a special knee brace was made that would enable her to play with a significantly lesser chance of re-injuring that knee in a similar fashion as had occurred. In practicing between the summer of her lost sophomore and highly anticipated junior year, she became concerned because when she wore the brace her kneecap turned "purple," in her own words. Apparently some of her teammates had also teased her, or noticed this and made some comments.

Deep in the heart (or mind), if you will, the seeds of her OCS were working. She reacted with extreme hypersensitivity to this "purpleness." It is very hard to be certain of the exact obsessive thought that was directly related to the sequence of events that then happened.

It began by her making offhand remarks of a vague and ill-defined nature suggesting some concern in regard to the wearing of the brace. Then in one of the early morning practices she put it on her leg but, in a Moment of confusion and indecision, never pulled it up over her knee, nor attached the straps that secured it in place. She proceeded to then have the best performance in practice of her life and later described having great practices ever since she stopped wearing that brace.

The injury, severe as it was, had happened the year before. It no longer mattered (seemingly) that another similar injury could terminate competitive basketball for this young lady forever, or even cripple her for life. Hey! When she wore it, her knee had turned purple.

She had even made comments such as, "what if it's cutting off the blood circulation to my leg?" and other seemingly preposterous notions. Then, as luck would have it, on the very day she decided not to wear it, she had the basketball day of her life. Here's a young lady who, if she does re-injure the knee, may eventually invent a knee brace that doesn't make the kneecap turn purple. Either that or she will give up on basketball altogether. Although this scenario may sound awfully silly to most who may read this, I assure you that, to the young girl described, it was as serious as a *forty-five pistol* pointed at your chest. These, I believe, are the roots of invention and also, at times, deep depression.

Thomas Edison is unarguably a brilliant man of many talents. In my opinion he displayed all the signs of significant ADHD and concomitant OCS. I doubt that many, if any, professionals knowledgeable about ADHD and familiar with Mr. Edison's life history would disagree with my Post Hoc diagnosis of ADHD, but the idea of OCS, though sound in my own investigations, may be new to many.

Mr. Edison has been described as a "lively child" by historians who "was always taking things apart and putting them together again, or, trying to put them back together." He started a little fire in the corner of the family barn once, to see what would happen, and ended up paying for the burnt down barn with a sound whipping by his Father in front of the townspeople in the village square. He was thought to be "a creative little fellow" by a neighbor who'd found him in the midst of his own barn sitting on a nest trying to "hatch" some goslings from eggs he'd found there. His Mother has been quoted as having said, "It's always interesting. I only wish he didn't get into so much trouble."

Thomas' first, and only, experience in an organized school setting was in Port Huron, Michigan after a family relocation out of financial necessity. Placed on a school bench for the more part of six hours a day was a hardly bearable experience and apparently not conducive to young Thomas' learning style. He bounced. He fidgeted. Mostly, though, he is reported to have been lost in his own thoughts and daydreams. This was probably the only way he could possibly remain cooped up in a small classroom for as long as was expected. Students of today who demonstrate this same tendency are described by teachers and classmates alike as: "out to lunch," "a space cadet," "off the wall," and "weird," to name just a few of the most common pejorative phrases and/or comments.

Thomas Edison, history records, would become so caught up in thought that he literally would not respond to the lessons of his teacher, even when directly called upon. Reportedly, after about three months of this, Thomas' teacher informed his Mother, in no uncertain terms, that her son was unteachable because he was "addled" or "addlepated" which, when translated, means essentially "retarded." Thomas Edison's Mother, as you might imagine, was furious at this pronouncement. In response, she thereafter kept him home and taught him herself.

Thomas set up his own "laboratory" in the basement of his parent's house. Although they allowed it, reportedly, they were also worried, perhaps understandably so. Their son did nearly blow up the basement while trying to make a cannon, and in the interest of studying "static electricity," once tied the tails of two Tom-cats together.

As a young man, Thomas Edison never kept a job for long, and by his twenty-first birthday, was considered by his family and those who knew him to be an out-and-out failure. He was also viewed, however, as "stubborn, independent, and hard working."

While he was courting the woman he was to eventually marry, she experienced much teasing and laughter from her co-workers directed at Thomas Edison and, of course, through an indirect association, herself as well. To this she was not immune, and it has been reported that she was flustered and embarrassed. Nevertheless, she did marry him.

Thomas Edison, historians reveal, was a man who simply could not understand mathematics, although he is said to have put forth-great efforts to do so. In spite of this, he has some 1,093 patents to his name, including the phonograph, the electric light, the motion picture projector, and dozens of other electronic devices most of us in this day-and-age take for granted as we use them every day.

Mr. Edison was once confronted and instructed by a reputedly well meaning individual to "remember, many famous scientists, people who knew all about how light and electricity work, have tried to make such a lamp – and *none* of them could do it. Maybe you should read what they have written about this very difficult problem before you spend a lot of time and money on experiments that might not work."

Thomas' reported reply is interesting, "that could just get in my way." He is supposed to have said, "when I start on an invention, I don't read books. I don't want to know what has already been done. I start from scratch." This may be exactly what Mr. Edison did, and why it is not, however, hard for me to imagine that the entire truth of the matter might just be a bit more complicated than it seems. Many individuals with OCS find reading an extremely tedious chore and, as such, avoid it inasmuch as they possibly can. This is not usually due to an inability to read, or a learning disability (although, it can be). It is most often the result of an active and obsessive mind-set that has trouble staying on the topic of the written word, even while reading. Thus, to comprehend what is read, the OCS affected may have to read and re-read a given page several times before they can "get it." Reading, for these individuals becomes a chore similar to mowing the lawn or doing the dishes. Perhaps reading was this kind of a chore for Thomas Edison but, not wanting others to know this and/or not realizing it him self and being frustrated often when he did attempt it, he reasoned it out as explained herein. Thus, he believed what he did in order to make sense out of what others may have charged, and perhaps he may have even felt him self, was senseless behavior. Perhaps if he had read what others had done in relation to the light bulb, it wouldn't have taken him some 2,000 experiments to invent the bulb. Then again, perhaps reading about others' failures would have narrowed or contaminated Mr. Edison's directions and/or limited his perceptions and locked him into a way of thinking that may have literally kept him from succeeding. We will never really know because of the way history has been recorded. It doesn't really matter, but the possibility of OCS affected reading difficulties does clearly exist.

Interestingly, I once heard a motivational speaker say that Mr. Edison had been asked by someone how it felt to have failed 2,000 times before finally succeeding with the invention of the light bulb. The speaker indicated that Mr. Edison had responded by looking the individual square in the eyes and saying, "I never failed, sir! It was a 2,000 step process." The speaker then used the comment to support the idea that everyone should endeavor to be as optimistic as Mr. Edison and so on.

Perhaps it won't come as a surprise to readers that I can conceive of an alternate, yet what I consider to be an equally likely rationale, for his having made the above related comment. Individuals with OCS tend to be extremely sensitive to the slightest perceived forms of criticism and can experience adamant denial even against the face of all odds. Incensed at the thought that anyone would even hint that he had failed, I can envision Mr. Edison's reported response as a brilliant quip meant to cut-to-the-quick of the insensitive jerk that queried him in such a way. Let historians interpret what they will. Of course, my interpretations are no more than educated guesses as well.

It has been said, and it seems clear, that Mr. Edison did not give up when he failed. He is reported to have never stopped forging ahead. I believe he might have given up, however, if he hadn't been obsessive about the things that he did. How many people, do you think, would really keep trying or experimenting after 100 failures, let alone 2,000?

Thus, I believe Mr. Edison's accomplishments epitomize what can be a very positive aspect of OCS, as well as ADHD. Depending on how strong the OCS is, an affected individual may never give up, once locked into a given task or project. Success in chosen endeavors is often just a matter of time and effort.

Mr. Edison, it has been reported, needed little sleep, and possessed an enormous amount of energy that propelled him day and night. He is said to have attributed this prodigious energy to the ten minute "catnaps" he took off-and-on both day and night wherever he happened to be when the urge for one occurred. I, however, attribute Mr. Edison's astonishing energy to ADHD and, perhaps a bit as well, to OCS. Mr. Edison's productivity as an inventor may very well have been due to one of the, sometimes, positive aspects of ADHD . . . an abundant and unyielding endurance, drive, and/or energy.

Mr. Edison has been considered "a strange man who gradually became deaf but never needed much sleep. After working all day, he would sit up till four in the morning studying electrical science. His first invention was one for killing cockroaches by electricity in the Boston telegraph office. At one time he was working on 45 different inventions at once."

*   *   *

Another individual worthy of note, that in my opinion also demonstrated what, because of his accomplishments, can be considered some of the most positive aspects of OCS and probably ADHD as well, is Albert Einstein.

A middle aged Albert Einstein once wrote, "Every reminiscence is colored by today's being what it is, and therefore by a deceptive point of view." I began my discussion of Mr. Einstein and his life with this statement because what I am about to describe is surely colored by today's being what it is. But it is also colored by what Albert Einstein perceived him self to be in his own writings, by how others perceived him who knew him, and sometimes by what others may have suggested, based on their perceptions of his writings or of the writings of someone else. Let us, therefore, keep in mind throughout this discussion the many possible levels of what can be called "deceptive points of view" that may have, at any given Moment, intertwined to provide the deceptive viewpoint I am most interested in presenting.

After exploring available information relating to the life of Albert Einstein, I have become convinced that genius though he was, he displayed throughout his life time evidence for what today would be diagnosable as an Attention Deficit Hyperactivity Disorder (ADHD). He also similarly, I believe, had significant concomitant obsessive and compulsive symptoms (OCS) in the mild-moderate range. In describing my case for Mr. Einstein, I hope to demonstrate sufficient evidence to make the case that many, if not all, genius level innovators such as him self are, at least in part, the products of their bioneurochemical "wiring" which "drove" them to the heights they often reached. By better understanding the lives of these "driven" great men and women, perhaps we can better understand our contemporaries and ADHD/OCS affected children and, hopefully, better enable their development and current life status. That which we understand, we no longer fear, and in fearing less comes dynamic changes that can work to foster healthy responses and attitudes that once were simply distortions made so by the unknown and our perceptions relative to our experience with similarities in the "known" world.

There are subtle hints made in relation to the parents of Albert Einstein that indicate to me the (what I have come to consider necessary) evidence of OCS tendencies demonstrating the genetic heritability link. Ronald Clark surmises that "Einstein was nourished on a family tradition which had broken with authority; which disagreed, sought independence, and had deliberately trodden out of line."

Regarding Einstein's memory, Dr. James Plesch wrote, "It has always struck me as singular that the marvelous memory of Einstein for scientific matters does not extend to other fields. I don't believe that Einstein could forget anything that interested him scientifically, but matters relating to his childhood, his scientific beginnings, and his development are in a different category, and he rarely talks about them – not because they don't interest him, but simply because he doesn't remember them well enough."

In reply to this statement, Einstein him self commented, "You're quite right about my bad memory for personal things. It's really quite astounding. Something for psychoanalysts – if there really are such people."

Interestingly, those with ADHD and OCS are often considered by parents and teachers to have "selective memories." Many of these children and adults can vividly, and with great detail, remember quite specific events or, information relating to areas of particular intense interest and study. This, I believe, tends to be an OCS related characteristic. The things for which one has an obsession (biochemically driven excessive interest) or a similarly driven compulsion, be it mild, moderate, or even severe, are remembered (often the affected individual couldn't forget even if they wanted to) with ease and with every intricate and minute associated component. Parents, teachers, and others can be frustrated in the extreme by the individual's seeming inability to remember common sense rules of behavior, the times tables, and even what time dinner is served, although the supper time may be at exactly the same day-after-day.

Einstein represents the epitome of what has become known as the "absentminded professor" and/or scientist. Clark points out, however, that Einstein was "absent-minded only about things that didn't matter . . ." He goes on to say something that, I believe, is a misinterpretation resulting from a lack of knowledge and awareness of what very-well may be the true underlying reason for the described behavior. Clark adds "Or Einstein was absent-minded when he knew there was someone to remember for him." From the OCS point of view, I will not argue that it undoubtedly seemed to others that when Einstein had someone there to remember for him, he was absent-minded (or forgetful). I would argue, however, that over time someone came to be there simply because he was absent-minded and that, if they had not been there, appointments would have been missed and every day things would not have gotten done.

It has been noted that there was nothing in Einstein's early history to suggest the presence of latent genius. In fact, some writers have insinuated that the exact opposite seemed more likely to be the case, citing the "lateness with which he learned to speak" as supportive evidence. It has been recorded that "even at the age of nine Einstein was not a fluent speaker." Einstein's own memories of his youth stress speech hesitancies and the fact that he would reply to questions "only after consideration and reflection." His parents reportedly feared he might be mentally slow. From an OCS perspective there is an alternative explanation that, in retrospect, cannot be proven one way or another. If OCS was a factor, though, there is a symptom characteristic that might make sense out of Einstein's apparent speech and language anomalies. In the past 15 years I have worked with quite a few children who, prior to seeing me, had been diagnosed with Elective Mutism, who demonstrated in addition to this, a wide variety of OCS characteristics. With initial treatment for the OCS consisting of a psychopharmacological intervention, the "Elective Mutism" improved dramatically. Common symptoms of OCS that appear to have been the main underlying factors relating to these children's unwillingness to speak include the following:

1.) An irrational, yet undeniable, fear of not saying the right thing

2.) An irresistible need to find *just the right* words before one answers

3.) The compelling fear that others will judge the worth of the speaker and reject or accept them as such based on whatever may be said.

Perhaps Einstein's delayed speaking, hesitancies, and tendency to respond only after carefully considering both question and answer were the product of the above-related very real OCS characteristics. Although in my experience it has been somewhat unusual for OCS affected individuals to experience symptom intensities at a level sufficient to render an individual mute, I have seen a few wherein this clearly seems to have been the case. Thus, I consider it plausible that Einstein's reported childhood language troubles might not have been language "problems" at all. Rather, they could have been secondary and tertiary reactions to the unidentified symptoms of OCS. His inherent genius, therefore, as reason would dictate, was always present, though well camouflaged amid a host of behaviors and reactions that tended to suggest otherwise. This, too, is common for the OCS affected in the public schools. Often considered underachievers, they are also frequently considered by teachers to be less intelligent than they actually are.

Another apparent secondary symptom common to the OCS affected demonstrated by Einstein has been reported by his son, Hans Albert. He has said that his Father was withdrawn from the rest of the world even as a boy and was a student for whom teachers held out only poor prospects. Einstein's Father had reportedly queried one of his teachers regarding what profession his son should pursue, and was told point blank: "It doesn't matter; he'll never make a success of anything."

Authors agree that Einstein grew to despise educational discipline and hated the Luitpold Gymnasium where he'd spent six of his boyhood years in school. Reportedly, Einstein did not seem able to express his dislike in regard to his Gymnasium (school) experience until his mid-life years, and even then was said to be unable to actually say he "hated it." Often the OCS affected have difficulties expressing some types of feelings and thoughts, especially when aimed at authoritative and/or established institutions and/or individuals. Sometimes this is due to an irrational fear of confrontation that is exaggerated biochemically to a point well beyond that which is reasonable. There may also be unrealistic fears with little, if any, basis in reality but, nevertheless, still inhibit the open expression of ones true feelings, especially when negative and focused on a societal institution or individually held office which is supposed to be beyond reproach.

Einstein left the Luitpold Institution without having obtained the necessary diploma of completion. It appears this would have been roughly equivalent to a high school diploma common in the United States of America. History reports that Einstein had apparently been attempting to leave the school to join his parents in Italy by means of a "medical" release relating to a "nervous breakdown." By report, however, Einstein had not yet received the medical certificate when he was summarily expelled from the school on the grounds that "your presence in the class is disruptive and affects the other students."

A description given of Einstein as he appeared to others during this time period in his life is also revealing. He was described as a "precocious, half-cocksure, almost insolent youth and young man." Some of the most difficult and disruptive students in the public schools of today could be described in the very same way, as was Einstein. Students of today might, additionally, be described as having and/or showing signs of ADHD and OCS.

Einstein had an intense disregard and dislike as well as suspicion against every kind of authority. A variety of reasons for his antiauthoritarian feelings have been postulated, the sum of which are undoubtedly due to the many combinations of factors experienced over time. One that has yet to be suggested, and yet still may have been a significant contributor to the whole, is the presence of possible OCS.

A substantial number of the OCS affected begin experiencing significant difficulties with authority figures early-on, starting with parents, teachers, coaches, rule oriented institutions and so on. These have been explained in some detail elsewhere and so, only a brief reminder will be inserted here. If the OCS affected has not finished an assignment and has a compulsion (as many do) to finish or complete tasks, and the teacher directs the class towards a transition to the next subject etc., the affected one is in danger of having an authority figure problem. The intensity of the students *need* to finish defines the extent to which a potential problem will occur. If the compulsion is strong and the teacher pushes the student to stop what they are doing and transition as directed, the student will appear, for all intents and purposes, to be actively defying authority even though they are simply responding to an unintentional, often inexplicable, desire for task completion.

An obsessive idea or thought that simply cannot be dismissed can lead to stubborn argumentative behavior if the idea is not in line or agreement with the content of the teacher's lesson. Thus, directions and instructions coming from a teacher, principal, parent, and the like can be perceived by the OCS affected as intrusions into the way they feel things must be and, therefore, must be rejected. Similar reactions can, and do, occur in relation to established rules and particularly when these rules are rigidly adhered to. If the "rule" interferes with the experienced needs, or compulsions, or perseverative thought processes, the affected one may appear to be flagrantly breaking those "rules." In reality, however, they are only following through on biochemically driven needs and impulses and only inadvertently breaking the "rule" because it just happened to be there and in the way.

If the presence of OCS/ADHD was a significant factor in Einstein's life, as I am herein suggesting, it would be easy to imagine how he might have developed the reported extreme and negative attitudes towards authority in all its forms. This could have even been the primary underlying factor influencing Einstein's experiences and perceptions relating to authority.

Einstein is said to have been "always sensitive to beauty, and abnormally sensitive to music." An abnormal sensitivity to many things, along with a predisposition, or tendency to over respond emotionally to practically everything that enters the OCS affected's consciousness, seems to be a central and perhaps essential response pattern relative to the mild-moderate OCS diagnosis. This extreme hypersensitivity seems to be a basal component related, either directly or indirectly, to all OCS symptomotology.

Colleagues spoke of Einstein's "single-minded determination with which he followed his star without regard for others." Also, he is said to have had a "desperate need to find order in a chaotic world."

Such descriptions fit easily into the OCS patterns of behavior. The OCS affected is often accused of being exceptionally egocentric and self-centered. The obsessive need to persist in and inability to let go of certain thoughts or ideas, as does the indefatigable need to do some things, interferes with the individual's ability to take notice of anyone and/or anything else that may be occurring simultaneously. Thus, it has been my experience that the OCS affected do indeed have, and hold deep and meaningful regard for others, and when accused of being otherwise, actually grieve very deeply and without guile to think that others could possibly believe, what to them, is such a preposterous notion. During Moments and/or periods of biochemically driven symptom expression, however, nothing else matters and there is virtually no awareness of anything beyond the undeniable thought and/or need of the Moment.

Einstein demonstrates another interesting idea in his writings relative to him self. He wrote, "but you must recognize it at least as a modest attempt to overcome the laziness in writing which I have inherited from both of my dear parents." This is of interest because it is not unusual for the OCS affected to experience significant difficulties in the area of writing relative to the complex interplay of symptoms that, to most others, can have no alternative explanation beyond obvious laziness. In fact, the OCS affected themselves, being unaware of interfering symptoms, let alone symptom interplay, typically come to accept what others have been suggesting all along which is that they indeed are "lazy". In my experience, when OCS is present, the appellation of "lazy" is very often far from the truth although as I have suggested, it certainly can look that way to the casual observer.

A fellow student's description of Einstein as a young man suggests some indications of ADHD-like behavior and hints of what seems to be evidence of OCS as well. This fellow considered Einstein "impudent" and further described him as "sure of him self, his gray felt hat pushed back on his thick, black hair. He strode energetically up and down in a rapid, I might almost say crazy, tempo of a restless spirit which carries a whole world in itself." He felt Einstein displayed an "intellectual disinclination to give a damn for anybody." He further was said to demonstrate a "prickly arrogance" and was "a young man of the world, well filled with his own opinions, careless of expressing them without reserve, regarding the passing scene with a sometimes slightly contemptuous smile." He was at times "moodily aloof" from his peers and companions.

Einstein was "casual of dress, unconventional of habit, with the happy-go-lucky absent-mindedness of a man concentrating on other things, which he was to retain all his life." "That young man," a friend's parent once said, "will never amount to anything because he can't remember anything." Einstein would frequently forget his key and have to awaken his landlady late at night, calling: "It's Einstein – I've forgotten my key again."

Emotional hypersensitivity and an extreme intensity relating to his music (playing of the violin) are displayed during "musical evenings" to which he'd been invited by friends. If attention to his performance were not adequate, he would simply stop playing, sometimes with a remark that would verge on impetuousness. He considered it an affront when a group of elderly ladies went right on with their knitting as he played.

A great deal of Einstein's "genius" has been attributed to "an imagination, which gave him courage to challenge, accepted beliefs." From an OCS perspective this could be restated as follows:

> Einstein's imagination was unfettered by societal rules, and accepted beliefs due to an inability, regardless of anticipated consequences, to ignore the internal workings, thoughts, and ideas conceived of within his own mind. His challenging of accepted beliefs may, therefore, have been more of an inability to see it any other way than he proposed, rather than a true challenge to the status quo. The inability to let go of new ideas, it seems, might easily be interpreted as a challenge to the ideas of old, for indeed it is, but not out of courage, although I suspect Einstein himself would prefer that explanation over the suggested biochemical drive. If accepted beliefs got in the way of the "drive," well, then, they may just have to be rethought out, or changed completely.

After failing the initial entrance exam to, essentially a college level type of institution, known as the ETH Switzerland, Einstein was eventually allowed to register because the principal of the ETH had been "impressed by his mathematical ability," but appears to have been more impressed with his "character." This principal set Einstein up in a nearby school where a year of specific study would, it was expected, enable him to pass the ETH entrance exam. Interestingly, Minkowski, who had been one of Einstein's teachers at the ETH described his student as, "the lazy dog who never bothered about mathematics at all." To the professors at the ETH, Einstein became one of the floundering scholars who might, or might not, graduate but who, nevertheless, was a great deal of trouble. A certain professor Weber, after admitting to Einstein's cleverness, then told him, "but you have one fault; one can't tell you anything." Again this type of comment is quite typical of parents and teachers when dealing with the OCS affected. Their obsessive and compulsive tendency locks in on the way things should be, often keeping them from being able to accept another's direction and/or advice.

Einstein's over sensitivity and tendency to over react is once again underlined in a comment made in later life regarding his four years spent at the ETH. "The coercion," he wrote speaking specifically of the obligatory examinations, "had such a deterring effect upon me that, after I had passed the final examination, I found the consideration of my scientific problems distasteful to me for an entire year!" He then sought employment at the ETH, but the refusal of this institution to hire him was a blow to both his prospects and his pride. Apparently he had been enough trouble as a student that no one wanted to have to deal with him as a colleague. It was said of him at this time, "Einstein was the graduate who denied rather than defied authority" and "the perverse young man whom 'you must' was the Father of 'I won't'. The keen seeker out of heresies to support; a young man who was written off as virtually unemployable by many self respecting citizens."

About a year later he was offered a position at a technical school by the name of Winterthur about which he wrote, "I have no idea who recommended me, because as far as I know not one of my teachers has a good word to say for me." In another part of this same letter he adds, "I am fully aware that I am a curious bird . . . ."

After just one year, though, Einstein was dismissed from the post because apparently his ideas about minimum routine and minimum discipline were quite different from those of his employer, Jakob Neusch.

"One thing that remains clear is that neither Zurich nor any other Swiss University would have refused to hire Einstein or sent him looking elsewhere for a position had they seen in him at the time anything more than an awkward, somewhat lazy, and certainly obstinate young man who thought he knew more than his elders and betters." I believe, however, that the impression of others that Einstein was a "know-it-all" is a fundamental misinterpretation that inadvertently occurs frequently with the OCS affected due to symptom dynamics.

Einstein's first marriage failed. This also is unfortunately not unusual for the OCS/ADHD-affected individual. They tend to be very difficult to live with. A student visiting him a few years after he'd married describes what he saw thus:

"He was sitting in his study in front of a heap of papers covered with mathematical formulas writing with his right band and holding his younger son in his left. He kept replying to questions from his elder son Albert who was playing with his bricks with the words, 'wait a minute, I've nearly finished'. He gave me the children to look after for a few Moments and went on working. The irresponsible cad! Did he care so little for his children that it didn't matter to him who looked after them?"

One could easily take a position such as this. In my opinion, however, the more correct explanation is that he was in the throes of an obsessive thought process with an accompanying compulsion that effectively filled his conscious mind completely and kept him from adequately considering any other thoughts and/or activities at that particular Moment in time. Caring was not the real issue at times like these although one could argue that it was. If he truly cared, one might say, he would never, under any circumstances, pass off his children into the arms of a practical stranger for safekeeping. This line of thinking, though common, does not take into consideration or even begin to understand what it means to be driven biochemically, as the OCS affected are, and I believe

Einstein was. This is not meant to excuse unsafe and/or thought-less behavior, rather it is meant to be of use as a basis for under-standing the OCS affected's behavior. Understanding is, after all, the essential initial ingredient to the most successful forms of man-agement and/or treatment.

A confession, in Einstein's own words, is of interest and hints further at the inner workings of, what for the OCS affected, is a common occurrence in their minds. He wrote, "I must confess that at the very beginning when the Special Theory of Relativity began to germinate in me, I was visited by all sorts of nervous conflicts. When young, I used to go away for weeks in a state of confusion." Confused thought processes along with significant anxiety (nervous conflicts) are both all too common for most of the OCS affected. In fact these tend to be the main reasons associated with difficulties in writing, as well as the fairly common compre-hension difficulties in reading that I consistently have seen in my OCS client population.

Einstein, it is reported, was always ready and eager to agree that "inventiveness, imagination, and the intuitive approach – the very stuff of which artists rather than scientists are usually thought to be made – played a serious part in his work." He has said,

"When I examine myself and my methods of thought, I come to the conclusion that the gift of fantasy has meant more to me than my talent for absorbing positive knowledge."

The OCS affected tend to be the obvious dreamers and are often described by others as "out to lunch" and/or "lost in their own world." This is both one of the positive and sometimes nega-tive aspects of the OCS affected. Only those "lost in their own worlds" can possibly envision "other" worlds as musicians, artists, and writers often do. Only they, can imagine what could, or might be because their thoughts are not locked into the common sense realities of their communities and societies at large. At the same time this tendency sets them apart from the group, the norm, and allows them the appellation of strange, weird, or down right "crazy." This can have a fairly negative impact on their social status and the willingness of others to include and accept them as members of a particular group, and/or a given community. Thus, the OCS affected tend to isolate themselves and withdraw from most, if not all, social groups. They may belong consciously to various social groups, but they are inclined to feel as if they are members but don't really "fit in". When asked they invariably describe themselves as "different" from the majority of group members within the communities and groups that they consider as their own. The experiencing of themselves as strange, or peculiar, when compared to others often seems to have a haunting quality that sticks with them throughout their lives. The feeling is always there, in the background, reminding them that they will never truly fit in with any group. It's often a dismal and lonely kind of a feeling.

Among his colleagues Einstein, "moved with a calm assurance and a quizzical smile; and both came, for all his innate humbleness, from an inner certainty (obsessiveness) of being right." He has been described as kind, but in a slightly casual fashion; and as friendly, "as long as others allowed him to get on with his work" (the underlying insinuation herein, of course, is that if people interfered with his work he could be quite disagreeable, surly, or seemingly malicious). This is a good description of the commonly seen reactivity of the OCS affected when a compulsion and/or obsession is interfered with by others, or attempts are made to block it's completion. They frequently over respond in the extreme or give up and completely abandon all efforts towards completion. Einstein, apparently, was one more apt to react with vehemence and hostility in relation to interference by other people.

Winston Churchill has been an individual to which Einstein's contemporaries have made comparisons. C.P. Snow wrote, "Of Churchill it has been written that almost obsessional concentration" (OCS?) "was one of the keys to his character. It was not always obvious, but he never really thought of anything but the job at hand. He was not a fast worker, especially when dealing with papers, but he was essentially a non-stop worker." In my opinion this "almost obsessional" state that Churchill (and Einstein) would attain to was indeed just that, an obsessional state of mind, probably at the moderate level on the continuum, but truly obsessive nonetheless. Einstein, it is said, demonstrated a "ferocious concentration on the task to be done" and "determination that nothing should be allowed to divert him from it." The comparison with Churchill seems true.

In 1908 Einstein wrote, "I am ceaselessly occupied with the question of the constitution of radiation." These incessant preoccupations seemed to change as capriciously as the wind, and over the years of his life Einstein apparently experienced a great variety of such obsessions, many of which were triggered by their associations with whatever currently occupied his mind, though sometimes just as easily not.

Obsessions and compulsions are known to change with time, situations, and circumstance, although exactly why this occurs is not well understood. My experience suggests, the milder the symptoms are, the more likely they are to shift and change from one to another and vary significantly over time. As one moves up the continuum towards the severe, it is more likely that fewer specific symptoms will be recognized and these are less likely to dramatically change with time.

In the early 1900's Einstein was seen as the man who was unsuccessful in his attempts to fit in or conform, was disrespectful of professors. The "dispenser of conversational bricks, the bumbling Jewish customer, and the man who at almost the age of thirty nevertheless, continued to prefer the company of students." This may have been due to what I suggest was an OCS related hypersensitivity and responsivity to especially, criticism. Einstein, it seems, was provided with more than his share of criticism from the professors and knowledgeable elders of his time. For Einstein, therefore, to associate socially with them would have been, in my mind, tantamount to a form of emotional suicide or masochism. Students would be far less likely to criticize and would, it seems to me, be the obviously preferred company. OCS affected children and adolescents do tend to associate with others that are several years younger and, at least in part, the reason appears to be that which was just suggested for Einstein.

Another revelatory characterization is offered by one of Clark's statements. "Einstein," he has said, "was, as he him self has admitted, the kind of man who did not work well in a team." This same difficulty is such a common one for the OCS affected that it nearly seems a universal symptom, although I know that it is not. The primary reason relating to this very real problem of working with others as a team lies in the, (inherent) inflexibility that invariably occurs when the OCS affected obsess or feel a need to do things in a certain way. Either that or their direction of focus is contrary to the direction that others in the group want to take. The OCS affected do not usually back down, bend, or compromise even a little and, of course, it is obvious what kinds of difficulties can occur given the dynamics of such a situation. The OCS affected also, however, tend to feel that no one else will do specific tasks at a level equal to their own (obsessive tendencies). Thus, they often feel a kind of resentment that their project grade, or the judgement of the finished project, could be the reflection of another's (often thought to be) inferior efforts. Thus, the OCS affected experience great anxiety regarding the other team members efforts and has trouble allowing another to complete his or her part of the project on their own. Like a Mother hen, they hover over the other team member's work, directing, suggesting, arguing, and sometimes demanding that it be done in exactly the way they obsessively and compulsively feel it should. Such behavior does not win friends and admiration, nor does it foster smooth running group dynamics.

Yet another essential element of Einstein's character, which is also a common ingredient of the OCS affected, is somewhat subtly suggested in another of Clark's descriptive statements. Einstein, he said, was always, "dissatisfied with earlier work . . . worrying round it until he unearthed the chance of providing experimental evidence." The imperative ingredients herein include the mention of his dissatisfaction with earlier work and the "worrying round it." The typical OCS affected individual, be it child or adult, is never satisfied with anything they may do. No matter the effort involved, it is never good enough. As a result two common outcomes seem to occur. The one is like that of Einstein who, always displeased with his work and performance, obsessively considers and reconsiders, writes and re-writes, striving for perfection. Although this type of OCS response never quite reaches the sought after perfection and is perpetually unsatisfied and forlorn about the work and or performance, this does not detract from the constant effort put forth in their attempts to get there. The need to get there overpowers all thoughts and frustrations relating to never actually getting there. In spite of the personally perceived failures, this OCS type does not give up. The other type can be a mixture or an apparent direct polar opposite.

These individuals demonstrate a similar need to reach perfection but seem more focused on the indisputable and constantly present awareness that nothing they do ever will be good enough. Thus, there is a tendency to resist work and performance activities, since they are already painfully convinced of their own inability to complete any task satisfactorily. Since each failure is essentially another biochemically driven exaggerated emotionally painful reminder of their own inadequacy, these individuals seem to be saying to themselves, "So, why even try." Depression seems more common for this group, though it is certainly not unheard of in the other. Whatever the factors may be that cause and/or influence one affected individual to go down this particular path, it appears to me that these reasons must be varied and interactively complex. It seems obvious that there will be no "simple" explanation, nor will there soon be, if ever, a comprehensive predictability that will enable practitioners to easily guide either polarity towards a more evenly dispersed responsivity and consequent healthier lifestyle. This, however, appears to be a worthy researchable goal of the future.

The strength and levels of Einstein's over focus (I suggest OCS) are hinted at in a verbal summary offered by Dr. James Plesch. He has said,

"As his mind knows no limits, so his body follows no set rules. He sleeps until he is wakened; he stays awake until he is told to go to bed; he will go hungry until he is given something to eat; and then he eats until he is stopped."

This statement came at a time when Einstein had become so severely ill that there was some concern that he might actually die. Apparently Dr. Plesch felt that the illness was a result of how poorly Einstein cared for the physical aspects of his being.

During the illness of 1917, his cousin Elsa took care of him and a relationship blossomed between them which eventually led to their marriage. It appears that Elsa's personality was that of a "Mothering" type. She was what Einstein needed. She took care of him and for all the reasons already mentioned, thus far, Einstein had a great need to be taken care of. She, it has been suggested, watched over him as one might watch over a child.

It has been implied that "It was part of his genius that he could isolate him self from his surroundings." I, however, do not see this "isolation" tendency as an element of genius, but rather as a symptom of OCS. At a time when one of his colleagues was expressing his joy regarding the results of an experiment that were viewed as proof of Einstein's previously long time unproven theory, Einstein him self bad been reportedly unmoved and said; "but I know that the theory is correct." The colleague then spontaneously queried of him, "but what if there had been no confirmation of the theory?" Einstein is said to have replied, "Then I would have been sorry for the dear Lord – the theory is correct!" Arrogance, or obsession? You know my thoughts on the matter.

Yet another factor related by Einstein's son, Hans Albert, is also quite common in the OCS affected population. He has indicated that his Father was always willing to exaggerate in his attempts to explain. There were also times, according to Hans, when Einstein would "delight in making up a story to please the audience." Common to the OCS affected is the tendency to frequently inadvertently exaggerate, and therefore distort, explanations and descriptions of events and experiences. This may have something to do with the OCS affected's common over-emotional responsiveness to much of what they experience in life.

Although I feel the desire to point out each and every recorded indicator of support for my conclusion that Einstein labored under the biochemically driven OCS and probably had at least some ADHD characteristics, I also know this is not the place to do so. In my opinion, sufficient information exists to make a post humus diagnosis of OCS/ADHD. In examining Einstein's life, it is my hope that the reader will now be able to draw parallels to their own and/or the lives of those who are OCS affected and ultimately recognize it for what it is. Those who are OCS affected are not alone. Although not yet well recognized, there is, and has always been a community of the OCS affected and, as you will begin to see in this chapter, if you haven't already, if you are one so affected, you *are* in good company. Some of the greatest and most productive men and women ever to live, it seems, owe, in part, their successes to the inescapable drive and seemingly boundless energy associated with the OCS/ADHD condition.

*　　*　　*

Let us consider Momentarily Mr. Alexander Graham Bell. Everybody knows that Alexander Bell invented the telephone. What many do not know is that "it was simply not in Bell's nature to fixate for long on any one specific area. All of his life he retained a child's joy in the world's diversity." But before he became world-famous, Bell's love of diversity raised misgivings in some who knew him. His eventual Father-in-law prior to his marrying chided him for his tendency "to undertake every new thing that interests you and accomplish nothing of any value to anyone." That was less than five months before the telephone was patented. What saved him though, interestingly enough, from mere aimless skittering was his reported capacity for total absorption in the concern of the Moment – another trait that might be called childlike. "My mind," he once wrote, "concentrates itself on the subject that happens to occupy it and then all things else in the universe, including Father, Mother, wife, children, and life itself, become for the time being of secondary importance." Even though very brief, this biographical sketch has components that clearly suggest to me the probable presence of, again, ADHD and OCS that appear to have surely enabled Mr. Bell and, perhaps, disabled him at times as well.

*　　*　　*

Of Marie Curie it has been reported, "with a passion to learn everything she possibly could, Marie worked far into the night and for weeks would live on nothing but bread and butter, fruit and tea."

*   *   *

During a short vacation from his university studies Albert Schweitzer reportedly made the decision that he would spend his time up until the age of thirty absorbing the things of the mind that he loved, and that thereafter he would devote his life to serving mankind. History records that he never wavered from this decision. It was his humanitarian efforts in Africa that earned him world fame and won for him the Nobel Peace prize. He was not only a doctor: he was a philosopher, a theologian, and a musicologist.

*   *   *

Eleanor Roosevelt's entire life was dedicated to service on behalf of others and steadfast accomplishments even in the face of quite serious setbacks. As a young girl, she was very timid and shy as well as withdrawn due to what, appeared to have been, persistent internal feelings of inadequacy. As first lady she has been described as "an energetic and outspoken representative of the needs of the people suffering from the Great Depression. She traveled broadly, held news conferences, corresponded with hundreds of men and women and, in both her private and public life, Eleanor manifested an unqualified concern for others. She taught at a school she had set up for poor children, ran a factory for jobless men, and was an advocate for equal rights when that was an unpopular thing to do." She is said to have had a lifelong yearning to be needed and loved.

*   *   *

Confucius believed that the purpose of life is for people to "obtain perfection within themselves." As his fame as a teacher grew, more and more people sought after opportunities to study with him. Once, he reportedly taught poetry, history, ceremonies, and music to a group of about 3,000 students. His standards though, were so high that he believed only 72 of these pupils had mastered the subjects taught.

*   *   *

Hans Christian Anderson's Father was a shoemaker who had dreamed of a greater career for him self. His Mother was uneducated and considered quite "superstitious." Hans school-age years were reportedly "not happy." In his teens he traveled to Copenhagen determined to win fame as a singer, dancer, or actor. According to available records, Hans was "a complete failure at all of these professions and was eventually reduced to almost begging." Throughout his life, Mr. Anderson had been considered "difficult" and of a "complex character." He has been described as "vain, sensitive to criticism, and bedeviled by his own moods."

*   *   *

The inventor of the modern day sewing machine, Elias Howe, ended up becoming more than a millionaire. Thereafter, right up until the end of his life, history records that Mr. Howe continually (compulsively?) built "small machines, some of them very queer ones for which nobody could figure out any use."

*   *   *

The most productive and greatest inventors clearly manifested OCS. The most prolific and widely known authors are and were OCS. The most diverse, impressive, talented and believable actors' have had OCS. Olympians' of all varieties are surely manifesting OCS. The most gifted master professional athletes. The most dedicated, ambitious, and well known artists. The most spirited, tireless, and prolific musician/songwriters. The most persuasive and successful salespersons, and so on. Perhaps you can now clearly see an emerging pattern. We, who make up the OCS affected population, are not alone and truly are in good company. The very best of the best in nearly every vocation, as well as avocation, research reviews and experience suggests, are typically the significantly OCS affected.

"All along this road of life we go
Where even the strongest will stumble
As well as sometimes fall
And all we'll ever really need to cope
Can only be found as we move
On down the road . . ."

Excerpt from the song "Along the Road" by Ron D. Kingsley

THE POSITIVE SIDE OF OCS:
FOR THE NON SUPERSTAR

Many OCS affected individuals simply never give up even in the face of apparent insurmountable odds. The affected artist draws, paints, sculpts, sketches, or whatever the artistic endeavor of focus, at every possible opportunity and situation. As a result of this unrelenting activity, the artist becomes very good at what he does. Michelangelo, Vincent Van Gogh, and Leonardo Da Vinci are historical figures that immediately come into my mind as probable examples of what OCS can do over time. Contemporary figures also come just as quickly to my mind as possible examples. These include myself (as can be seen in the few out of my thousands of drawings that have been in this book). Others that should be recognizable to all include Gary Larsen of the popular "Far Side" (although I am not making a diagnosis in relation to these contemporaries, the evidence, nevertheless, seems reasonably clear), and Charles Shultz of, "Peanuts: Featuring Good Ol' Charlie Brown", fame.

Similarly, musicians such as Beethoven, Bach, and Mozart to name a few of the well known historical examples, seemed to be clearly OCS driven, as well as gifted musically, which may account for their productivity as well as frequently recorded sometimes very strange behaviors and inconsistent emotional volatility. Well known contemporary figures that seem both gifted and OCS driven might include some of my personal favorite singer-songwriters: Cat Stevens, Carly Simon, Elton John, Neil Diamond, and the late John Denver to name only a few. Again, it must be made clear that I am not making a diagnosis in relation to these individuals. I have not evaluated them. What I am doing is suggesting that from the literature and information I have read over the years, they seem prime candidates and I mention their names only to suggest that it is possible that this might be among the main reasons why they have been so very successful.

Authors or writers that seem to demonstrate the OCS drive that pushes them to prolific heights of historical significance might include: Shakespeare, H.G. Wells, and Charles Dickens (a few among many). Contemporary writers, that seem obvious candidates (but for whom, of course, I am not formally diagnosing) include a few of my favorites: Stephen King, Judy Blume, Orson Scott Card, and perhaps Louis L'amour. Again, this names only a few of the many, many other writers that almost assuredly manifest significant OCS.

The above related groups of artists, musicians, and authors, if OCS affected, would have in common a relentless drive to produce, to perform, to persevere to the extent that they typically turn out work after work after work. This productivity alone, over time, engenders even greater expertise. Thus, for these individuals the OCS, if present, would enable them to be ambitious and prolific well beyond the norm. It gives them a ferocious undeviating drive without which they would undoubtedly not do the things that they do.

Actors and salespersons that are OCS affected seem to have commonalties between their respective groups as well. There is a dynamic that begins early in the life of those who are OCS affected that, in my opinion, shapes these individuals inexorably towards their, if you will, destinies. Early in life when OCS begins to show up, individuals are typically faced with a variety of problems. Their behavior is frequently repetitive and often annoying to parents and teachers, and they have no idea why they do these things again and again, especially after being told not to do them anymore. A fair amount of the things they do are downright strange, and it makes no sense that they act in such ways. As a result, I suggest they begin to learn how to provide others with explanations for their behaviors that are reasonable and therefore believable. To cover up for their actions, which they too frequently do not understand, they learn to be very good liars, storytellers, and chicanery artists. In order to survive they spend a good part of their lives learning to convince others, as well as themselves, that things are not how they seem, that they themselves are not who they seem. In short, they experience a life time of practice in the art of lying and, what are actors, if not people trying to get us to believe that they are actually someone different from who they really are? A good salesperson can sell people things they wouldn't normally even think of buying themselves. Both these groups are extraordinarily convincing in part due to the years of practice foisted on them. Also in part because they too, like all the OCS affected, tend to be so hyper-focused and intense about what they do that they will go to any lengths possible to make themselves more believable.

If an actor playing the part of someone that is supposed to have been chased through the streets and alleys of a big city for three days without sleep prior to a specific scene may actually spend three days and nights out in the streets without sleep. All this in order to make the character become the more real. No one, in my opinion, can be more convincing playing the role of another person than someone obsessed with getting it right and compulsive about doing so. When ADHD is a component, as it often is, the actors and salespersons will have an abundance of energy and be able to work long grueling schedules that can sometimes seem almost superhuman. If you think about who are many of the best actors and salespersons of today, I would be surprised if at least a few names don't come to mind that, as you learn more about them, seem to fit the descriptors I have been suggesting.

Professional and Olympic athletes, usually starting at a very young age, tend to be intent on becoming the best. To do so requires practice. The best of the best eat, drink, and breathe their sport. They put in unbelievably long hours day-after-day and year-after-year to attain their goal. Having OCS, as might be expected, provides these individuals with the never ending drive necessary to remain motivated and continue perfecting the skills required of their sport long after they are already better than most. The highly touted "will to win" these individuals demonstrate can be more of an "obsessive need" than an actual will.

Thus, having OCS can be considered a tremendous asset depending on your point of view, the situation in which it occurs, and the determination of how much interference it is causing in a given individual's life experience. It can also be an unimaginable burden even when manifested in what may be considered an eventual positive outcome. To treat or not to treat medically depends on the intensity and frequency of the symptoms and the perceived interference. Awareness or knowledge, however, regarding this insidious and pervasively present potentially disabling condition that affects so many people is extremely valuable whether or not formal treatment efforts are instigated. Education is always important as truly understanding what is going on enables individuals to better manage responses to the symptomatology whether they, or someone else in their family or workplace, are OCS affected. Remember, OCS, like so many other physiological conditions is managed and not cured.

CHAPTER EIGHT

A NEW FRAME OF REFERENCE

Sometimes I wake up late at night . . . I cannot sleep . . . no reason why
And I lay there . . . thinkin' about this life
What I've done and where I've been . . . where I'll yet go before it ends
And writing songs that come into my mind
Each song in a way is an open book . . . waiting to be read
And sometimes to them back I look . . . just to re-read what I've said
And there's still some I don't quite understand . . . especially those written from the heart
Or from that place way down deep inside . . . where demons hide like thieves in the dark
Sometimes I wake up late at night . . . I cannot sleep . . . no reason why
And I lay there . . . thinkin' about this life
What I believe . . . and others too . . . the things I need . . . and have yet to do
And wondering . . . "will there be enough time?"
We're all running out of time
And time is a burning candle . . . growing shorter day by day
And it makes no difference if we fight for more . . . there's just one hand dealt with which to play
And the world we know so much depends upon . . . the world we want and need to see
And it's a player's game that must go on . . . until the final act is complete
Sometimes I wake up late at night . . . I cannot sleep . . . no reason why
And I lay there . . . thinking about this life
The words still come so easily . . . I arrange them into shapes I see
Making rhymes . . . that feel right to me
Oh . . . they feel so right to me

From the song "Sometimes I wake up late at night" by Ron D. Kingsley

THE GRIEF PROCESS:

As it relates to Newly Diagnosed Disabilities with a Special focus on ADHD, OCS/OCD, and Tourette's Syndrome, by Ron D. Kingsley MS, Ph.D., NCSP (Structure adapted and borrowed from an article titled "The Grief Process: As experienced by parents of handicapped children," by Ann E. Witcher)

The emotional changes that occur when someone is first told that they, or a child of theirs, have a potentially handicapping or disabling condition such as those listed in the title of this article are often quite similar to those experienced by people having lost, or facing the loss (expected death) of a loved one. Almost invariably after it has been determined that true ADHD, OCS, and/or Tourette's does exist, individuals go through what is known as "the grieving process." Typically this process is made up of five identifiable stages. These are, **DENIAL; ANGER; BARGAINING; DEPRESSION; and ACCEPTANCE.**

Each of these stages will now be reviewed as they relate to the parents of children so diagnosed, and in relation to the diagnosed individual (adult or child) as well. These people must come face-to-face with the reality that a bioneurochemical condition has been suggested to exist within themselves or in their child. Unfortunately, the diagnosis of ADHD, OCS, and Tourette's are commonly missed, misunderstood, and misdiagnosed right through childhood, adolescence, and on into adulthood.

The initial emotional transformation often comes at the time that the diagnosis is first suggested. Essentially the underlying factor here is the idea that the one with this diagnosis can no longer be considered to be "normal." Although some may be thrilled at the prospect of being thought of as "different", and to some it really doesn't seem to matter, others may be rather upset. This can be a time of shock that frequently leads to a complete rejection of the diagnosis. We immediately think, "this can't be true." Parents and individuals facing such a discovery will sometimes feel that their entire world has just collapsed. Those of us in this situation also commonly feel that we are very much alone.

Disabilities such as ADHD, OCS, and Tourette's can be diagnosed at virtually any age. It is somewhere around the time of diagnosis that we will usually begin to experience the first stage of grief. As soon as unexpected, shocking, or traumatic news is disclosed, our minds put up a hasty defense in an effort to protect our emotional stability. The first such defense is almost always a form of **DENIAL.** Most of the time we aren't even aware that this process of denial is in operation. This "mechanism of defense," as it is called, is not planned, but acts instead as a shield to deflect unwanted information that we are not yet able to handle. Because inconsistency is a hallmark symptom of ADHD, OCS, and Tourette's, we may very easily fool ourselves into thinking the problem behaviors and incidents are purposeful, and this can lead us into the trap of long term denial.

It is at this point that "doctor shopping" can, and sometimes does, occur. A second opinion is often a very good option to choose. In the case of true denial, however, it is not really a second opinion that is sought after. We may go from professional to professional, hoping that the diagnosis will be reversed and it will be revealed that we, or our child if that is the case, are actually quite normal after all. If not found normal, it is at least hoped that some other, perhaps more knowledgeable professional, will be able to figure out the exact cause of the identified problem and fix it. Of course after the problem has been corrected, we believe, sometimes desperately, the so-called ADHD, OCS, or Tourette's will have been exposed for what it really was and, as a result, proof will exist that we, or the affected child, are, not only currently, but have always been "normal."

Some of us become very sure that the tests themselves must be in error or that the diagnostic reports must have been somehow accidentally switched. Even though, in our hearts, all that are involved may sense there is something surely wrong, no one is yet able to consider or acknowledge the existing problem as it has been diagnosed.

At this time in the process of grief, denial often plays a very important role in enabling us to keep from quite literally "going off the deep end." Not having to face the immediate and mind-numbing truth can allow us needed time to slowly adjust and reorganize or rearrange our thoughts. To stretch our minds and make room for new possibilities. Most of the time it isn't so much a complete refusal to see that there is a problem as much as it is an inability to even consider it might be a permanent fixture in our lives, or in the lives of one or more of our children. ADHD, OCS, and Tourette's, though, are managed, not cured.

Tied in with this first stage is the unshakable feeling of being the only one. Along with the new diagnosis comes the fear that we are all alone, singled out, and somehow set apart from everyone else. This can be especially true if there are no local support groups available consisting of others with similar problems. These feelings of isolation can foster an active withdrawal from our usual ways of life, which can then actually create the very isolation that we fear, at least for a time.

Another common reaction during the denial stage is fear itself. Usually this fear is the result of the unknown enormity of the problem. What does it mean to us, our child, to friends or to our immediate family, not to mention relatives? How will it affect personal, family, and social situations? What new responsibilities will be added to or expected of us as a result? What will this mean in relation to our child's school experience, to our own current or future employment, social relationships, and the ability to remain or even become self-sufficient?

Other commonly experienced feelings anticipated during the denial stage are guilt and shame. Parents often view their children as extensions of themselves. In the case of diagnoses such as ADHD, OCS, and Tourette's, one or both parents may have experienced the very same kinds of problems growing up and been told they were *bad* and been told just as frequently that if they would "just try harder" and so on. As children the Parents may have been placed in special education classes and had a horrible experience because educators did not understand what the problem really was, and not understanding, did not know what to do. Parents may be treating their child in much the same way that their own parents treated them. Sometimes, if not physical, there may have been actual mental or emotionally abusive reactions. Parents do not do this on purpose. When they are faced with the proposition that they may have been, even if only on occasion, abusing their children, when the child's actions were in part the result of a very real Neurobiological cause, it is no wonder the diagnosis is rejected. The guilt and shame we feel and would have to face if we accepted the diagnosis can be tremendous. This can be further complicated by the feelings we may have towards our own parents for those of us who, with the child's diagnosis, begin to recognize our own similar symptoms (or for those initially diagnosed an adult). Questions arise like, "you mean I wasn't really bad?" "I wasn't lazy?" I'm not dumb?"

"I was unknowingly bio-medically influenced?" Feelings of both love and hate (known as ambivalence) toward the child, our parents, and even ourselves may surface and make emotional reactions much more difficult to understand and deal with effectively.

Fortunately the stage of denial along with the related emotions of isolation, fear, and guilt is usually only temporary. As we complete this stage, we begin to experience what can be thought of as a "partial acceptance." The initial reaction of "**NO!** This can't be true!" is exchanged for "Well, I guess it could be."

Whenever our children or our selves are unable or unwilling to meet our own expectations, the disappointment of shattered personal and parental hopes and dreams engenders **ANGER**. This is the common second stage of the grief process. The anger may be directed at the child, others, or even ourselves. Anger may also build in relation to our perceived "lost opportunities" and the belief that we will now be unable to adequately meet our own, as well as our children's, complicated needs. Doctors are suddenly blamed for the medical condition they have diagnosed, or teachers can be blamed, and attempts made to hold them responsible if there have been academic or learning problems. Parents themselves may be blamed by a newly diagnosed adult or by older children. The spouse of a married adult may be blamed for creating all the problems, especially, if the spouse was first to recognize the symptoms leading to a diagnosis. Honest outrage at the ignorance of others that consistently misunderstood what was going on and then judged our children or us mercilessly is also common when ADHD, OCS, or Tourette's is the diagnosis. There may also be justifiable anger directed at doctors and professionals who misdiagnosed the condition and then minimized the observable symptoms. These often well meaning (though ADHD, OCS, and Tourette's ignorant) doctors may have made statements such as: "He's a boy" or "She'll grow out of it," and even one such as: "Have you ever thought about taking a class on parenting skills?"

The third stage in the grief process is called **BARGAINING**. As the reality begins to sink in, we may try to put off or postpone this thing that can no longer be avoided with promises of good actions and behavior. Most of the time these commitments are made secretly and are religious in nature. Common bargains include promised conversions or large religious donations to be exchanged for granted requests and prayers. Sometimes these oaths are driven by added feelings of guilt for not having been faithful in attending religious services regularly or been consistent in offerings and donations. This, it is pledged, will be changed . . . if only.

When we finally realize that the act of bargaining has not and will not alter the final outcome relating to our situation, the fourth stage in the process of grief has been reached. It is **DEPRESSION**. Hope and anger are abandoned as useless. The new focus is on the great loss that we feel for all the things that "might have been." Usually each family member and sometimes close friends share in these sorrowful feelings. It is during this stage that we may actually begin to accept that which cannot be changed. It is also at this point that we newly diagnosed adults may start the process of correcting faulty and distorted memories of past events to more accurately reflect the reality of our new found knowledge. This is a very difficult and sometimes overwhelming task and we may need experienced professional help to succeed.

After the depression has run its course, there is often a period, which may best be described as a lack of feelings. We are no longer depressed, nor are we angry or even envious. It is at this time that we truly begin to understand that things really could be worse. This is the gateway to the last of the stages in the grief process, that of **ACCEPTANCE**.

Acceptance has at its heart two distinct and separate levels, one emotional in nature and the other intellectual. In order to work through this stage, we need to be able to talk about, as well as understand, the realities that go along with a particular diagnosis (or any disability) at a clear intellectual level. We must also, however, be able to experience and support this objective knowledge at an emotional level too. Either level without the other does not constitute a complete acceptance. An example of real acceptance might be: "I know it takes Rebecca a lot longer than most of her peers to do her school work. Most of the time she can only finish about half of what has been assigned. I need to let her do it by herself, however, because it is important for her to experience the benefits that come from personal accomplishments. She has the right to do her own work at her own pace and at her own level."

The acceptance stage is the beginning of the process that marks a healthy adjustment. Adjustment, though, is an on going process that covers every aspect and phase of our entire lives. Each new phase of life brings new challenges and sometimes, new grief. A few examples of such phases include age, physical development, social expectations, marriage, and personal expectations. We who have been recently diagnosed must work through all previously held beliefs and experiences of which we are aware from a vantage point that includes the new-found knowledge such diagnoses bring. Perhaps for the first time, old misunderstandings and emotional wounds can be successfully cleared up and eventually healed. The diagnosis cultivates new insight regarding why certain events and incidents may have happened while growing up, and the reason things were the way they were. This insight can lift what has often been a tremendous lifelong burden of anger and guilt. Most times such insight has the literal effect of changing the past we thought we knew. Looking through this new frame of reference at life's events, long believed to have been caused by specific people and circumstances, often results in some radically altered perceptions. When this happens we are in the process of actively reconstructing who we are today through a redefinition of our past. Much of what we believe about ourselves, who we were and what we did, we realize, may not be altogether accurate. In trying to determine what was accurate, misperceived, exaggerated, distorted, or simply misunderstood, we may fear that our entire existence up until the present day has been a lie. This, of course, is not true, but the actual fear itself is very real. A rediscovery of the self must be undertaken when an unrecognized lifelong condition such as ADHD, OCS, or Tourette's is finally diagnosed, if a true healthy adjustment is to occur. This is a difficult task that requires patience, persistence and hard work and usually takes a significantly lengthy period of time. It can only be done truly and with the depth needed to insure success during, or following, the resolution of the acceptance stage. And, as in some of the other stages, professional help may be needed.

It is essential to clearly understand that even though we may have reached the acceptance stage this is no guarantee that our prayers and hopes for a cure will have stopped entirely. The true meaning of this stage is that knowledge and emotions have evened out and become stable. With this stability, we can now successfully face the reality of our situation and begin to make the best of it. The previously held hope that the doctor's were wrong has now matured and become the new hope of making as normal a personal and family life as possible.

CONCLUDING REMARKS:

We should be careful not to assume that, once emotions have been acknowledged and explored these same emotions will never bother us again. Even when our emotional wounds are successfully healed the scars generally remain, as do the memories. It is equally important to understand that the stages in the grief process do not always arrive one right after the other in a nice, neat, and ordered package. Some stages may run into each other or may even take place at the same time. All people, too, do not as deeply experience emotions, and as a result we will respond differently to the feelings and challenges associated with moving through these stages. For some, it may not take such a long time to complete the grieving process and yet, for others, it may require years. Throughout the process of adjustment, certain stages can resurface and may need to be once again worked through. Usually this is the result of a different, though similar, incident having occurred. We should always keep in mind humans are extremely complicated beings and, as such, we are never entirely predictable.

It is of import that we understand the grief associated with the news that the presence of a bioneurochemical diagnosis represents an honest struggle in adjusting to what can be considered a "symbolic death." The child that parents had expected, or the person we once thought we were is gone. That strongly held hope and belief was buried by the diagnosis. The essential role of spouses, friends, parents, and teachers is not to actually counsel those in the process of grieving, as professionals and specific support groups are better suited to fulfill that responsibility. The healthiest role and the undeniable responsibility of these here-to-fore designated others is more appropriately one of awareness, understanding allowance, and support.

As more and more children and adults with ADHD, OCS, or Tourette's are identified, teachers, employers, spouses, and friends will be most helpful if they are sensitive regarding the expected stages in the grief process. It would also be helpful if they are also aware that people must be allowed the time and space needed to experience the stages. A supportive and nonjudgemental attitude can be a powerful and comforting element, much like a shelter in a storm.

One final thought worth repeating is that, for true healing to occur, the grieving individuals must be allowed to work through these emotionally laden stages. They must redefine and set new expectations for their children and/or themselves, as well as learn new skills with which to cope. Another's willingness to empathize, respect, and keep communication lines open during this traumatic period of life can actually speed up the healing process.

CHAPTER NINE

"And the courage it takes to get through each day
He somehow collects along the way
And if you ask him he just might say, 'you'd better believe it'
'Cause what goes up must come down as this old world keeps spinnin' 'round and gravity confines us to the ground . . .
though we can't see it

And some think he's lost . . . they say his mind's all but gone
While others see him as kind of strange . . . yet feel nothing else is wrong
But it doesn't seem to matter much at all . . . to him . . . how they carry on
And you know . . . there are those who believe . . . that's what makes him strong . . ."

Excerpt from the song "The Innocent" by Ron D. Kingsley

ASSESSMENT OF OCS:

"TO BE . . . OR NOT TO BE . . ."

Those famous words of Shakespeare, "To be, or not to be . . ."
seem right at home with the attempt to assess a group of symptoms that, no one readily wants to admit they may have. Individuals tend to be incredibly embarrassed, confused, very frightened,
and unable to accept the idea that something could be wrong.
They are also often totally unaware of the true reasons they do
some of the things that they do. Furthermore they may be in-
credulous that such behaviors could be biochemically driven, and
convinced that "everyone" does things like that, sometimes. This
last idea is frequently especially difficult to get past because the
fact of the matter is that most of us, if not all, do have OCS behaviors at times. The difference lies in how much these tendencies
may or may not interfere with our lives as we wish to live them.

Thus, evaluators have their job cut out for them right from
the beginning. They must find a way to enable the examinee/
client to remain calm in the midst of asking a host of what may
seem to them strange and/or silly questions. Questions that, in
spite of their strangeness, tend to hit nerves. "I can't believe you're

asking me that question," is a fairly common response. So, also is the intense recognition that these strange sounding symptoms are very much right on the nose for those who are truly OCS affected.

Through the course of evaluating individuals over the last decade, I have, I believe, learned some quite important elements that tend to make an OCS evaluation go more smoothly than it otherwise might. Also, it would appear more validly as well. One of the first and maybe most important assessment discoveries learned is that most OCS affected individuals, when confronted with an inventory designed to identify severe OCD symptoms, tend to flatly deny that any such symptoms could possibly exist, at least initially. I hesitate to use the word "all," but thus far, in my experience, every OCS affected individual I ever attempted to evaluate with an OCD scale in the past denied the presence of OCD symptoms as they are presented on the "typical" OCD questionnaire/ scale. OCD symptoms are usually expressed with such bizarre intensities that the OCS affected are completely incapable of relating to or even envisioning any kind of a relationship between their own troubles/symptoms and those commonly descriptive of OCD, although a relationship often truly does exist.

In my search for a tool that would enable me to assess more appropriately and adequately both OCD and OCS, I was introduced by a professional colleague, Eric Benjamin M.D., to The Leyton Obsessional Inventory for Children. I immediately found this instrument to be far less intrusive and/or intense in both content and wording of the queries presented.

Often a child's symptomatic picture of a disorder (initially diagnosed almost exclusively in adults) can tend to be thought of in terms of less severe symptoms (whether true or not). To me the children's version of the Leyton inventory seemed to be just that, a minimized, or milder, version of the more intrusive and severe OCD questionnaires. I began to use this inventory exclusively before long, not just with children but with adults as well. There were still some questions that seemed awkward and worded in ways that appeared to invite denial. However, on the whole, this instrument has proven very useful in not only the initial diagnosis of OCS/OCD but also as a pre/post instrument to aide in the monitoring of an individual's response to treatment. This has been especially true when a medication is used. Over the last ten years I have taken the liberty of rewording many of the questions to enable them to be more easily asked. I have also eliminated some of the questions that experience suggested were not really that useful, and added a few of my own that are particularly common to the OCS affected, but were not on the original inventory.

This was because as I made use of the instrument I found myself instinctively rewording the same questions again and again, as well as leaving several unasked and even adding a few of my own. Finally, in an attempt to be consistent, as well as ask the questions more appropriately in relation to the population intended, I rewrote, revised, deleted, and added to the Leyton. I still refer to it as the Leyton Obsessional Inventory because the framework, in my mind, remains much the same.

I have also come to rely on another instrument in the assessment of OCS that was not originally created to assess such symptoms. It does so nonetheless from the perspective of an observer, and it does it very well if one knows what to look for. Since the time I initially began working as a School Psychologist (1980-82), I had been introduced to a behavior evaluation scale that I connected with and enjoyed using most of the time as an integral part of my behavioral assessments. My liking towards this instrument may have been due, perhaps, to it's relative ease of administration, fairly comprehensive outlook (measuring 18 or 19 categories of behavior), sensible sounding results, and parent/teacher's positive responses relating to its usefulness upon completion. This instrument is called The Burks' Behavior Rating Scales.

When a conscientious professional utilizes a given instrument of assessment over time periods extending over many years, it is not unusual for such a professional to begin to see patterns. Often such patterns may not be specified in the original manual. Nevertheless, such data can be valid indicators of issues and/or diagnoses worthy of careful clinical consideration. Thus, the OCS pattern, as rated by an observer, emerged. Time and time again when OCS was present, the Burks' patterns were very similar. This pattern did not make sense until I began carefully reviewing single items of significance. Both the direct as well as the indirectly related scored descriptors of OCS were negatively skewing so many of the 19 categories that make up the Burks' profile as to render it uninterpretable, as far as normal procedures were concerned. Invariably, when I first began noticing the pattern, or more simply the problems, relating to the Burks' being essentially unreadable as a result of this pattern, my tendency was to look to other assessment tools for my answers. The Burks', however, I would still consider from the viewpoint of singular items of significance, as indicated earlier. These single items could be grouped into a category that reflected the OCS pattern. In time a consistent pattern seemed to emerge.

A third element, not to be left out, in the assessment of OCS is the clinical interview, and more specifically a history of symptomatic presence should be documented. While doing so, it is important for the clinician to keep in mind that in the initial stages of assessment, the affected individuals and/or parents/guardians involved are typically quite naïve in regard to what may, or may not, have constituted a symptom. They may initially fail to appreciate the significance of past experiences that could have been either directly and/or indirectly related to, or resulting from, mild-moderate OCS. When OCS is thought to be present, clinicians should always look for indicators suggesting its presence throughout the life span of the individual. Intensity levels typically wax and wane over time, and symptoms can be incredibly varied as well as "here today and gone tomorrow", meaning that it is not unusual to experience quite different symptoms off-and-on throughout one's life time. It is also not uncommon, though, to have a few symptoms, or symptom threads, stay with you off-and-on throughout life as well. The presence of recognizable symptoms, characteristics, and/or "tendencies" is almost a requisite for the diagnosis when the Serotonin levels seem to be the underlying precipitating factor relating to the OCS. Eventually affected individuals can learn in what ways, and get a sense of to what extent; this insidious malady has influenced their decisions, life experience, and past/present behavioral repertoire.

Within the context of the clinical interview, a brief exploration of the OCS suspected's extended family, and family of origin is warranted. The question needs to be asked, "do other immediate family members appear to have similar "tendencies"? Consideration should be given to each brother and sister, as well by both parents. At this point I routinely ask diagnostic questions regarding not just the possibility of OCS, but also regarding the possibility of ADHD and/or Tourette's Syndrome. The research suggesting a genetic relationship between ADHD, OCS/OCD, and Tourette's, along with my own clinical experience, is sufficient in my mind to warrant such a procedure. In my experience, it seems an affected individual will typically have a sibling(s), parent(s), aunt(s), or uncle(s) and so on that could have been or may already have been similarly diagnosed. Any of these three apparently genetically related problems might appear in any combination in family or extended family members as well.

When pursuing this line of questioning with parents of, or older affected individuals in regard to extended family members, it is often helpful to describe, using ordinary terms, how others might have perceived someone with OCS at a time before most people were even aware of its existence. For example, I often begin with the following type of statement:

"Well, if your Grandmother or Grandfather had OCS, others might have said things and make comments about them such as: "She's a little *off-the-wall*," or, "Yeah, he's kind of *eccentric*, a little *strange*, or even *weird*."

As a child when it was time to go visiting at these grandparent's home you might have tried to hide, or wished you could have hidden. Anything to keep from having to go. Complaints similar to the following, if not in context, at least in flavor, might have filled the air.

"You can't even sit on a couch at their house".
"Remember not to touch grandpa's newspapers . . . even if they are old . . . and all over the house."
"Grandma follows me through the house with a dustpan, broom, wet rag, and Lysol . . . for cryin' out loud."
"Aw . . . we get yelled at over there just for breathing wrong . . ." and so on.

By the time I get through a diatribe such as the one above, awareness begins to dawn on the faces of those listening. If not aware of a grandparent with such idiosyncrasies, children and adolescents will often recognize another extended family member who fits such a pattern.

"You know," they may comment. "My Uncle Bob, my Mother's brother, always has been really weird. He does the stupidest things and no one ever seems to want to be around him . . . at least not for long."

The motor and vocal tics of Tourette's are easily described (or demonstrated) and, if present, in familiar extended family members, tend to be recognized immediately. When tics are ascertained, a brief explanation of the severity and kinds of tics is warranted and may eventually prove beneficial in the affected individual's treatment plan.

The point is, when OCS is an appropriate diagnosis, it is highly unusual not to be able to trace one or more of the three related bioneurochemical problems (ADHD, OCS/OCD, Tourette's) back through either one, or both, parent's extended families. This is not true, of course, when there were adoptions or, for some other reason, the extended family information is not known. Belaboring over extended family issues is not recommended, as the role this gathered information plays in the evaluation is actually one of support for the possible diagnosis.

ADHD tends to be a better known condition due to its current diagnostic popularity. A description of a few of the current established "core" symptoms typically results in immediate recognition. Even if an individual's perceptions about ADHD are somewhat distorted, the general sense of the disorder usually allows for a fairly quick determination of its possible familial presence.

NOTE: It is beyond the scope of this paper to describe in specific and/or comprehensive detail, the genetically related conditions of either ADHD or Tourette's Syndrome. The interested reader is referred to the following texts for their excellent descriptions of these related conditions:

Children With Tourette Syndrome: A Parent's Guide: Ed. Tracy Haerle 1992.

A Mind of its Own: Tourette's Syndrome: A story and a guide: Ruth Dowling Brunn and Bertel Brunn 1994.

Driven to Distraction: Recognizing and Coping with Attention Deficit Disorder from Childhood through Adulthood. Edward M. Hallowell, M.D., and John F, Ratey, M.D. 1994.

You Mean I'm not Lazy, Stupid, or Crazy? A self-help book for adults with Attention Deficit Disorder: Kate Kelly and Peggy Ramundo, 1993.

Taking Charge of ADHD: The complete, authoritative guide for parents: Russell a Barkley, Ph.D. 1995.

When behavior ratings, inventories, and clinical interview information are all consistent in suggesting the presence of OCS a provisional, or working diagnosis should be made. An integral part of the assessment is also to try and determine the severity of, or intensity levels of, the interference experienced from identified symptoms. Not unlike the diagnostic criteria found in the DSM IV in relation to an Obsessive Compulsive Disorder, the goal is to estimate the amount of time lost in an average day as a probable result of current symptomotology.

Next I attempt to ascertain, in as much as is possible, the emotional impact the OCS is having on the affected individual, as well as on those who are consistently interacting with the person (i.e., family, close friends, and co-workers). How distressed is the one affected by their symptoms and related problems stemming from the OCS? How distressed are family members? What is the relationship stability in relation to occupational authority figures and/or underlings? Are such changes considered critical? Does the individual have good or poor insight in relation to identified symptoms and resulting dynamics? Answers to questions such as these provide valuable information that enables the experienced clinician to formulate appropriate treatment strategies and interventions.

CHAPTER TEN

LIFE WITH OCS

OCS AND THE FAMILY

This is where it all begins. The OCS affected child typically is born into a family in which one and often both parents are symptomatic themselves. In my experience most affected parents, particularly when the symptoms are in the mild-moderate range, are (as I've hinted at elsewhere) as unaware of their own symptomotology as they are of breathing. It just happens. It's the way things are. Similar patterns existed with their parents, who also had no idea regarding the biochemical-inherited nature of the condition, and so on.

Interactions between family members of the OCS affected tend to be very serious. Attempts to kid and/or joke with one another typically fail miserably because the intended scapegoat frequently takes all comments directed towards them soberly. It's as if they cannot hold in their minds what the words mean and the aspect of humor at the same time. And, since humor often depends on subtle connotations and fine vocal intonations, the OCS affected hear it straight. Since many jokes also tend to be exaggerated either in the intensity of the way they are presented (vocal tones, etc.) or in the words chosen, the meaning, and so on . . . the OCS affected tend to hyper-respond, that is exactly what tends to occur. They over respond. Efforts to laugh a bit and make light of difficult situations often end up in bitter arguments and family strife.

Growing up in such a family tends to be difficult, and it is made even more difficult by the fact that no one knows why the family members react to each other and to the outside world in the way they do. There is often an unconscious awareness that things are not right or "normal", if you will. At the same time there is a desperate need to at least appear "normal" to others. This dissonance plays heavily on each of the family member's lives over time.

A Mother of three in an intact OCS affected family will joke that she really has four children. These would be the three she gave birth to and her husband. She'll laugh with the others who may hear her statement that smile while nodding their heads, but in secret she sheds real tears over it.

When obsessive thoughts and compulsions are actually intruding, chores, homework, special requests and the like are not completed.

An eleven-year-old girl is walking through the family room in front of her Dad who is sitting on a couch watching TV She is headed towards the kitchen.

Her Dad, who has noticed her socks simply dropped on the carpet by the end of the couch, says, "Ellen!" in somewhat gruff and frustrated tones, "will you PLEASE pick up those socks and quit leaving your clothes scattered all over the house!"

Ellen stops leans over to retrieve the socks, and continues on her way.

From the kitchen the sound of a refrigerator door being opened and eventually closed is heard.

Ellen once more starts to cross in front of the couch where her Dad is sitting. Suddenly his voice fills the room. "Ellen," he exclaims. He sits up straight and literally glares at her. "Where are your socks?"

Frozen in her tracks, eyes wide, a tear trickles out of the corner of her right eye. She hesitates, and slowly rolls her eyes as if looking, considering. Then, in a soft but choked whisper she replies, "I don't know." And she doesn't.

"You've got to be kidding," says the Dad as he pushes him self from the couch to his feet.

Ellen immediately shies away from him as if fearing she might get hit, even though she was four years old the last time he spanked her.

The Dad heads straight for the kitchen. "Where could they be?" He adds.

Later, many times, he is able to laugh as he tells this story about his "brainless" daughter to others. He laughs especially hard when he gets to the "punch line" of this very real joke of life.

"They were in the refrigerator," he roars. Most of the time those he tells laugh right along with him just as hard as he does.

Ellen never did, laugh that is. To her it had never been funny. She was incredibly embarrassed when it happened and even more so at each subsequent telling.

These are the dynamics of which I speak that become entrenched within the affected families. A single related incident like the one above by itself is not usually a devastatingly psycho-emotionally-ripping event. What makes it so overwhelmingly devastating are the hundreds, perhaps thousands, of other similar incidents, situations, and events that go undetected and roll on and on through the years that a family is together, and often carry on even when they are, later in life, quite apart from each other.

Family members learn early on to "walk on eggshells" in relation to each other much of the time.

A wife complains, "I can't tell him anything important! When I do, he just blows up and then he doesn't hear a thing I say past that point."

"When I tell him he's done a good job, he comes back (lots of times angrily) with all the reasons why it's not a good job. If I don't say anything, he complains that I don't notice or care about the things he does. If I happen to suggest one more thing that could be done, or a different way something could have been done, he goes ballistic. I can't win!"

"He never does ANYTHING around the house." she complains in a loud bitter voice.

Later, in confidence, he shares, "Why should I do anything? No matter what I do, no matter how much or how hard I try, it's never—ever good enough. She wants me to do it again, or, she does it again. What's the use?"

Parents often remark, "The kids are addicted to playing. They never come home when they're supposed to. They don't listen. They don't mind, and they don't care. Grounding doesn't work.

Neither does spanking. Yelling doesn't work. Nothing does. They don't care about consequences of any kind. They just don't care."

In my professional opinion, no book will ever be able to capture in detail the practically innumerable ways in which OCS can affect a family. This is because symptoms vary, they come and go, environments are different, individual chemistry is variable and so on. This is why it is often useful and perhaps even essential (at least to begin with) that families seek out a knowledgeable professional counselor, psychologist, or psychiatrist that can work with them to disentangle the often subtle and insidiously complicated family dynamics involved in OCS. The descriptions herein are offered as fairly common examples, but the depth of the potential problems and related problems has barely been touched. It is hoped that extrapolations from the text of this book will be used to aid in the process of this commonly needed disentanglement.

In spite of the inability to accurately describe all possible conditions, dynamics, and situations, there are a few common threads that I believe families and professionals can keep in mind that will more easily enable therapeutic progress to continue successfully.

• OCS affected individuals, and therefore families, tend to be hypersensitive and over respond in the extreme. Many arguments, fights, and misunderstandings have this factor at the heart of the situations. When this is so, tracing it back can be a helpful intervention, and eventually a prevention tool.

• Affected individuals frequently are unable to listen and/or focus long enough to allow new information to be processed and stored in the brain when experiencing a compulsion or obsessive thought patterns. Tracing this back to the source can relieve feelings of frustration and anger associated with perceptions of another's irresponsibility, and beliefs that they don't care, as well as perceptions that they purposefully do not listen. Once it is recognized, it can also lead to creative and successful techniques of intervention that might be tried to better manage this type of problem. For example, I know a professional man whose briefcase only opens from one side, and he always takes it to work every day. He tapes a piece of paper to the outside so that every time he goes to open it, the things he doesn't want to forget are right there in front of his face. He also writes things down immediately so they are not forgotten. I also know a child (now a man) who hated having anything in his right pants pocket. When he wanted to remember something important, he wrote it down or put it in that right pocket. It bugged him so much to have something there, he'd touch and pull it out throughout the whole day. This worked for him.

- Affected individuals get doing something and do not want to quit (compulsion). This problem can be at the heart of unfinished chores, missed meetings, unfinished homework, arguments, temper tantrums, threats, extreme anger, and physically violent acts.

- When affected individuals want something obsessively, they want it bad. They will ask and ask again. They will cajole, wheedle, whine, and demand. They may even make threats that they truly do not mean to carry out, but can be frightening nonetheless.

- If one parent says no, they will usually go straight to the other. Parents need to stay in close communication with each other and check up with one another on any questionable subject in relation to their children.

- Extreme and over reactive fear of intensely imagined consequences, literal beliefs (again over reactive and unintentionally exaggerated) that if they cause parents to be disappointed (by disobeying, etc.,), they will lose all their love (the parent will hate them), will engender a perceived need to be deceptive. Adults and children alike will lie or hold back on all the truth and so on. This can be difficult to deal with, because the very falsehood they tell can also cause parents to be disappointed, and since that is still over reacted to if parents catch them in a lie, they will expend much energy and time denying that it's a lie. They may creatively rationalize a way that what they've said could be viewed as the truth, or simply deny vehemently that the lie is a lie. Eventually, when calm, most can admit the lie but while biochemically driven, most cannot.

- OCS family members sometimes need their space. While the action and reactions are biochemically charged, much of the time nothing else will get through. Verbal reasoning is useless; screaming exacerbates everything, as does touch or attempts at restraint. At these Moments, all parties involved need to be left alone in order to facilitate their calming down. Creative use of time-out procedures is extremely helpful in these situations. Professionals can work to create a family time-out sequence with backup plans in case someone gets too out of control to respond.

- A family cue system can be beneficial. This would consist of a "cue" that could be verbal, visual, or kinesthetic. Each member would agree to "cue" any other member at the Moment they perceive a biochemically driven situation has commenced. This depends entirely on the family members and should not be used if agreement can't be reached. I know a family that, once things were understood, would cue each other by playfully saying, "are you obsessing again?" This worked for them quite positively as treatment went on to help prevent many of the previously common household fights and episodes.

- Changes in routines tend to be extremely difficult for OCS individuals and families. Often this difficulty can be at the heart of why the family members don't do much together or go places much. Vacations are frequently disasters in relation to the amount of family energy and emotional intensity involved. There are some tried and proven strategies that can make changes, transitions, and vacations go more smoothly. One of the best is, don't go! I say this somewhat facetiously here but, unfortunately, this happens all too often. Vacations and changes sometimes become so hard on the OCS family that they simply give up and quit trying to go. I don't believe this strategy is any healthier than rekindling disaster after yearly disaster. Of course, treatment in the form of awareness, knowledge, and medication is extremely helpful. Other methods that typically help, whether before or after successful treatment, include mainly one thing, preparation. The family should start a couple of months in advance, talking about a planned trip or vacation. The closer the date of departure gets, the more often and detailed the discussions need to be. In this way each member is being prepared mentally for each and every important aspect and change planned, of which the planners, of course, are aware. This reduces mental anguish regarding the fear of the unknown, anxiety, and worry. When prepared well for changes, transitions, and vacations, the family members are much less likely to experience "disaster," and things will go more smoothly.

- All family members need to practice, practice, and practice their PATIENCE with each other as well as themselves. One of my favorite phrases to utter is "practice your patience" whether it be in reference to myself or to others.

OCS AND THE INDIVIDUAL

There are significant scattered bits of information pertaining to the affected individual throughout the body of this work. The recommendations relating to family factors just reviewed, for the most part, are appropriate for the individual as well. Thus, I will try not to make this section tediously and/or redundantly long.

When individuals from the age of about 10 years and up first realize and truly understand the ramifications of what it means to have a genetically transmitted biochemically driven symptomatology, they are often ecstatic. Suddenly, all the years prior to their finding out begin to make perfect (or at least good) sense. They understand for the first time much of why they have been the way they were, and experience real hope for the present and, for what often had been, a truly dismal looking future.

Many seem to become excited about life again. Parents frequently find their children's positive responses hard to believe. They are thrilled. Initial positive responses tend to be greater than those eventually achieved over time. Sometimes being excited, or thrilled, is far from what the initially diagnosed individual or parents experience.

An article written many years ago caught my attention when it came out and triggered what I have considered a very useful and important personal insight that, I believe, is also capable of being generalized. The article was by Ann E. Witcher and was titled "The Grief Process: As Experienced by Parents of Handicapped Children."

The idea that parents of handicapped children would experience, after initially being informed about a handicap, and the stages of grief, was new to me. It felt right immediately, and I gratefully accepted its' wisdom and truth. Ms. Witcher's article focused on the parent's experience in relation to what seemed to me the more obvious and debilitating kinds of childhood handicaps. It occurred to me; however, that this same process of grief might have to be experienced, as well, by the parents and individually affected them even when the conditions being initially diagnosed are of a more subtle and less than obvious nature. In particular, I found myself pondering the insidiously chronic condition of ADHD, and soon thereafter, those of mild-moderate OCS and Tourette's Syndrome.

Ms. Witcher's thesis suggested that parents whose child was born handicapped experience the same well known grief process associated with the actual loss, or death, of a loved one. This is due to the parents being faced with the loss, or death, of their expectations for a "normal" child. Just as in the case of a loved one's literal death, they go into mourning over their hopes, plans, and dreams regarding what they would become, which are no longer appropriate in relation to what they have. They must be changed (sometimes dramatically) or shifted to incorporate the child from a new frame of reference. It is essentially a kind of paradigm shift. Their grief over what they perceive has been lost, through the process, enables them to eventually accept the reality of all that they still have. Life goes on.

As I read and pondered the article, a seeming flash of inspiration came to me. I began to wonder about those parents who, upon the birth of a child, were informed by attending physicians as well as their intact five senses that this child was perfectly healthy and "normal," only to find out, usually many years later, that the child actually had not been "normal." After having already been engaged in parenting for a period typically ranging from about 2 to 18 or 19 years, they find out their "normal" child has an Attention Deficit Hyperactivity Disorder, mild-moderate Obsessive Compulsive condition, or previously undiagnosed (and/or misdiagnosed) Tourette's Syndrome. This among also other subtle and difficult to recognize and diagnose potentially disabling syndromes, disorders, and conditions. It seemed obvious to me that these parents must also face significant grief and also face having to go through the stages of grief. An added element for this group of parents is the frequently experienced immense guilt associated with their, at times, bordering on abusive actions and reactions in their efforts at parenting such a child as if he/she were "normal." Parents can feel they have been the targets of a great deception pulled off by the delivering physician, and later maintained by the child's Pediatrician. The initial grief stages of Denial, followed by Anger, can be especially severe and difficult to work through for this group of parents.

In considering those parent's faced with working through the delayed discovery of these insidious and difficult to detect chronic conditions that directly and often indirectly affect and influence their child, I couldn't help but wonder about the child as well.

Not only the child, though, what about the adolescent? What about the adult, who just like their parents, had been living with the constantly held affirmation that they, themselves, were "normal" and just like everyone else? These are they who had been holding themselves up in comparison to societal norms and expectations with a strong internalized absolute belief that, because they were "normal," they should be able to meet all these societal standards of normality. Wouldn't, I thought, theseindividuals go through the grief process too? It made such good sense it hardly seemed worthy of an answer. Of course they would.

As an affected individual moves through the grief stages, I have found that there is an essential and incredibly therapeutic task that must be undertaken in addition to the mourning for that which was lost, and a re-establishing of more realistic expectations. Quite frequently the older child, adolescent, and especially the belatedly diagnosed adult must come to accept themselves through a redefinition or rediscovery of the past. Because these previously unknown chronic conditions typically influenced, interfered with, and may have dramatically affected life's experiences up until the Moment of awareness, these individuals usually have a distorted view, though inadvertently so, of their pasts and all others with whom they had had significant personal relationships and associations. The reasons, or causes, of specific events, relationship struggles, and experiences of the past are all too often, given the new perspective engendered by the diagnosis, found to have been partially and even totally inaccurate.

Thus, affected individuals can benefit immensely by exploring personal significant historical experiences and relationships with awareness of, and taking into consideration, what it means to have lived without knowledge of these chronic interfering factors. From the perspective of this newly achieved point of view, history can literally be changed. Of course, what has actually occurred cannot be changed but, since humans themselves record history, one never knows for sure how much the attitudes and perceptions of each individual recorder may have distorted, or viewed differently, the events and situations pertaining to what they write. Therefore, as perceptions and viewpoints change so, also, can previously held beliefs and realities of one's past.

The adult, for example, who grew up feeling abused and neglected by parents and/or guardians, may be harboring excessive significant anger and hostility towards them in relation to these experiences. The adults in this situation may be resentful and angry at the entire world, and at God, as well. After being diagnosed with an ADHD/OCS combination, and truly learning about the effects these chronic conditions can have on a given individual, along with receiving knowledge of the genetic nature of such problems, the adult who looks back may begin to suddenly understand in a way never possible before. All of a sudden they may clearly see and begin to appreciate how difficult to parent, as a child, they must have been. They start to get a sense of how overly sensitive and over responsive to little things they often were, as well as how such exaggerated responsiveness may have led to personal misperceptions and distortions of incidents and situations. Perceived abuse may not have been nearly as bad as previously believed. There may be times when remembered incidents were not truly abusive at all. Individual extreme hypersensitivity may have intensified most emotionally charged experiences, to the extent that the individual's perception of abuse was real and became embedded in the memory as such. This is not to suggest that true abuse may not have also occurred. It often does.

By understanding the underlying dynamics that commonly result in misperceptions and distortions, the affected individual can use this comprehension to explore memorable events and relationships of the past and carefully consider possible new interpretive viewpoints. This previously perceived history could be transformed via a redefinition of the whys and wherefores of events.

Another factor that can significantly aid in the healing of long standing wounds can occur with the knowledge that the individual's current diagnosis is primarily of genetic origin. The understanding and application of this awareness, in relation to the parental behaviors of the past, allows for a possible redefinition of the individual's perceived motives for their parents actions and reactions.

One can come to understand that not only were they, as well as their parents, in the dark about the initially diagnosed individual's symptoms; they, as parents, were also totally unaware of their own. Thus, not only was the OCS individual chronically hypersensitive and hyper-responsive, so were the parents, as undoubtedly were their parents and so on.

This examining of the past through new eyes often enables the healing process of long standing emotional wounds to begin. Chronically held intensely bitter feelings and related, sometimes all consuming, anger can finally be worked through, and meaning or sense can be brought to them both.

The adolescent and adult whose diagnosis was postponed can eventually begin to realize that their parental figures may have been, and/or might be, doing the best they could, given their specific circumstances in life. As this occurs, the profoundly felt deep-rooted anger accumulated over a life time can subsequently dissipate. Open emotional wounds similarly heal and become dispassionate scars instead. Management of the diagnosed chronic bioneurochemical conditions is then made much easier.

As was true when dealing with OCS families, the affected OCS individual may benefit from being aware of some of the more common tendencies associated with the individualistic experience of OCS. They are as follows:

- There is an insidiously woven tendency for the OCS individual to be perceived by others as extremely self-centered and/or overly self-occupied. Most of the time when such a perception prevails, I believe, as a result of years of experience this perceived notion is actually false. The problem, though, is that for all intents and purposes, OCS individuals do look very much self-absorbed. In my opinion, this appearance is given as a result of their active obsessions and compulsions. In the individual's mind, much of what they do is perceived as entirely for the benefit of others. The problem lies, however, in how their preconceived selfless actions are implemented. This is a difficult concept to understand and also, I have found, to believe.

A simple example may help. Let's say a child comes to visit his Grandfather. In the backyard of the house they happen to have two big and healthy Navel orange trees growing. The child loves oranges. So, upon arriving, he asks the Grandfather if they can go out back and pick one so that he can eat it.

The Grandfather is thrilled at his grandson's request. After all he'd hand planted them both for this very reason more than 25 years ago. They go out back together.

The Grandfather, whose entire purpose for planting the trees was for this grand Moment, begins to tell the story of the trees to his grandson.

The boy wants an orange. But the story must be told first. Grandfather insists. The boy must know it in its entirety.

The Grandfather begins by telling him exactly why he chose the Navel orange.

The boy reaches his hand out towards the nearest tree.

"Not yet," his grandpa takes his hand. "We're getting to the good part. I went to 32 different nurseries before I found these two . . ." the Grandfather drones on.

Need I go on?

Obviously the Grandfather appears to be forcing this story on the boy to fulfill his own needs. This is exactly how it looks.

To the Grandfather, however, caught up in the obsessive need for this Moment to be just right, it's all . . . every single word along with 25+ years of care totally for and in behalf of his grandson.

But the boy only wanted an orange.

Knowledge and awareness (and sometimes medication) are needed to make positive forward progress on this problem, that and time, as well as patience and commitment. The affected individual must be open, completely clear of significant denial, and non-defensive. They must try to "catch" themselves in the act, so to speak. Most of the time, especially in the beginning, they will need to rely on others to identify and cue them that an apparent self-centered and self-absorbed act has begun. This is why the individual needs to be open and non-defensive, so they can readily acknowledge and accept such cues. At the time the cue is given, they must stop what they are engaged in doing. It often helps to shift, or redirect themselves to another, perhaps incompatible activity or response. With time and effort, this obsessive pattern can be reduced significantly, which then leads to better relationships with others and less likelihood of having actions misunderstood.

- The tendency to be hypersensitive, and hence over responsive can also be diminished in intensity with persistent effort over time. Medication typically dramatically reduces this hyper-responsivity and also allows the individual a unique opportunity to learn about the true biochemical nature of OCS. As awareness is increased, so is the likelihood that when medications are not being used, the individual will be much better able to consciously choose responses during hypersensitive moments or when triggers occur, rather than simply over reacting as was done in the past.

. Since the OCS individual's mind is constantly occupied the resulting perception is that there is never enough time. There is no way they will be able to do all that needs to be done. As a result, it is not unusual for the affected individual to attempt to gain more time by cajoling others into essentially doing some of the work for which they are responsible. Often the individual is quite unaware of this tendency and has, similarly, no idea what kind of an emotional strain such behavior can have on others. They very quickly can become frustrated, angry, and intensely resentful. Let the OCS affected be aware and work to consciously avoid creating such a psycho-emotionally harmful dynamics amid family members, friends, and those others in the workplace.

. Personal and obsessive standards of perfection: This trend is usually a no-win situation for all those involved. The OCS individual is constantly experiencing frustration as person after person fails to measure up to the affected's expected measures. These expectations are commonly out of reach for most, if not all, others on which they are placed. No individual's performance is exactly the same as another's. Thus, non-affected individuals who are persistently up against the affected's out of reach contingencies can quickly become demoralized, frustrated, angry, and may, as a result, perform well-below their own capabilities. Resentment, as might be anticipated, towards the OCS individual is a frequent outcome. Awareness can help the OCS affected to refrain from impinging on others with their own obsessive and/or compulsive standards. Expectations can be high, just try not to allow them to become obsessively high and out of reach.

- Be aware of distortions and misperceptions. These are prominent and frequent in the case of the unaware OCS affected individual. As treatment progresses and understanding and awareness grow, the affected is typically better equipped to handle this tendency and it's occurrence tends to diminish greatly.

OCS AND SOCIAL LIFE:

Depending on one's frame of reference, this may not be considered to be much of a problem at all because there often isn't one; a social life that is. Social difficulties are quite common throughout the life span of those who are OCS affected. I suspect that by the time this portion of the text is being studied the reader, through extrapolations, has assimilated a host of ideas in relation to symptoms and their associated dynamics that could be simply plugged in here. All of the previously shared OCS descriptors come together and have an impact on the affected individual's social life.

There seem to be significant numbers of the OCS affected who can be grouped, for the most part, in one of two clusters that to the casual observer appear to be polar opposites.

A large group of the OCS affected have developed fears and anxieties that become so uncomfortable in social situations (where they are triggered) that these individuals tend to actively avoid social gatherings in as much as they possibly can. A few of the more prominent, understandable, and more obvious symptoms underlying this group's responsivity socially include the following:

- A heightened fear of what others may be thinking about the OCS affected individual.

- The affected's personal fear that they may say, or do the wrong thing.

- Significant discomfort relating to being so physically close to so many people at the same time.

- Feelings of a claustrophobic nature.

- Extreme generalized anxiety for which no apparent cause has been found. In my experience there are invariably specific underlying causative factors, although they may be well hidden by secondary and even tertiary behavioral symptoms enter-twined and counter entwined so thoroughlyas to make it difficult for even the most savvy and aware to disentangle.

- Problems accepting personal responsibility. This actually seems to be a hallmark characteristic associated with OCS which also has a similarly hallmark polar opposite symptom. To accept responsibility, or blame, for ones misdirected/problematic actions and/or reactions means to admit a personal mistake was made. This is so incredibly difficult for many of the OCS affected because, in their own distorted and exaggerated perceptions, to do so would be tantamount to personal emotional suicide. For them things are "black or white" and in quotients of "all or nothing." To accept responsibility for an error or mistake is to acknowledge one's worthlessness as a human being or as an individual acting in whatever role or position currently being played. So, there is an almost universally subconscious need to immediately and adamantly deny responsibility for any and all mistakes, no matter how seemingly insignificant these may be perceived by others. The opposite can also be true, and neither of these tendencies seems to be mutually exclusive. OCS affected individuals can also have a proclivity towards blaming themselves in an intensely exaggerated manner and attempt to take responsibility for any and every problem, error, and/or mistake occurring within their sphere of existence. This, too, can be tremendously exasperating for the individual as well as all others that are connected in life and must deal with them. Medication, awareness, cognitive restructuring, patience, practice, and time, all need to be combined in order to successfully intervene, manage, and eventually change this particularly insidious mindset.

The other major direction of a great many of the OCS affected in relation to social activity appears to be a direct opposite position to the one just explored above. The key word in the sentence before this is "appears", but we'll come back to that in a minute. This group of individuals seems to love attending various social gatherings, events, parties and the like. This, it seems, is their chance to shine. They can be (although just as often not) the "life of the party." The various prominent observable actions (symptoms) displayed socially by the individuals of this group tend to be tremendously varied but lean in the same direction. They are loud, and often perceived by others as obnoxious, intrusive, and also hilarious. As a result they can become the "life of the party," or the scourge. They can be admired and loved for their frequently offbeat comments and antics, or barely tolerated as annoying buffoons. Many others perceive the individuals of this group, as desperate attention seekers whom it seems would sell their souls for a laugh. The dynamics that lead people down this particular path are not yet very clear, but it does seem obvious that it is no single event. Rather, it is a complex series of events that interface with an individual's unique and specific bio-physiology. Hypotheses I have generated thus far that seem to make sense include the following:

- To regulate, control, or be in charge of any given social event or situation. The more the OCS affected feel in "the drivers seat," the more it seems anxiety, worry, and fear are diminished. Thus, the OCS individual's "acting out" in social situations may, at least in part, be due to the subconscious need to be in charge of all that happens to them. This in turn significantly reduces what might otherwise consist of an extremely uncomfortable, or overwhelming, amount of uncontrollable free-floating anxiety and/or fear.
- The incompatible response mode. There is a well known behavioral modification technique called the Incompatible Response Method that can be implemented to diminish the frequency of a given undesired behavior or series of thoughts. It consists of a purposeful change in behavior and/or thinking, from the undesired to the more desirable ones that, when occurring, literally interferes with a person's capacity to engage in those behaviors that are considered undesirable, or not wanted. For example, a right handed person who is engaged in the act of writing on a piece of paper with pencil or pen cannot, at the same time, chew or bite the fingernails of the hand that is writing. The act of writing in relation to biting the nails is an incompatible response. As Rapaport et al. have

pointed out in their OCD research, affected individuals who keep themselves "busy" experienced a significant diminishing of various symptomatology. The OCS individuals of this group therefore, when in social situations may, in part, be unknowingly acting in concert with a need to diminish whatever symptoms they would otherwise experience as a result of their presence at a social gathering. This suggests to me that this group may not be actually all that different symptomatically from their apparent polar opposites. The difference seems to lie more in the manner that these individuals respond that serves to reduce their symptoms.

- Energy levels. Although controversial at this time, I have a notion that the individuals compromising this subgroup may very well be many, if not most, of those who experience equally significant co-morbid ADHD and OCS. The ADHD component appears to be comprised of mainly the subgroups having as a significant symptom an identified element of hyperactivity. Impulsivity and impulse-control disinhibition seems of secondary importance in this subgroup. Remember, however, OCS itself, at times, can be viewed by others as evidence of impulsivity or considered due to impulse control problems. The frenetic and boundless energy of this hyperactive ingredient, which we know is frequently intensified in the presence of overwhelming external stimuli, may hold a significant share of the pie in relation to the reasons certain OCS individual end up in the subgroup we have been herein considering. Social events and gatherings are often replete with numerous assorted and frequently changing externally produced intrusive stimuli that can tax the sanity in the best of us. When overwhelmed, the intensity of the ADHD symptom increases, which means, in the case of hyperactivity, you may get, essentially what may constitute a temporary state of, SUPER hyperactivity.

- Entertainer. On the more positive side, the OCS affected in this group can be particularly astute comedians and actors. The perspectives of these individuals can be astonishingly refreshing and inventive, while the intensity they bring to the characters in the roles they play could convince even the vehement skeptical critics to disregard their skepticism and believe.Again, as has been said before, knowledge of OCS and conscientious awareness tend to be essential elements to positive progress and success. The OCS affected's social behavior can be dramatically improved. It does, however, seem to take a fair amount of time and persistent effort to both achieve and maintain social success.

We need to remember this:

There is no key to life: It has a combination lock.

Hence: There is also no key to OCS: It, also, is locked via combination.

CHAPTER ELEVEN

Theoretical Perspectives

There comes a time when we must
Pack up the bags and leave our inner child behind
So the signs say
There's a thing takes place
When we reach a certain age
Considered older
Suddenly it's sir
Hey . . . I never really wanted to grow up
In a world like this
If I were to step right off do you think I might miss
Something?
Well . . . bring me a little sunshine . . . oh yeah
Down my way
Sing me a little good times song . . . I'm sad today . . . yeah
I'm sad today

From the song "Reflections" by Ron D. Kingsley

OCD, OCP, and OCS: A DISCUSSION

Obsessive Compulsive Disorder (OCD) is a diagnostic category listed in the DSM IV, as is OBSESSIVE COMPULSIVE PERSONALITY DISORDER (OCP) as well. Obsessive Compulsive symptoms at a sub clinical level (not sufficient to be classified as a "disorder") or what I have referred to, as in the mild to moderate range, are also listed in the DSM IV in a sort-of back seat kind of way. That is, they are indicated as characteristics or symptoms that are subsequent to another specific disorder such as Major Depression, Bipolar, and even Generalized Anxiety Disorder among others. It is my contention that OCD, OCP, and OCS are all related manifestations of the same problem that are simply at different stages on a continuum, and that OCS can be just as valid a problem in need of intervention as OCP and OCD. In this section, I will attempt to give the reasons why I believe this to be true.

The DSM IV defines OCD (Obsessive Compulsive Disorder) as:

> "Recurrent obsessions or compulsions that are severe enough to be time consuming (i.e., they take more than one hour a day) or cause marked distress or significant impairment. At some point during the course of the disorder, the person has recognized that the obsessions or compulsions are excessive or unreasonable."

If another disorder is present, the content of the obsessions or compulsions is not restricted to this other disorder. The problem also cannot be due to the direct physiological effects of a substance (e.g., a drug of abuse, a medication) or a general medical condition.

DSM IV goes on to define Obsessions as "persistent ideas, thoughts, impulses or images that are experienced as intrusive and inappropriate and that cause marked anxiety or distress".

There is, in my opinion, a problem with the above definition that is important to point out. In my mind the problem lies in the statement that the, obsessive thoughts are experienced by the affected person as "intrusive and inappropriate". In my experience affected individuals are often desperately trying to make sense out of their obsessions and will go to great lengths to justify and rationalize them, to the point that they are no longer thought to be intrusive. As a result it can be difficult for those so affected to admit to themselves, and especially to anyone else, that they are experiencing intrusive obsessions. On the contrary they may argue that they enjoy making their minds think in such ways. It makes them "different", "set apart", more interesting or whatever to other people. This can be especially true for the mild-moderate OCS affected. It is due to the diminished severity (compared to actual OCD) of their symptoms. For them it is much easier to adopt the obsessions as their own, and completely deny any hint of intrusiveness whatsoever as they work to protect and preserve their own sanity and often their fragile egos.

Another word from the DSM IV definition, "inappropriate," has a similar problem among the OCS affected population. For many of the reasons identified throughout this book, those affected with OCS may work very hard to make the inappropriate appear or seem appropriate (through rationalizing, re-framing, lying, and etc.). They may go as far as blocking out the inappropriateness of their actions or thoughts, rejecting this notion out right, and adamantly insist that the obsession, or whatever, is indeed quite appropriate. A large part of the resulting anxiety can be due to the tremendous cognitive dissonance (battle of the mind) involved in this internal fight over the appropriateness and intrusiveness of their ideas, impulses, thoughts, and/or images.

In the "Disorder" or severe form of obsessions and compulsions called OCD the DSM IV indicates the obsessions are "not simply excessive worries about real life problems and are unlikely to be related to a real life problem." In my experience with OCD, I have found this to be mostly true as well, however, in OCD the obsessions and/or compulsions tend to be so all consuming and pervasively manifested that there is practically no room in the Affected one's mind for any other thoughts. I believe the reason these individuals (those with true OCD) do not seem to obsess over real life problems is simply due to the single, or several, very severe symptoms that take up most of their time, thoughts, and energy.

Experience over the last 15 or so years has led me to the conclusion that literally anything and everything could develop into an obsession or compulsion, in particular as I have defined them in OCS. Consequently, those with mild-moderate OCS do indeed obsessively worry about real life events and problems, although they can be somewhat distorted. They also obsess over "inappropriate" things, but these things tend not to seem nearly as bizarre and are not as severe as in OCD.

DSM IV defines compulsions as "repetitive behaviors or mental acts the goal of which is to prevent or reduce anxiety or distress, not to provide pleasure or gratification." DSM goes on to indicate, "in most cases, the person feels driven to perform the compulsion to reduce the distress that accompanies an obsession or to prevent some dreaded event or situation."

One of the difficulties I have with the above-related portion of the definition of a compulsion involves the casual way in which it is indicated compulsive behaviors do not occur "to provide pleasure or gratification." Although I agree with this pronouncement, I feel a need for a careful explicit exploration of this notion because it has seemed, in my experience, to be used to exclude many of the mild-moderate OCS affected from being taken seriously and from receiving proper treatment and care.

For example, there are those who have emphatically stated that relentless overeaters cannot be considered compulsive because eating is a pleasurable activity. I do not believe this to be true. This is not to suggest there aren't those who overeat, because it is pleasurable, who become overweight and obese. Rather, it is to suggest that the truly "driven" eater is demonstrating a compulsion and is not eating for the pleasure of it, even if they get in your face and SWEAR it *is* pleasurable. Remember, they know inside that they just can't seem to stop eating, but what would admitting that get them? Perhaps, others would be disgusted, call them names, and pass them over for jobs considering them weak-willed and on and on and on.

Sexual compulsions appear to be in this same category. What one of us with a compulsion to have sex with as many individuals as possible, or at least 3 times a day, or in as many different positions that exist, will admit when caught, or sharing escapades;

"Oh . . . yeah . . . Well, I kind of have to, you know. If I don't do it at least twice a day, I feel like I'm going to die. Then I can't think straight, work, or even have fun until I've done it again. If I miss even one day, you know, I'm dead!"

This is a large and populous world. Although I have never seen someone admit this openly or easily, who's to say that it hasn't happened? I just happen to believe it rarely, if ever, does. I have had clients reach the point therapeutically, usually after many sessions, wherein they become able to begin to see and verbalize such things to me in the privacy of our sessions. I assure you, however, that this admittance has never come easily, nor has it been said "off the cuff" in such a frivolous manner.

No. The man or woman with such active sexual compulsions will typically work extremely hard to try and get others to believe they're doing it because they "love it", they're macho, they BELIEVE in their sexuality, and so on. It is their defense. It is often the only rationalization they know that can enable them to avoid having to face what frequently they conceive of as the only other possible alternative, that there is something really wrong with them. They are SICK or, at least crazy. What else can they do? They don't know why they feel this way and have no idea there is something that is wrong. What would you do?

Thus, although I agree that true compulsions are not performed to provide pleasure or gratification, they can appear as if they are. Professionals need to be careful to refrain from spontaneously dismissing OCS as a possibility, simply because the individual may appear and even adamantly indicate their actions are purely for pleasure. Do not be fooled. Remember, the OCS affected are the champion prevaricators of the world. They've had a life time of practice.

The same situation as described in the above-related paragraphs exists for others who can too easily be excluded from an OCS diagnosis and exploration. Compulsive gamblers are not really gambling for pleasure and/or profit, although they may work to make you believe that they are. So it is, also, I believe with those obsessed and compulsive about shopping, dare devil risk taking, workaholics, and so on.

Interestingly as DSM IV further defines OCD, the statement is made that:

> "When attempting to resist a compulsion, the individual
> may have a sense of mounting anxiety or tension that is
> often relieved by yielding to the compulsion."

I find this interesting and bordering on contradictory because if I engage in a compulsive action that immediately relieves or diminishes significant anxiety and/or tension, might this not be perceived as "pleasurable" and/or "gratifying." Indeed, experience has suggested to me that this can often be the case, particularly with the OCS affected. The twisted and sometimes knotted dynamics associated with OCS/OCD must be carefully scrutinized and re-explored at times from several different viewpoints to insure evidence leading to a more complete understanding of symptoms and behavior is not inadvertently missed or misdiagnosed.

DSM IV itself helps make a case for one of the reasons relating to what I consider might be the most common misdiagnosis when OCS is present and significant in stating the following:

> "Because obsessive intrusions can be distracting, they frequently result in inefficient performance of cognitive tasks that require concentration, such as reading or computation."

To this I would add, obsessive thought also tends to interfere with listening and attending. So, what do I think just might be the most common misdiagnosis when OCS is present, unrecognized, and the primary factor of interference? Why ADHD of course.

Another reported diagnostic requirement that I have found to be somewhat problematic in making my case for mild-moderate OCS is the following statement from the DSM IV:

> "The obsessions or compulsions cause marked distress, are time consuming (take more than one hour a day), or significantly interfere with the person's normal routine, occupational (or academic) functioning, or usual social activities or relationships."

In my experience over the years, physicians not specializing in OCS/OCD have had a tendency, when confronted with treating an OCS identified individual, to open up a DSM IV manual (or pocket manual) and read the diagnostic criteria to the patient or to themselves. Those who have done so are simply double-checking the diagnosis. Diagnostic criteria, however, are quite different for OCS than for the more severe OCD. These physicians, in glossing over the criteria, will often ask, "do you wash your hands, re-fold clothes, check your stove (and so on) for an hour at a time every day?" Even the OCD affected often answer "NO" when the question is stated in such an unclear manner, however, the OCS affected nearly, if not always, answer no anyway. Physicians have concluded such brief visits into little known territory by making statements such as, "You don't have OCD, it must be something else."

What they inadvertently miss is that the "hour" of time spoken of may be cumulative throughout the day and rarely does it in OCS, and sometimes even in the OCD population, it may not occur in a single solid block of time. However, said carelessly, the client typically interprets this to mean for an entire hourly block of time, and so, has no trouble saying "no," to the question. These usually well meaning physicians often do not seem, as well, not necessarily through any real fault of their own, to have carefully considered the important last part of the sentence stating:

"or significantly interfere with . . ."

Thus, obsessions and or compulsions must last cumulatively for at least an hour a day or interfere significantly with day-to-day life activities. OCD does this, but often OCS does this as well.

The idea of considering OCS/OCD as a syndrome might make it easier to integrate other diagnostic categories into the continuum when appropriate. According to DSM IV criteria OCD is not diagnosed: "if the content of the thought or the activities is exclusively related to another mental disorder (e.g., preoccupation with appearance in Body Dysmorphic Disorder, preoccupation with a feared object or situation in Specific or Social Phobia, and/or hair pulling in Trichotillomania, and etc.).

I can easily agree with this statement that Body Dysmorphic Disorder, Social Phobia, Trichotillomania, and so on should not be diagnosed as OCD as it is currently defined in DSM IV. In the past 15 years, however, I have had the opportunity of working with many individuals previously diagnosed with such things as related above. I have been struck by the finding that above and beyond the specific recognized problem that brought them into treatment, each and everyone of those I've worked with, when interviewed with the Leyton Obsessional Inventory, have also had significant numbers of symptoms consistent with mild-moderate OCS. The primarily visible, or bothersome, manifestation may be the reason for seeking out treatment, but the bottom line has generally seemed to suggest underlying generalized OCS.

Similarly I have come to believe there are certain depressions that are not primary, but secondary to significant underlying OCS. These, in my opinion, appear to be the depressions, as suggested in previous chapters, that respond best to Anafranil and the SSRI, as well as some of the other "atypical antidepressants" that have a strong action on Serotonin. Also, Generalized Anxiety Disorder, I have come to believe, seems to result from underlying OCS as well.

Finally, in my clinical work over the past 15 years with those truly diagnosed as having OCD, I have found time and time again evidence of mild-moderate OCS having usually been recognized in as far back as infancy that by parents and caretakers, and almost certainly during the toddler years. Perhaps the reason OCD typically begins in late adolescence or early adulthood is because OCS has been present, essentially, all along. Maybe stress, over time, accumulates and eventually overwhelms some OCS affected individuals, to the point it becomes OCD, although certainly not all of them are thus affected. It could be that being higher symptomatically on the OCS continuum, eventually, under the right stressors or circumstances, it becomes OCD. We know that OCD does wax and wane as time passes, and it seems that OCS does this as well. Perhaps this is at least one of the reasons why.

"There is nowhere to run to . . . there's no place you can hide"

Reality is gonna get you . . . by and by
You wake up every morning . . . with dreams for a brand new day
By the night they are forgotten . . . or mislaid

And sometimes I wish my life was over
Then I stop and wish again
I wish that things could be more certain
In this life my friend
And who knows? . . . maybe someday
We'll find a way to make it right
Open up all the window shades
And see the light . . . let in the light . . ."

Excerpt from the song "Maybe Someday" by Ron D. Kingsley

OCP

(Obsessive Compulsive Personality Disorder)

As a result of my experience and, I admit, somewhat limited readings over the years, I now believe that OCP (as it is currently defined in DSM IV) is made up of a group of life time OCS affected individuals. These individuals were previously never diagnosed, nor did they experience levels of severity sufficient to lead to a diagnosis of OCD. These individuals did, however experience a life time of OCS symptoms and characteristics to such a significant degree that their very personality structure was formed and solidified while heavily influenced by their mild to moderate obsessions and compulsions. Thus, a complicated combination of bioneurochemically induced, environmentally induced, and learned behaviors persisting over a life time in the OCS individual seem to form what in DSM IV has been called personality disorder. It makes perfect sense to me that untreated significant OCS (as it is being presented in this book) would certainly have lasting and long-term effects on a developing "personality". The fact that such individuals would end up in time in a fairly homogeneous group manifesting similar "personality" styles and/or characteristics seems sensible too. According to the DSM IV, the OCP "pattern" begins by early adulthood, which again makes sense as "personality" becomes most established at about this time. The DSM IV defines OCP as follows:

"A pervasive pattern or preoccupation with orderliness, perfectionism, and mental and interpersonal control, at the expense of flexibility, openness, and efficiency, beginning by early adulthood and is present in a variety of contexts . . ."

This pattern is indicated, or diagnosed, based on the presence of four (or more) out of eight, listed symptom patterns. The diagnostic features of OCP as presented in the DSM IV are very similar, and identical in some ways, to those I have chosen to label, or call, OCS.

A personality disorder, by definition, develops from an individual's long term patterns of functioning, and must, as a result, have an onset in adolescence or early adulthood. Over the years, however, I have been recognizing toddlers, children, and early teens, essentially with sufficient symptom clusters to meet the diagnosis of OCP delineated in DSM IV. Such a diagnosis, of course, of a personality disorder, did not then, nor does it now make sense. How can a child of 3, 6, or 12 years of age be manifesting symptoms and characteristics of a personality disorder? How can they, that is, unless the root of the problem does not originate in the personality which, as pointed out by the DSM IV, is an "enduring pattern of inner experience and behavior." What if a previously unidentified factor (or factors) was responsible for both the childhood symptom manifestations and, later, the similar though more entrenched, diagnosable symptoms of a disorder in personality?

It then would make sense that young individuals, including the very young (1-4 years in age) could demonstrate like characteristics and similar behavioral responses tempered by age and experience, but similar nonetheless. As these children, affected with the hypothetical underlying core problem that frequently leads to OCP, grow their symptoms wax and wane with stress and time and influence behavioral responses as well as the development of their "personality." Of course not all OCS pathways would, I believe, lead to OCP. Some, I believe, may lead to OCD and others to chronic depression, anxiety, panic states, and so on.

In discussing OCP in the viable literature, researchers seem to hold to the oft referenced statements by professionals in the field (as an argument against a strong association or connection between OCP and OCD) that while OCD responds to Anafranil and the SSRI, OCP typically does not. In my opinion, however, this is not necessarily true. This I will attempt to explain.

OCP, as I see it, is not a disorder of the personality. Rather, it is a biochemically initiated compilation of characteristics and/or tendencies that are similar throughout the life span. Taking into consideration some undeniable differences that are inescapable due to age and the cognitive capacity of individuals involved, lead five-year-old children to behave in parallel fashions to the diagnosed OCP adult.

The five-year-old with OCS appears to be working to gain a sense of control by rigidly adhering to every single rule, trivial expectation, and plan of action of which their young minds are aware. They may be anxious and fearful beyond reason out of a hyper-elevated concern that they will make a mistake. Thus, they check and recheck with available adults and teachers on every tiny step and detail of an assignment or task, trying desperately to refrain from making any mistakes at all. Like their OCP diagnosed adult counterparts, they are usually totally unaware that others are often very annoyed at the constant disruptions resulting from such behavior. The OCS 5-year-old, again just like the OCP adult counterpart, may self-impose such a level of perfectionism and unreachable high standards that significant dysfunction and distress are inevitable. The adult may become so intensely focused in trying to insure that every microscopic detail of a project or task is so categorically perfect that the project is never finished. The 5-year-old experiencing this biochemically driven need, in my experience, more often than not may shut down and refuse to perform. Such a child may become sad and dejected, or tantrum wildly and with extreme and seemingly exaggerated passion when, as it must, a mistake is made and/or the overall performance is not up to par, and so on.

Adults can also shut down, but this is not as frequent of a response as it seems to be for the affected children. Undoubtedly the limited experience and immature cognitive capacity of the 5-

year-old, as compared to that which is available for the adult, remains a significant and instrumental determinant of available responses specific to the individuals in question. Obviously the longer lived and experienced adult has the advantage of many more potentially available responses than the child thus, the young child's responses to symptoms are raw, simple, and often straightforward while the adult's can be tempered, indirect, and sometimes distorted. The foundation of the shared behavior between these two disparate individuals, however, I believe is ultimately the same, although for the above related reasons and many others, it's manifestations may differ somewhat. The difference is in years upon years of experience with these unexplainable intrusive drives and needs that have shaped them and often had a great impact on choices and decisions made. Over time the initial primarily biochemically induced OCS can become so well entrenched in the patterns and psycho-emotional fiber of the affected individual that it is perceived, not only by the individual, but by others alike, as simply an integral, though often annoying, fragment of what is viewed.

The "enduring patterns of inner experience" that meld in the creation and maintenance of an individual's "personality" come to the melting pot, we know, from a variety of pathways and sources. This only makes sense. Many are learned, some via forced choice, some through the modeling and observation of others, and some from the experience of life. Some personality pieces may be derived from disease, or illness and the dynamics that occur as a result. Some parts may be formed as a direct or indirect result of physique (or body type), physical prowess (or a lack thereof), physical beauty, stature, as well as physical deformities and the accidental loss of body parts. Similarly, one or more of the five most well known senses to man can have an impact as well. Neurological conditions, biochemical deficiencies, and/or disruptions, as well as the environment, along with those things which, may yet be unknown, come together and continue to come together over the course of a life time. These elements come together to add a little here and delete a little there, in the constant formation and reformation of the self commonly referred to as the personality.

In working with adolescents and adults that demonstrated characteristics and symptoms consistent with an OCP diagnosis and would have been so diagnosed (a few already had been), I began to see a pattern of responsiveness and success that eventually led me towards the conclusion I am suggesting here.

I began to see evidence that the recommended medication, be it Anafranil or an SSRI, was having a positive therapeutic effect on my "OCP" client's symptoms too. This was indicated and tracked by successive administrations of my slightly modified version of the Leyton Obsessional Inventory for Children (which I choose to administer in the assessment of adults as well). As I tracked symptom responses to the medication, I found the Leyton symptoms following the same fairly immediate improvements as the OCS diagnosed clients. OCS symptoms are often responding positively on the very next day after an initial dose is taken. I wondered if those researchers reporting a lack of efficacy in relation to symptom improvement, when those that are OCP diagnosed were treated psychopharmacalogically, had been tracking the appropriate symptoms likely to respond to such an intervention. Perhaps, although it may seem like a preposterously boorish notion, those researchers had not been tracking the primary, or direct, underlying symptoms and characteristics that seem initially affected by Serotonin fluctuations. What if they had been actually following secondary and/or tertiary symptoms that, not being directly related to the brain chemical situation, of course would not respond to a direct medicational manipulation of a given chemical's levels in the brain right away.

In my experience working with those whom, it could be easily argued have bad symptoms that fit, or very nearly fit, the criteria for OCP as defined in the DSM IV, it has been a standard practice of mine to conceptualize them as manifesting OCS as defined in this book. Symptom determination was made via clinical interview, family and extended family histories, the Burks' Behavior Rating Scales, and a slightly modified version of the Leyton Obsessional Inventory for Children. Progress in symptom amelioration was tracked by re-administering the Leyton and sometimes the Burks'. My working hypothesis was that the symptoms tracked by these instruments would improve, become less intense, and/or less problematic within days of having started either Anafranil and/or one of the SSRI as a direct result of their mechanism of action in the brain, and thereby demonstrate an effect.

I also hypothesized that such biochemically driven symptoms had been significantly influencing the individual's behavior and internal thought processes unchecked for anywhere between 20 and sometimes 60 years. Thus, there would surely be patterns of behavior and thought that developed secondarily and even tertiarily as a result of the primary OCS symptoms. OCS, I hypothesized, is more directly connected to the biochemical insufficiency at the heart of the condition. These secondary and tertiary symptoms, characteristics, and behaviors, not having a direct connection to the biochemical, would take a longer period of time before treatment effects would be noticed and therapeutic change would be observable and eventually successful.

One other element that I believed, and continue to believe, is essential if treatment is to be successful in this population and especially when significant secondary and tertiary symptoms are present (as in the OCP profile), is knowledge and awareness. For example, without the knowledge and awareness that an antibiotic will, over time, cure a bacterial infection, who would continue to ingest the pills which, typically don't result in obvious positive effects for 2 to 3 days. Who, as well, would continue to take the medicine for a full 10 days when, by day *five* your senses are telling you everything is fine? Why would someone do this if not aware in advance that it needs to be taken for a specific length of time, regardless of how one feels, or the bacterium will not be destroyed and will reestablish the infection in the body. The common assertion that "knowledge is power" is clear.

A final working hypothesis is that many secondary and tertiary symptoms should weaken, significantly diminish, or eventually fall by the wayside the longer the primary symptoms are held in check by a psychopharmacological agent. Thus, client awareness is crucial if success is to be achieved.

Patterns of behavior do not change easily. Surely some of this complicated behavioral pattern is not caused by the biochemical condition. It is more a reflection of and reaction to a complex combination of events, or experiences, as perceived by the individual. It is affected by the person's perceptions of the past, present, and the future. This needs to be understood by the client in treatment.

If there is an expectation on the part of the professional or the client that the medication will dramatically and directly affect behavioral patterns, the client, especially if not made aware, is likely to discontinue medication. It makes sense that a client would do this long before reaching the point wherein behavioral pattern changes can more readily and more easily be accomplished. Since the initial driving force underlying a given pattern may have one or many elements directly connected to a biochemical causative factor it seems plausible that these elements may indirectly serve to maintain a pattern's integrity. Thus, when the biochemical is adjusted via a psychopharmacological agent in a positive direction, the elements directly connected are immediately affected. These elements, or "symptoms," diminish in intensity or fall away. The pattern itself remains relatively unaffected as no single element makes up an entire behavioral pattern. The pattern persists by virtue of the other elements that have no direct or real connection to the biochemical. Also because those that were initially the result of a biochemical influence or cause become secondarily or tertiarily associated and, at least for a while, are held in place within the pattern by the other elements of that pattern. In effect the pattern sustains itself for a time.

Prior to the initiation of a psychopharmacological intervention, as the affected individual would make attempts at changing or rearranging undesirable behavioral patterns, those actions would reactivate the elements more closely connected to the biochemical. As these elements became set in motion, they would give rise to the biochemical, which in turn would re-affect the elements and the behavioral pattern would reassert itself. Attempts to change the pattern would be thwarted time and time again.

With the underlying biochemical problem ameliorated psychopharmacalogically, as attempts are made to reorganize and/or completely change the related behavioral patterns, there is no biochemical reassertion. The transition from a specific maladaptive pattern to another more desirable one does not encounter the same levels of interference and the change is more likely to transpire successfully, given adequate time.

Thus, I am suggesting that the longer an OCS affected individual lives with the symptomotology unawares, the more likely it is that the symptoms will become incorporated into the self and interwoven into their behavioral patterns which are then interpreted by them and others too, as components of "personality." This makes it more difficult to affect change but not impossible.

Ultimately I am suggesting that OCP may in actuality result from having to deal with life long unidentified mild-moderate OCS. As such, it may be more conducive to treatment if the helping professional, as well as the affected client, view the problem as biochemically initiated very early in life and sustained thereafter in the same way over time. As the years pass, the biochemically affected components, usually experienced early-on as alien to the self become so insidiously intertwined with the other aspects of the self that they are viewed as portions thereof. This hypothesis seems further supported by the very longevity and consistency of the condition.

Obsessive and Compulsive Symptoms therefore, in my opinion fall on a continuum ranging from, hypothetically, none, to the mild, moderate, and the severe. When symptoms are in the severe range, the usual diagnosis is Obsessive Compulsive Disorder (OCD). When symptoms are in the mild-moderate range and go undetected until adolescence or adulthood, and are sufficiently problematic to come to the attention of professionals, there is a high likelihood that the diagnosis will be Obsessive Compulsive Personality Disorder (OCP). As such, it tends to be exceptionally resistive to interventions of any kind. Individuals from both of the above related diagnostic categories have also been frequently misidentified, or diagnosed, as having the following: Attention Deficit-Hyperactivity Disorder, School Phobia, Separation Anxiety, Major Depressive Disorder, Dysthymic Disorder, Bipolar Disorder, Cyclothymic Disorder, Panic Disorders, Social—Phobia, Generalized Anxiety Disorder, Anxiety Disorder NOS, Hypochondriasis, Body Dysmorphic Disorder, Primary Insomnia, Intermittent Explosive Disorder, Adjustment Disorders, as well as various relational problems. This is because along the OCS continuum, symptoms can mimic or bring about any one, or more, of the above diagnoses. In particular, if the helping professional is not aware of the OCS continuum and how, at times, it can mirror and/or precipitate the actual development of another disorder, as it commonly does, such as various depressions, and anxiety disorders.

When OCS is determined to be present and underlying another viable diagnosed condition (OCS can evoke extreme anxiety and is without question frequently quite depressing), the efficacy of treatment may be enhanced and more likely to endure over time if the OCS is identified and thoroughly explored with the client. Treatment, however, may or may not be appropriate, although awareness or knowledge is usually, if not always, appropriate.

As aptly pointed out in DSM IV:
> "Obsessive Compulsive . . . traits in moderation may be especially adaptive, particularly in situations that reward high performance."

The thing DSM IV seems not to have considered is how these same traits (or symptoms), also in moderation, might be significantly maladaptive to the extent that aggressive treatment is warranted, even though symptoms are not diagnosable as OCD. Neither has OCS been considered or conceptualized as a potential underlying causative factor relative to such a wide variety of diagnoses as I have suggested in this book. Perhaps it is time to do so.

The Effects of Stimulants on OCS: A Hypothesis

When ADHD and mild-moderate OCS coexist, it has come to
my attention, through experience in working with these individuals,
that there are times when the client will report that the use of stimulants seems to make certain OCS behaviors more intense, or worsens
them. I have also read in the ADHD literature of instances in which
stimulant doses were considered too high because the result was a
demonstration of obsessive and compulsive behavior that had not
been visible prior to whatever the dose was at the time the behavior
was observed. This has led in the literature to a hypothesis that stimulants (at too high a dose) caused obsessions and compulsions in some
individuals.

Since obsessive and compulsive behaviors generally seem to relate
to Serotonin levels in the brain, and ADHD behaviors are generally
attributed to levels of Dopamine and Norepinepherine, this research
hypothesis, along with some of my client reports, did not make sense
to me. Perhaps, I thought, because all of the above related brain chemicals fall into the group known as Monoamines, there is a relationship
not yet understood between these chemicals.

In time, however, a connection occurred that although still only
hypothetical seemed to not only make sense behaviorally, but also
may represent what is going on biochemically as well.

As defined by DSM IV, ADHD consists of various combinations
of inattention, hyperactivity, and/or impulsivity. Mild-moderate OCS
is not so easily encapsulated, but it also can falsely appear as hyperac-
tive-like or impulsive-seeming behavior and a hallmark feature is also
inattention (although it is primarily internally caused rather than
externally), plus the tendency to experience repetitive thoughts and
over focus on tasks, ideas, and actions. In fact, the last portion (repeti-

tive thoughts and over focus) is what causes the inattention and im-pulsive-seeming behavior associated with OCS.

Many professionals who are experts in the area of ADHD have found that often the ADHD diagnosed individual may have periods of hyper-focus that seem paradoxical to the very definition of ADHD. Usually, when this happens, it is only in areas of great interest, excite-ment, or thrill that it occurs. It is my contention that this apparent "paradox" in behavior is not truly paradoxical at all; rather, it is a manifestation of the so often co-morbid condition of mild-moderate OCS. When both of these are present, over focus or hyper-focus be-comes possible. Depending on the severity levels of either problem, there may be more or less evidence of the mild-moderate OCS. When OCS is weak, or mild, and ADHD is mild-moderate, the OCS tends to be fairly concealed and not as frequently observed, or seen for what it is. When ADHD is strong, or severe, and OCS is moderate, the same pattern tends to occur and the OCS is camouflaged and diffi-cult to detect. When OCS is moderate, or strong, and ADHD is less strong or not present at all, it has been my experience that the OCS is very commonly diagnosed as ADHD (usually the non-hyperactive type).

When both conditions coexist and the ADHD component is effectively treated medically by a stimulant, it has been my experi-ence that initially the symptoms of both improve. Those related to the treated ADHD more so than those associated with OCS. Since the symptoms of both of these biochemically driven disorders are clearly exacerbated (made worse) by significant stress, fatigue, and/or emotional reactions, the effective treatment of one or the other would result in noteworthy stress reduction. As the symptoms belonging to ADHD and the dynamics connected to these are reduced or im-proved, stress is the natural by-product that simply fades away. As the anxiety associated with this stress lessens due to the medical interven-tion, the symptoms of the co-morbid OCS also tend to decrease due to the fact that stress has been reduced overall.

Years of experience have suggested that, at least some of the time, these reduced OCS symptoms may seem dormant, or insignificant for weeks, months, and even years before they (not being treated directly) begin to return, interfere, or become noticed by others. Often, when such is the case, parents and teachers begin to report that the previously effective stimulant is no longer working. Medicational doses are raised. Stimulants may be changed two and three times. Symptoms described, however, in these situations typically seem to be more representative of the OCS types of inattention, apparent over-activity, and impulse control problems that frequently include extreme mood swings at any given Moment throughout the course of a day.

It appears, in my experience, that misunderstood situations involving the OCS/ADHD combination may be the reason Barkley (1995) identifies a 30 percent group of the ADHD diagnosed as "non-responders" to the stimulants. These may be the mainly OCS affected (or otherwise affected) individuals whose symptoms mimic those commonly attributed to ADHD. It may also be the reason the ADHD literature reports a group of ADHD diagnosed individuals who respond favorably (that is with significant symptom reduction) to Prozac and other medications classified in the same category which are the Specific (or Selective) Serotonin Reuptake Inhibitors, or SSRIs. Medications in this group are considered to be "antidepressants," however, all have demonstrated their effectiveness as effective anti-obsessional and anti-compulsive agents. It appears to me that the SSRI group is not truly effective in the treatment of ADHD, but rather they treat the similarly symptomatic co-morbid mild-moderate obsessive and compulsive symptoms.

It, therefore, seems plausible that even the depressions that respond positively (in 3-6 weeks) to an SSRI may actually be secondary to, or the result of, the biochemically induced primary symptoms of mild-moderate OCS. This is because, with the introduction of a medical intervention (psychopharmacological agent-SSRI), provided there are no unwanted side effects, symptoms of OCS show improvement within a few days, and even the very next day. It stands to reason that if the SSRI-responding depressions actually are derived from these hypothesized primary OCS, and related non-biochemically caused dynamics, that the depressive symptoms would be some of the last to decrease or improve. Therefore, perhaps the depression only lifts after the OCS primary symptoms improve and are brought under control as has been suggested in earlier pages of this work.

Getting back to the focus of this paper, however, the idea that the stimulants may worsen OCS when present, may now make better sense. When ADHD and OCS are co-morbid disorders and the OCS factor is unrecognized, and/or ignored, while the ADHD component is diagnosed and treated with stimulants, there do seem to be times when the OCS is intensified. From oncophagia (nail biting) compulsions to extreme over focused computer use to the inability to turn off certain ideas and thoughts and probably any other of the incredibly varied OCS symptoms, all could potentially become worse.

How? The stimulants improve inattention, impulsivity, and hyperactivity. This allows the affected individual to better attend, stay with regular tasks longer, and be less hyper in all areas. If such is true for these areas of functioning, it makes sense that similar effects might, even if indirectly, have an impact on other aspects of the self as well.

If, for example, when given stimulants I can now sit for longer periods of time, focus better and longer on my math homework (or any given task), it seems perfectly reasonable to assume (or suspect) that any currently experienced obsessions and/or compulsions might similarly respond to such treatment. Thus, compulsions may last longer and be experienced as stronger (or more intense) because the previously potentially interfering ADHD symptoms interfere no more. Not only can I focus on, and stick with reading, math, and mowing the lawn. I can also compulsively work at the computer longer and chew my fingernails with even better focus, and, I can similarly stick with obsessive thoughts and perceived needs too. One other contributing factor should also be considered. When psychopharmacological treatment successfully reduces ADHD symptoms and significant OCS remains, these remaining symptoms may suddenly become observable in ways they never were before. With the ADHD component ameliorated, or partially ameliorated, the OCS factor is revealed, or forced out into the open. Confusion then arises sometimes from the vast symptom similarities between OCS and ADHD.

A final thought. In co-morbid ADHD/ OCS, even if only one of the factors is treated by direct medical intervention, knowledge of, as well as awareness of, both disorders and their interrelating dynamics are essential ingredients if the individual is to be treated appropriately.

"For dreams are like melodies
Deep in our minds
Long hidden memories
Hoping to find
A life line . . ."

Excerpt from the song "Stardust in Aspen" by Ron D. Kingsley

Obsessive Compulsive Symptoms (OCS): Alternative Hypothesis

Ron D. Kingsley MS, Ph.D., NCSP

It is a well accepted notion today, by most professionals working in the mental health field, that broad based diagnoses such as depression and anxiety can be considered as a side effect, secondary to, or the result of another often quite specific, problem. One such problem is found under the category of Obsessive Compulsive Symptoms. Experience suggests OCS (mild-moderate symptoms) and OCD (severe symptoms) are strongly genetic and are a primarily Serotonin based biochemically induced/influenced or related problem.

When significant OCS is present, it is quite common for the undiagnosed individual to experience chronic depressive episodes that can range from mild discomfort and dysphoria, to what can be diagnosed as a full-blown Major Depressive episode. Typically the depressive characteristics experienced when OCS is the underlying influencing factor are difficult to pin down. Symptoms come and go erratically and are inconsistent in duration and intensity. When OCS is identified and treated with Anafranil or one of the Specific Serotonin Re-uptake Inhibitors (SSRI), symptoms usually ameliorate and diminish, often as much as 50 to 95%. In several weeks to about a month-and-a-half after starting medication, when therapeutic doses are reached, these individuals tend to "realize" that they are simply not depressed anymore. The situation is similar when OCS is identified and the initial broad target symptom had been "anxiety" with or without panic attacks. After the recognized OCS has been treated appropriately and directly, the anxiety seems simply to "slip away". Most often, however, when OCS is the driving force, individuals will experience both depression and anxiety at varying degrees and levels. Often the chronicity of an individual's depression/anxiety is related to the unidentified underlying causative symptom factors. When depression, anxiety, and etc., result from unidentified underlying causal factors, interventions and professionals' treatments are frequently a hit-and-miss proposition.

At times a medical doctor will prescribe one of the SSRI out of sheer popularity of their use, and a person will experience significant relief, although (when OCS driven) they usually have great difficulty expressing in understandable and specific terms exactly what it is that seems better. This uncertainty or confusion among unidentified OCS influenced patients, as well as their treating professionals, is not unusual in my experience. Therapeutic levels may never be reached. This can result in further changes in medication. It also may result in a hesitancy to raise a dose or change it in view of the heightened uncertainty professionals may very well have. It is sometimes unclear what a specific medication may actually be doing and why it may have been working. Similarly it may be confusing when a medication suddenly seems to have stopped being effective.

The question as to why a specific psychopharmacological agent or specific class of agents will seem to relieve depression, anxiety, and etc., in certain individuals and not others has been a perplexing problem since the advent of psychoactive medications. Clinical experience, along with extrapolations pulled from reviews of the literature, have led me towards a still tentative conclusion that those individuals diagnosed with "depression" who respond positively to the SSRI may actually be misdiagnosed mild-moderate OCS sufferers. When an SSRI works, the depressive characteristics typically improve, or are finally recognized as improved, in 3-6 weeks. In the treatment of acknowledged, or diagnosed, OCS, slight yet specific improvements are very common in just a day or two. As the dose is increased, and/or maintained, symptom amelioration typically continues, and in the case where significant depression was also a recognized co-morbid condition, interestingly enough, as the OCS is alleviated, so also is the depression (in about 3-6 weeks). The relationship between broad, sometimes vague, diagnoses and other more specific symptoms has brought me to, yet another, seemingly far-fetched, yet possible, notion or hypothesis in regard to the OCS itself.

Researchers are fairly confident that the brain chemical Serotonin plays a large role in the creation and/or maintenance of Obsessive Compulsive symptomotology. The most cited reason is that symptoms tend to decrease when Specific Serotonin Re-uptake Inhibitors are introduced and tend to increase when the medication is stopped as well, as when psychoactive Serotonin blockers are used. Exactly this occurs is unknown.

My experience in treating individuals over the last 15 years who have demonstrated OCS, Obsessive Compulsive Disorder (OCD), Attention Deficit Hyperactivity Disorder, and Tourette's Syndrome, all of which research suggests are genetically related problems, has led me to wonder openly about biochemically direct, and/or indirect, causation. I am not hesitant to admit that I have a hard time believing that the Serotonin link to OCS is direct. Of course logic may not apply in this situation, however, it seems clearly illogical to posit that the levels of Serotonin are directly responsible for the myriad of obsessions and compulsions documented in the literature and in my practical clinical experience. Other, as yet unidentified chemicals, may be involved. It has also occurred to me that perhaps OCS itself, not unlike the depression seen that is OCS related, may be an actual response to some other factor that is the real underlying problem directly related to the Serotonin levels in the brain. This would make OCS an indirect secondarily caused problem, and depression one that is tertiary, at least in its relationship to the actual Serotonin levels. Indeed, if such a situation were found to be true, then perhaps the term Obsessive Compulsive would not be the most descriptively accurate and/or best one to use other than in a cursory fashion when treating an individual with such a symptom picture. Medication may relieve the underlying factor that then is expressed in what has traditionally been referred to as Obsessive Compulsive behavior and/or symptoms.

Experience over time has suggested to me that a core problem for individuals with OCS appears to be what might best be described as an extreme hypersensitivity to anything and everything that the individual may experience. The specific expressions of this hypersensitivity to many of the same and/or similar incidents are often variable. This appears to be the result of the probable biochemical inconsistencies or fluctuations that reason dictates must occur. When emotionally distraught, stressed, fatigued, and/or anxious the tendency to respond in an extremely hypersensitive manner is heightened.

I began to wonder, what if, at the heart of the behavior that we have defined as obsessive and compulsive in nature, one of the actual primary biochemically direct components involved is an immediate and extreme hypersensitivity? During this biochemically activated period of time, all responses to external events are exaggerated many times over so that each event is literally experienced by the individual (at least Momentarily) as the equivalent to a "life or death" situation. The intensity of the event as well as the reaction to it can be so extreme that uncontrollable behavioral outbursts (that look very much like a child's tantrums) can occur. When the event persists and no relief is forthcoming, the intensity can increase until the individual appears to have completely lost all emotional control. There seems to be a, what I like to call, "point of no return," wherein the intensity must play itself out before the individual can once again regain control. Frequently, after such outbursts are over and the individual is calmed, there is a seemingly heartfelt sorrow (after a while others begin to view this as a manipulative tactic) in regard to the explosive reaction and apologies may abound.

Another dynamic that also can occur that is very often misunderstood involves self-mutilating acts. These include a range from the mild (scratching oneself, hitting a hand against the ground, etc.) to the moderate and sometimes, severe (cutting oneself with a razor blade or knife, banging one's head on the ground or walls, and suicide). When this dynamic is in play, the individual is feeling so badly (hyper-exaggerated of course) that there is a sense within that they need to be punished. Since no one else really understands how very "bad" they are or how bad what they did is, they take it upon themselves to do the punishing. There appear to be many levels of intensity at which the biochemical may trigger this extreme hypersensitivity. Thus, the immediate reaction can range from mild irritability to a loss of emotional and behavioral control, even though the apparent precipitating event can seem of very minimal concern and in some cases, seems absolutely senseless and completely unbelievable as a cause of such behavior.

Perhaps the experience of intense hypersensitivity gives rise to obsessive and compulsive symptoms because it is our body's natural reaction to extremes of emotional, physical, and behavioral hyperreactivity. If true, this hypersensitivity hypothesis, suggests that individuals may feel constantly overwhelmed by both external life events and their own internal reactions as well. As a result, one might expect emotions to be downplayed and even hidden. Control, it seems reasonable to believe, would become a constant issue of concern. Since research has given evidence that over control is linked to over responsiveness, and this reaction may be quite self-defeating especially over time, it seems the above-related postulate is at least a tenable one.

Another factor must be considered herein as well. The brain's primary function, research supports, in regard to the physical body is to maintain homeostasis, or equilibrium (balance). If a chemical imbalance in the Serotonin levels creates extreme hypersensitive reactions (or overreactions) to events . . . leading to emotional instability and eventual "loss of control" both emotionally and at times behaviorally; perhaps the brain's response to this situation is to seek alternative methods of control. Control may then very well become the central issue of immediate concern. In such a situation the focus of attention may then become the sole outlet of the intense emotional response, thereby creating an intense hyper-focus, or Obsessive Compulsive response. In an attempt to regain homeostasis the brain may force a singular hyper-focus on one thing, and one thing only. The strength of the response would be related to the level of deficiency in the Serotonin. Thus, a mild deficiency results in over focus at a milder level and so on. This could explain the reason so many individuals do not "fit" current DSM IV criteria for the diagnosis of Obsessive Compulsive Disorder (OCD), and yet still have definite obsessive and compulsive tendencies that are insidiously and persistently interfering with their day-to-day life functioning.

In the mild-to-moderate versions of this problem one might expect, if the above-related hypotheses are true, that less severe depletions in the Serotonin levels would result in a shorter duration of, and perhaps a more variable symptom picture. In other words, symptoms should be less strong, less likely to persist at the same level of intensity, and subject to a higher probability of being ousted, or replaced, by more intensely experienced symptoms, the will, and/or the need of the Moment. This, in fact, appears to be the case.

Why, then, can the symptom picture be so similar and yet so variable? It makes very good sense when the hypothesis stated above is connected to this ever-changing picture for a given individual. As the brain works at the mild-moderate level of intensity to regain equilibrium, the individual's focus can be derailed by a thought or experience that, at the Moment, is at a higher level of concern, or intensity, than the one of current or previous focus. This could be the reason individuals will be actively engaged in a specific project and then, in a seemingly spontaneous (or impulsive) fashion, suddenly leave what they are doing. They frequently forget entirely, for the Moment, that they were ever engaged in the other project. They immediately commence activity on a new and/or completely different project. Often, when this dynamic occurs, the individual may never complete the initially abandoned project at all. When actual OCD (severe) is involved, the level of intensity of a given symptom seems to be so strong that this shifting of focus is much less likely to happen.

Individuals with the mild to moderate symptom picture that are the primary focus of this treatise tend to respond to issues and events in an "all or nothing" or "black and white" (no middle ground) fashion. This tendency leads to a seemingly controversial and paradoxical finding.

Obsessive and compulsive symptoms at the mild-moderate levels in children often result in a need to do things as perfectly as their perceptions perceive they should be. Early on in school, the printing of letters and other writing tasks commonly reflect this experienced need when present. At first, providing there are no other interfering factors such as learning disabilities, physical, emotional, or additional biochemical problems, the OCS child tends to perform marvelously in this academic area. The letters and words they form are raved over by teachers and parents alike because these children are not only willing to take the time necessary to accomplish such extremely good writing, but they also feel compelled to do so.

As more work becomes required in the natural progression of communication through writing that is expected as a child is promoted from grade to grade, the OCS child (depending on finger dexterity, as well as the intensity level of the compulsion to write neatly) often begins to fall behind. Either that, or, ends up spending an enormous amount of time completing class assignments and homework. Each letter and word must be "just right" or it is erased. If erased too many times, or the pencil mark does not erase adequately, the entire paper may be crumpled-up and thrown away (no matter how near to completion it may have been). It is easy to see, then, why many of these individuals (though not all) may start to fall behind academically.

This particular situation gives rise to a host of dynamics that can lead to problems in school, at home, and personally as well. The one we are considering at this point is the one I've labeled *Paradoxical Inclination*. The child who experiences this feels trapped. If the child continues to write "perfectly" (just right for their perceptions) work is not going to get done (sometimes there is a compulsion for that as well) but if the child ignores this inner compunction to write "just so," the resulting emotional impact tends to be experienced as "devastating". Thus a double bind, or emotional trap, is encountered. Sometimes the child will become an expert at coming up with excuses as to the reasons for his incomplete work, or, will simply shutdown and refuse to work. Paradoxical Inclination occurs, however, when the child's response is to rush through work, often paying little or no attention to accuracy, and certainly not at all to specific letter and word formation. An "I don't care" demeanor appears to replace the "I care so much it hurts" experience that used to be there. Of course, this doesn't happen overnight or quite as simplistically as stated herein.

The way in which many OCS children handle the experienced need to write "just so" tends to be through self-talk and specifically directed thought that can be quite unconsciously engaged in. They tell themselves (silently) things such as, "It doesn't matter that it's sloppy or incorrect because I'm not really trying my hardest anyway". Through, just such types of self-talk, the OCS child performs in such a way that it appears to their teacher's, parents, and even their peers that they simply do not care. The paradox is, however, that they do care. By acting as if it is not important and doesn't matter to them, they attempt to relieve the incredible strain and burden that having to do it "just right" has placed on them. This pattern can soon turn into a monster.

In careful clinical interviews, most children experiencing the above described situation will indicate that they really would like for their papers and writing to be as neat as they once were. To do so, however, causes them such intense feelings of exhaustion, weariness, self-anger and of being overwhelmed that they typically have "given up even trying". Most of them will also indicate this predicament has made them at least a bit sad and still does. Thus, what I have nicknamed "little pockets of depression" is formed and carried with them everywhere they go. It is generally upsetting when a person's inner desires are kept from being expressed and/or experienced for whatever reasons. Anger and depression are common side effects of Paradoxical Inclination.

Another quite common area in which Paradoxical Inclination abounds is in the cleaning of one's room, house, etc. Having things excessively clean and ordered is common to OCS.

The bottom line with Paradoxical Inclination is that the excessive need is thwarted frequently enough that the individual finally "gives up" trying to keep things clean and in order, but the resulting mess creates another "little pocket of depression". Each time, the person is faced with seeing, or acknowledging, this "mess" they re-experience their own intensely felt failure, unless (as they sometimes are) they are able to block it out of their consciousness completely (at least for a time).

Wherever the word "perfect" has been used in this document, the intended definition is as follows: "to do something in exactly the way a given person feels or believes that it must be done." In this sense "perfection" varies with the individual and yet can still be the intended goal.

I believe this tendency to be either "perfect" in an area of human functioning or the exact opposite (black of white) is a hallmark condition of mild-moderate OCS. Since these individuals are easily overwhelmed by situations requiring many responses, many choices, and their own overly intense reactions and expressions, they tend to be "all or nothing" kinds of people. They want to win or they don't want to play (or the excuses fly when they do not win, along with often ill directed anger and fury). They will either do it well (the way they feel, think, and absolutely believe it must be done) or they would rather not do it at all. Is it any wonder that OCS people usually have difficulties working in pairs, and/or groups with others? If someone else wants to do a task differently that the OCS affected person feels it needs to be done the "fireworks can really fly". A child tantrums. The OCS adult is fired, put on probation, or may be considered a troublemaker. If in the position of "boss" the OCS affected may be barely tolerated by those workers for whom they are responsible and, as a result, their morale may become a serious problem. Such a boss appears "never" to be satisfied with anyone's performance, including, ironically, their own.

"There must be more to this life than what I've seen
There has to be . . . there has to be
There must be some way to find out what it all means
Is it just a dream . . . oh . . . what can it mean

There'll be those who will try and tell you what they do not know
And the lies you'll be forced to wade through will take their toll
Sometimes you may feel that you know life well
But even then you will doubt yourself . . . you'll doubt yourself

And you and me could be just like leaves blowing in the wind
Going round and round . . . again and again
And if you want to find out who you really are
It seems to me you've got to learn to read your own heart . . ."

Excerpt from the song "There must be more" by Ron D. Kingsley

OCS: SYMPTOMS OR SYNDROME?

Although there are symptom similarities among the OCS affected, it may be best not to label or stereotype these individuals. Labeling may be necessary in the diagnostic and treatment stage in order to get things going, but it need go no further. Stereotyping and labeling beyond what is needed for accurate diagnosis and appropriate treatment tends to lead to misconceptions.

Misperceptions already abound in relation to OCD, Tourette's and even ADHD, particularly in the early literature and even in some more recent books on the subjects. OCS is a fledgling diagnosis that is frequently misinterpreted as OCD. This occurs in spite of how clearly it may be stated. As soon as someone hears the word "obsessive" and/or "compulsive," there occurs a preconceived automatic notion as to what is meant. They think and often say "oh, yeah, OCD." Perhaps the way in which I describe the mild-moderate obsessive and compulsive condition or symptoms (OCS) needs to be changed. Such a change might be worthwhile if it kept others from automatically assuming that what I am referring to is OCD as it is outlined in DSM IV. Ostensibly, the appellation of "syndrome" could possibly do the trick.

A syndrome is a compilation of symptoms or characteristics associated with a specific condition. Unfortunately the general public may misconstrue the meaning of even the word "syndrome". When individuals hear the word syndrome, they may tend to entertain mystical and sometimes frightening images in their minds of what this may mean and feel it must be something truly horrible.

Nevertheless, if a diagnostic category were created to represent the group of individuals, characterized in this book by the designation of Obsessive Compulsive Syndrome followed by the most appropriate adjective such as mild, moderate, or severe, there would be problems. This is in spite of the fact that it might more appropriately represent the Obsessive Compulsive condition and the continuum hypothesis contained in this book. Although it does have a certain appeal, such a syndrome would undoubtedly have to include the OCD group. Thus, not only would a new diagnostic category need to be added, but an already agreed upon diagnosis would have to be changed. It would seem that this makes such a re-designation highly unlikely. As a result, I fully anticipate that I will continue to refer to this group of individuals as OCS, which I have defined as not OCD but Obsessive Compulsive Symptoms in the mild-moderate range.

APPENDIX

OCS RELATED ILLUSTRATIONS

THE OCS-ADHD CONNECTION

In order to insure clarity and understanding, for the purposes of this article, it is important to define terms. Whenever the term Obsessive Compulsive Symptoms, or the abbreviation (OCS), is used in this communication, it refers to these symptoms at a mild-moderate range, or level. Obsessive Compulsive Disorder (OCD), as currently defined in the DSM IV, consists of symptoms at a much more severe and intensely interfering level. OCD symptoms are typically quite alien to those experiencing the mild-moderate version of, essentially, this same problem. Thus, when asked questions relating to OCD, those individuals with OCS usually deny the presence of these very severe symptoms (and rightly so, since they are not present in the form being presented). The questioning professional, thereafter, often queries no further.

The professional may dismiss the possibility of obsessive and compulsive symptoms entirely or, if they do recognize some tendencies, they often conclude that such symptoms are of insufficient intensity and/or duration. Thus, they determine that such "tendencies" could not possibly be interfering significantly enough in the individual's day-to-day functioning to actually consider it a worthwhile focus of treatment. In fact the current DSM IV description of OCD appears clearly restrictive and narrow in its approach (it's as if you either have it *BAD*, or you don't have it at all). This seems to give credence to and foster the kinds of perceptions many professionals experience as stated above. The common assumption, then, in regard to the treatment for OCS by most professionals not specializing in this area, tends to therefore be rather nondescript and unhelpful. The tendency is to believe that, if obsessive and compulsive symptomotology is not frequently "all consuming" as suggested in the DSM IV, then such a diagnosis is not viable and aggressive treatment and/or intervention is not warranted. Such an attitude, however, has not proven useful to the many individuals manifesting such a mild-moderate symptom picture.

When affected individuals or parents of OCS affected children are initially present with this seemingly vague and inconsistent symptom picture, misdiagnoses are quite common. It is also not uncommon for the professional to conclude that no *"real"* problem actually exists. Frequently parents are given what can be an emotionally demeaning directive to "try taking some parenting classes". Depression (for both the parent, as well as the identified child or affected individual) along with frustration, severe stress, anxiety, and blaming, are typical out comes.

Obsessive and compulsive symptoms are usually treated by medications known as the Specific Serotonin Reuptake Inhibitors (SSRI). With the use of an SSRI, obsessive and compulsive symptoms often decrease dramatically. As the OCS decreases, secondarily related depressive problems improve shortly thereafter as well. Relationships with family members, teachers, and others also improve, as does self-esteem. Emotional outbursts decline and at times even disappear altogether. Irritability and moodiness follow the same path of improvement, as does attentiveness and a sometimes surprising new level of concern and awareness for others needs is achieved as well. The Behavior Modification technique known as Exposure and Response Prevention has also been shown to diminish the strength of obsessions and compulsions. It is, however (in this writer's experience), a very difficult treatment strategy to follow, and tends to be especially so for children.

There is evidence that ADHD is genetically connected to OCS/ OCD. When ADHD is determined to be a co-morbid factor that is also interfering with daily functioning, the addition of a stimulant (such as Ritalin, or Adderall) in conjunction with an SSRI is a common viable treatment with quite positive outcomes. Neither the SSRI nor the stimulants can effectively treat both conditions alone. Research points mainly to the brain chemical Serotonin in relation to OCS, and to Dopamine in relation to true ADHD. Interestingly, many of the observable symptoms and behaviors of the OCS affected look exactly like those of ADHD, making it difficult to distinguish between the two.

The most essential treatment factor, whether it is for the individual, parent, or treating professional, is without question, accurate knowledge. This can be obtained through pertinent articles, books on the subject, and an up-to-date knowledgeable counselor, psychologist, psychiatrist, or physician. In fact, counseling is typically only beneficial to the extent that it focuses on coping skills with an understanding of the dynamics associated with OCS/OCD and ADHD. Many families and individuals have lived for years with these specific undiagnosed problems, and enabling them to untangle the chronic misinterpretations, cognitive distortions, and long standing emotional distress can be invaluable.

It is a fairly easy task for most professionals to talk an individual with mild-moderate OCS (or parent of an affected child) out of the desire and/or need for pharmacological intervention or, for that matter, any kind of intervention. Usually affected individuals have already experienced long term self doubts about their own sanity and spent a great deal of energy rationalizing, hiding, and/or camouflaging symptoms. Often they have also created and/or accepted a host of rational sounding reasons for their uninvited thoughts and sometimes rather odd seeming behaviors. Any hint of disbelief, hesitation, or active cross examining on the part of a treating professional tends to push them closer to the ever present fear that something truly is seriously wrong with them; something like "I really *am* crazy." This terrifying thought makes it very easy to believe, and even cling to, the unknowing professional's testament that the individual is actually quite fine.

The medications commonly used that can alleviate and/or ameliorate obsessive and compulsive symptoms (though not all inclusive) include the following:

Fluoxetine (Prozac)	Sertraline (Zoloft)	Clomiprimine (Anafranil)
Fluvoxamine (Luvox)	Paroxetine (Paxil)	Citalopram (Celexa)
Efazodone (Serzone)	Venlafaxine (Effexor)	Mirtazapine (Remeron)
Welbutrin (Bupropion)		

All psychopharmacological agents have potential side effects. Sometimes there can be a side effect severe enough to warrant discontinuance of a specific SSRI or other of the medications listed above. There is, however, mounting evidence that if one of these medications causes uncomfortable side effects, it doesn't necessarily follow that another will do the same. Thus, if unwanted side effects do occur, it is often worthwhile to attempt another of those medications listed above and so on.

BRIEF QUICK-RESPONSE GUIDE:

OCS/OCD INTERVENTIONS
FOR TEACHERS AND PARENTS

Knowledge: Without question, in my opinion, knowledge about these symptoms, the disorder itself, and the psycho-emotional inter-related dynamics as they relate to both school and home environments is the most essential and potentially helpful intervention for any individual in relation to how to deal with this problem.

Medications: Generally these are in the SSRI (Specific Serotonin Reuptake Inhibitors) category which include most of the following: Anafranil, Prozac, Zoloft, Paxil, Luvox, Celexa, and those that are related like Serzone, Welbutrin, Tenex, Remeron and Effexor.

- The affected individual can keep track of symptoms and associated behaviors and practice substituting an incompatible response.

- The behavioral modification technique of Exposure and Response Prevention has been demonstrated in research to be the most successful behavioral method available. It, however, does have certain problems when used with children, and when attempted for symptoms and charac-

teristics in the mild to moderate ranges that are nevertheless significantly interfering with a person's day to day life
successes.

- Work resistance and work refusal: There are a host of
  possible and viable reasons why students may resist and
  refuse assignments. In fact, even when OCS or OCD have
  been found to be the underlying causative factor, teachers
  almost universally had been inaccurately attributing the
  behavior to another, although possible, unrelated cause.
  This is one of the reasons attempted interventions can be
  notoriously ineffective. Affected students either don't
  know why the resistance/refusal occurs or, similar to the
  teachers, assume an inaccurate cause. One begins to sense
  why confusion has run rampant in relation to OCS/
  OCD.

- If this student is having anxiety, fear, anger, and etc., that
  appears due to time constraints, the extension of such
  time constraints may prove beneficial. Often these
  students take an incredibly long and even unbelievable
  amount of time to complete their work for a variety of
  reasons that don't really need stressing here.

- Shortening certain assignments can also be beneficial if
  the student will allow it. Many affected students absolutely do not want to be viewed as different than from
  their classmates do, and when this problem is present,
  cutting their assignments may not work.

- If a student adamantly insists that there is just no way to
  get done in the time allotted, suggest that the work be
  taken home.

- Avoid power struggles. The biochemically driven obsessive
  and or compulsive student will hardly, if ever, give in no

matter what the cost. To them the situation is of "do or die" intensity not unlike the well known fight or flight syndrome of animals.

- Do not try to force the OCS/OCD student to become involved, answer a question, or respond when their body language and words are telling you they **WILL NOT.**

- There is a commonly experienced symptom of an unrelenting need to always know they are right in what they are doing. This can be very frustrating to a teacher as it looks like the student is craving attention. Patience is of paramount importance when working with these students.

- Counsel with the School Psychologist for ideas on how best to work with such a student and also the possibility that the psychologist can speak with parents about medical diagnosis and interventions through their pediatrician.

- Help these students to structure their day and prioritize tasks. These are notoriously problematic areas for the OCS/OCD affected.

- When the student over responds emotionally and/or physically, do not get immediately in their face unless they are a danger to self or others. Give them space and use time out procedures to enable them to calm down.

- These students tend to have great difficulties working in-groups. Consider allowing them to work alone.

- Be careful about touching such a student. Their over reactivity extends to all areas and it can be very hard for them to be touched. Also, however, the exact opposite can be true as well. Be aware and be careful.

- Report excessive sadness and evidence of possible depression to the school nurse and/or School Psychologist.

- Always keep in mind the following: **OCS/OCD IS AN EXPLANATION, NOT AN EXCUSE.** Also remember that this condition is managed and not cured.

BIBLIOGRAPHY

Baer, L., Ph.D. (1991), *Getting Control: Overcoming Your Obsessions and Compulsions.* Little, Brown & Company.

Barkley, R.A.(1998), *Attention Deficit Hyperactivity Disorder: A Handbook for Diagnosis and Treatment. Second Edition.* New York/London: The Guilford Press.

Barkley, R.A., Ph.D. (1995), *Taking Charge of ADHD: The Complete Authoritative Guide for Parents.* New York/ London: The Guilford Press.

Braun, ~A., M.D. (1993-94), *Neurobiological Relationship of Tourette Syndrome, Obsessive Compulsive Disorder, and Attention Deficit Hyperactivity Disorder.* Tourette Syndrome Association; No. 3.

Bruce, R.V. (1988), Alexander Graham Bell. *National Geographic,* September (1988) p. 360.

Bruun, B., & Bruun, R. (1994), *A Mind of Its Own: Tourette's Syndrome: A Story and a Guide.* Oxford University Press.

Hyman, B. M., Ph.D., and Pedrick, C., R.N., (1999), *The*

OCD Workbook: Your Guide to Breaking Free from Obsessive Compulsive Disorder. New Harbinger Publications Inc.

Johnson, A.D., (1981), *The Value of Creativity—The Story of Thomas Edison.* La Jolla CA: Value Communications.

Johnson, AD. (1984), *The Value of Self-discipline: The Story of Alexander Graham Bell.* La Jolla CA: Value Communications.

Johnson, S., M.D., (1979), *The Value of Dedication: The Story of Albert Schweitzer.* La Jolla CA: Value Communications.

Johnson, S., M.D., (1979), *The Value of Fantasy: The Story of Hans Christian Andersen.* La Jolla CA: Value Communications.

Johnson, S., M.D., -(1979), *The Value of Honesty: The Story of Confucius.* La Jolla CA: Value Communications.

Kelley, K. & Ramundo, P., (1993), *You Mean I'm Not Lazy, Stupid or Crazy?!: A Self—Help Book for Adults with Attention Deficit Disorder.* Tyrell & Jerem Press.

Leonard,H.L., M.D., & Rapoport, J.L., M.D., & Swedo, S.E., M.D., (1992), *Childhood Obsessive Compulsive Disorder.* Journal of Clinical Psychiatry 53:4 (Suppl-, April).

Leman, K., (1985, 1998), The New Birth Order Book. Fleming H. Revell.

Leman K., (1989), Growing up First Born. Delacorte Press Bantam Doubleday Publishing Group.

Levert, S., & Murphy, K.R., Ph.D., (1995), *Out of the Fog*

Treatment Options and Coping Strategies for Adult Attention Deficit Disorder. Skylight Press.

Levinson, H.N., M.D., (1990), *Total Concentration: How to Understand Attention Deficit Disorders.* M. Evans & Company.

McLean, P.D., and Woody, S.R., (2001), *Anxiety Disorders in Adults: An Evidence-Based Approach to Psychological Treatment.* Oxford University Press.

Nadeau, K.G., Ph.D., (Ed.) (1995), *A Comprehensive Guide to Attention Deficit Disorder in Adults: Research-Diagnosis-treatment.* Brunner/Mazel.

O'Neal, J., M.D. & Pharm, R., M.A., & Preston, J., Psy. D., & Talaga, M., B.S., (1994), *Handbook of Clinical Psychopharmacology for Therapists.* New Habinger Publications.

Penzel, Fred., Ph.D. (2000) *Obsessive Compulsive Disorders: A Complete guide to Getting Well and Staying Well.* Oxford University Press.

Peterson C., Maier S., and Seligman M., (1993), *Learned Helplessness: A Theory for the Age of Personal Control.* Oxford University Press.

Pratt, F. (1955), *All About Famous Inventors and Their Inventions.* New York: Random House.

Rapoport, J.L., (1989), *The Boy Who Couldn't Stop Washing.* New York: E.P. Dutton.

Rapoport, J.L., (1991), *Recent Advances in Obsessive Compulsive Disorder.* Neuropsychopharmacology, 5(1): 1-10.

Rosenberg, D., M.D., Holttum, J., M.D., and Gershon, S.,

M.D., (1994), *Textbook of Pharmacotherapy for Child and Adolescent Psychiatric Disorders.* University of Pittsburgh Medical Center. Brunner/Mazel Publishers New York.

Schwartz, J.M., M.D., & Beyette, B., (1996), *Brain Lock:-Free Yourself From Obsessive Compulsive Behavior.* Harper Collins Publishers.

Shimberg, E. F., *(1995), Living With Tourette Syndrome.* Simon and Schuster.

Singer, H.S., (1993), "Tic Disorders." *Pediatric Annals.* 22:1 January, 1993 (p. 22-29).

Steketee, G., (1993), *Treatment of Obsessive Compulsive Disorder.* Guilford Press.

Steketee, Gail., Ph.D. and Pigott, Teresa., M.D., (1999), *Obsessive Compulsive Disorder: The Latest Assessment and Treatment Strategies.* Dean Psych Press Corp. Compact Clinicals.

Steketee, G., Ph.D., and White, K. M.D., (2001), *When Once Is Not Enough: Help for Obsessive Compulsives.* New Harbinger Publications, Inc.

Vasey M.W., and Dadds, M.R,, (Editors), (2001), *The Developmental Psychopathology of Anxiety.* Oxford University Press.

Witcher, A.E., (1989), "The Grief Process: As Experienced by Parents of Handicapped Children." (p. 31-32), *Principal,* March 1989.

BVG